THE COLLECTED WORKS OF JULIAN FANE
VOLUME SIX

THE COLLECTED WORKS OF
JULIAN FANE
VOLUME SIX

THE TIME DIARIES

❖

ODD WOMAN OUT

❖

A DOCTOR'S NOTES

BOOK GUILD PUBLISHING
Sussex, England

The Time Diaries
first published in Great Britain 2005
by Book Guild Publishing
Copyright © this edition The Sussex Heart Charity 2012

Odd Woman Out
first published in Great Britain 2006
by Book Guild Publishing
Copyright © this edition The Sussex Heart Charity 2012

A Doctor's Notes
first published in Great Britain 2007
by Book Guild Publishing
Copyright © this edition The Sussex Heart Charity 2012

This edition first published in Great Britain in 2012 by
The Book Guild Ltd
Pavilion View
19 New Road
Brighton, BN1 1UF

The right of Julian Fane to be identified as the author of
this work has been asserted by him in accordance with the
Copyright, Designs and Patents Act 1988.

All characters in this publication are fictitious and any resemblance to real
people, alive or dead, is purely coincidental.

Typesetting in Bembo by
Keyboard Services, Luton, Bedfordshire

Printed and bound in Great Britain by
CPI Group (UK) Ltd, Croydon, CR0 4YY

A catalogue record for this book is available from
The British Library

ISBN 978 1 84624 780 4

CONTENTS

THE TIME DIARIES

To
G

CONTENTS

MARKING TIME

It might be thought that, owing to my age, the title of Part One of these diaries is synonymous with the modern catch phrase 'Waiting for God'. Not so – marking time is part of our military vocabulary and describes marching on the spot, preparatory as a rule to receiving the order 'Forward march!'

1999

11 June 1999

Patsy Grigg, wife of John, wrote me a letter appreciative of *Evening*, but saying she was worried by the final paragraph of the book. *Evening* has just been published, and balances my first book, *Morning*, published nearly fifty years ago. I end the story of *Evening* by announcing that it is my last puppet show, my adieu to fiction, at least in principle.

12 June

It is the next day; and, like all authors, I have more to say – and to say on the same subject. I cannot retire, authors don't, authors won't – I would be ill if I did, or under ground. What then am I to write? The answer seems to be this diary. My approach to the undertaking is diffident. I have never before kept a diary, and feel I do not belong to the strange tribe of diarists. I have never begun a book that has no end in view.

But there is really no alternative. Notwithstanding my lucky facility in respect of plots, stories, inventions, I am not sure that I could produce another novel which was new.

Questions touching my diary remain. The brave modern answer would probably be: 'Go for it!'

13 June

My half-sister June was named after the month of her birth. Our mother was married and widowed three times before she was fifty-six. By her second husband, Arthur Capel, she had two daughters, Anne [Higgins] and June. June married first the distinguished pianist Franz Osborn, and produced her only child Christopher, and after

Franz's premature death married Jeremy Hutchinson, Queen's Counsel and now peer of the realm.

Yesterday afternoon G and I went to have tea with the Hutchinsons in their home in the Sussex Downs. June for the moment is well, and in her brave way has thrown off memories of her lifelong battle against ill health, and Jeremy looks twenty years younger than his age. Their hospitality is exemplary – and I am the most objective of guests. Their welcome could hardly be warmer, they concentrate on you for all they are worth, listen to you without interrupting, allow general conversation, steer clear of controversy, and do their utmost to feed you well and make you comfortable. June supported my bid to become a writer – from my schooldays onwards – when others were against it. She bought the house in London where I lived for nearly two decades, and without which I would have had no settled address.

14 June

Spoke to Patsy Grigg on the telephone yesterday. She explained to me that the last page of *Evening* worried her not because it was incomprehensible, but because it seemed to signal my decision to write or to publish no more books, fiction in particular. I thanked her for the compliment, and said, 'Well, perhaps and maybe'.

But I have not yet changed my mind. The distance increases between me and Grub Street, where rats race and backs are bitten, and I note the receding prospect with complacence.

Also, yesterday, the first night of the revived production of Handel's *Rodelinda* at Glyndebourne. G loved every minute, I enjoyed it, and the audience applauded loud and long. But I am not a critic, except of unqualified journalists who air destructive views of the life-work of artists in newspapers.

16 June

Tonight is G's big night at Glyndebourne. She has free use of the Glyndebourne Box and its ten seats: that is her annual reward for being a director of the main Glyndebourne board. She is the longest-serving director apart from George Christie himself, and only the second female director ever since George's father and mother, John and Audrey Christie, founded the opera house in 1934. G is due to retire at the end of this year and before the next millennium begins. She may be sad to call it a day; but all she cares about in this context is the good of Glyndebourne and the art of opera.

18 June

In the night, just as we were dropping off to sleep, our dog Meg began to bark under our spare room with a couple of guests in it. Meg is over a hundred in human terms if her age is multiplied by seven, and goes in for long spells of irritable spaced-out barking, whether for the sake of food or to attract attention or for other reasons. We told her to shut up; let her out into the garden, although she is accustomed to make messes in the kennel if taken short; we scolded, threatened, attempted to bribe her – all in vain. She stopped until we were back in bed, then began again. The tailpiece to the story – no pun intended – is that our guests vowed at breakfast that they had not heard a single bark during the night: could it be true?

I have revised the TSS of the last two of my fifteen little books in the Harlequin Edition, *The Harrison Archive*, descriptive of the schizophrenia of the twentieth century, its humanity and its barbarism, and *In Short*, my tribute to Ursula Codrington, who lived for art and typed for me for some years.

19 June

Saturday morning, and for me business as usual. My routine of work for half a century has been five hours of writing or trying to write until one p.m. for seven days a week. That makes only thirty-five hours of writing weekly, not much in comparison with Tolstoy's boast that he sometimes wrote for twelve hours at a stretch, and not a great deal relative to the average forty-eight or forty hour working week.

But William Douglas-Home, the playwright, advised me when I was nineteen or twenty that I had better learn to sleep at any old hour of the day or night, since writers can only get away from their work by sleeping.

20 June

Tony Shephard has recently moved into the basement flat of the house next to ours, and we were told he was keen to meet us. Had he read my books, I wondered, as authors will. Eventually we were introduced and he invited us in for a drink and a great surprise. He has turned his flat into a mini-museum dedicated – consecrated almost – to the upper crust. Life-size cut-outs of Queen Victoria and other royal ladies have been padded, robed, bejewelled and crowned. Crowns and coronets are everywhere. Chairs bear the royal insignia, and have been sat on by peers and peeresses at functions. There are pictures of royalty, books about royal personages, family trees, menus of royal repasts. Tony guided us from treasure to treasure with charm and expertise. And he dealt diplomatically with his special interest in me. He had a complete list of everybody in Westminster Abbey for the coronation of King George VI in 1937, and my name was included as Page to the Marquess of Cholmondeley.

Tony was born and brought up in the East End; gravitated to Sussex; has spent his life, and is spending his retirement, in looking after people; and mounts exhibitions of his royal collection to raise money for charities.

★   ★   ★

What are these: The Chinese Character, The Common Pug, The Sallow Kitten, The Dingy Footman, The White Ermine, The True Lover's Knot, The Clouded Drab, The Snout? Answer is caterpillars.

21 June

My friend Carlo, the playwright and translator Carlo Ardito, a recent convert to the Internet, is not so interested as he used to be in our domestic politics. Our country is becoming a cipher, he tells me. Great Britain or England or whatever we are now meant to call it is not even mentioned by the international media as participating with the USA in the bombing of Kosovo.

23 June

Politics for me is like cheerfulness was for Oliver Edwards – it keeps breaking in (see Boswell's *Johnson*).

John Grigg wrote to me yesterday about *Evening*. He is not only a historian, but a literary man in the old-fashioned, widest and most admirable sense. He pays me a compliment in urging me not to regard *Evening* as my last book; but has discovered it is what he calls a 'tract', and says he has a prejudice against 'tracts'.

I am afraid I have done it before – there always seems to have been a 'tract' in me struggling to get out. And I like 'tracts' as much as John dislikes them: I like an author to generalise, to illustrate a truth or a truism, and always to have morality or a moral in mind. *Evening* has the humblest of links with Plato's *Symposium*. It was meant to be the summing-up of my experience of the grades of love. I respect John so much that I can see his point and differ from him without difficulty.

24 June

Sir David Frost OBE merits congratulations. He first made his mark as a guerrilla satirist in the class war, but now he himself is an internationally respected member of the Establishment. Can it be true that he too is heading for that Eldorado of entertainment, crime? There is a rumour going round that he is a backer of a film about Nick Leeson, who betrayed the trust of his employers, defrauded and broke Barings Bank, and ruined innumerable lives. The film, good or bad, will make Leeson into a hero or anti-hero, and rub salt into the wounds of his innocent victims. I expect the scurrilous rumour is unfounded. We have all hoped Sir David had become the sort of knight who is *sans reproche*.

25 June

People of my age are surprised and not necessarily displeased when I ask them about their medication – in layman's lingo, what pills they take. They are apt to bridle and reply that the subject is boring, that polite people are supposed not to show the scars of their operations, and the less said the better. But I am pleased to inform them: 'At last we have something of mutual interest to talk about.'

Today I am giving away the hefty volume entitled: Debrett's *Distinguished People of Today* 1990. I have replaced it with a 'classless' edition of the same work entitled: *People of Today* 1999.

26 June

I note, and almost begin to enjoy, the relaxation of discipline in writing a diary in comparison with the writing of my kind of books.

A strong socialist wins the Lottery – what does he do with five million pounds, what do five million pounds do to him? He could have a wife whom he adores – she could have bought the Lottery ticket. He could have a daughter with expensive tastes. Subject of the story: the contradiction between socialism and human nature, or, to put it another way, between the idealism and the corruption responsible for the hypocrisy that has ruled in my lifetime.

Do-gooders live in another world, where realism is out of order. In my hearing a friend of ours told liberal-minded X that he and his neighbours were scared of a local criminal, a convicted car thief, mugger, burglar, who is large, strong, probably mad, and threatens everybody when he is out of prison that he is planning to break and enter their houses; to which X commented sympathetically, referring to the criminal, 'Poor chap!' Yet X fights like a tiger for his own and his wife's privileged way of life, and I cannot believe he would like it if he and his family in their first, second or third homes were burgled and beaten up.

A do-gooder is a person who attempts to please somebody (singular or plural) at somebody else's expense.

27 June

Is it a new horror or an old one? I used to think that the upper classes and people in authority were stereotyped by popular entertainers, and denigrated as morons and buffoons, owing to ignorance. But I have recently come to suspect that they are not mocked for fun, not in the P G Wodehouse manner or in music-hall terms, but in a politically motivated attempt to rob toffs and bosses of their humanity and turn them into objects fit to be hated, like the stuffed dummies we were trained to bayonet in the army. The Russian communists did the same thing to the kulaks before liquidating them, and the nazis did it to the Jews.

Spoke to Ben Glazebrook, Chairman of Constable, my publisher and friend, yesterday afternoon. He rang me and apologised for having been hard to reach for the last fortnight – he has been in Paris and America. He said he had had enough of life in the fast lane, and longed only to crawl along in the slowest of all possible lanes.

30 June

If I knew more, was learned, a historian, and had time to burn, I would write a book entitled *Second Sons*. I believe they are an interesting class of person in countries where primogeniture is more or less in force in the top families – that is, the principle of the first-born son's entitlement to the lion's share of family treasure.

Primogeniture is a good idea, in fact essential in order to conserve the social fabric, especially when an inheritance includes a title, a stately home and a great estate. The alternative is some sort of division of the spoils between the children, probably the end of the family home, the break-up of the estate, and disputes and litigation.

Primogeniture however, for all its advantages, can raise awkward questions. What happens if his lordship happens to sire male twins? The twin who politely ushers his brother into the light of day and follows a few minutes later may be renouncing a fortune. What if the twins are identical – it would seem to aggravate the injustice – and what if they are delivered by Caesarean section? – the surgeon in charge could be enriching one and impoverishing the other.

Exemplars of the good or the bad luck of second sons abound. King George V obtained both the regal destiny of his deceased elder brother and his brother's fiancée, Princess Mary of Teck. George VI was a second son, enthroned thanks to Wallis Simpson, who rid us all of Edward VIII. The late John Wyndham, 6th Lord Leconfield of Petworth and 1st Lord Egremont, and two dukes, Devonshire★ and Beaufort, were raised to the seats of power when their brothers were killed in the 1939–1945 war: what were and are their thoughts on the subject of fate?

I donate the above to whoever is able to mine this seam of drama and perhaps of gold.

★Andrew, 12th Duke of, deceased.

[13]

1 July

Last night at the Final Rehearsal of Puccini's *Manon Lescaut*. The Romanian Adina Nitescu sang Manon, as she did in the original production two years ago; but she has become beautiful in the interval, a beautiful actress and a lovely singer.

2 July

Harriet Bridgeman, of Bridgeman Art Library fame, and more to the point our friend, wrote me a postcard that includes the gratifying sentence: 'I heard [my mother speaking] of the rare excellence of the modern morality story she was reading.' The morality story was *Evening*, which is a tract to John Grigg.

We were speaking of the difficulty some men have in extricating themselves from the arms of some women, and, of course, vice versa. Franz Liszt, pianist, composer, irresistible magnet for the opposite sex, and eventually Abbé, did it with wit and charm according to the following anecdote. He spent the night with his mistress of the moment at the hotel where she was staying, then walked out on her. In the morning the lady – to give her the benefit of the doubt – discovered she had been abandoned and created a tremendous scene, breaking everything she could lay her hands on. Later in the day she prepared to depart and to pay the bill for her room. The manager of the hotel informed her that the gentleman had paid for it. She then offered to pay for breakages, the crockery, mirror, vase for flowers and picture frames she had smashed. The manager said that the gentleman had left enough money to pay for breakages too.

4 July

Yesterday evening, the first public performance of the revival of *Manon Lescaut* at Glyndebourne. Apparently the star of the show, Nitescu, said at midday that she was too ill to sing; at 2 p.m. she said she might sing; George Christie talked to her and at 6.15 p.m. she did sing – she sang marvellously throughout and was cheered to the echo.

A well-known, not to say notorious, opera critic refused Glyndebourne's invitation to be present, and therefore, like most critics, failed to give great art its due.

Pat Gibson was there, we met him in the garden and talked briefly. He said how happy he was to be eighty-three – he needs to do no more fund-raising. He has had a brilliant career, ending up a lord covered in honours of one sort and another. Pat and Dione Gibson are or could be our friends if my reclusive and their gregarious tendencies could ever bring about meetings. Dione's sister Lavinia Smiley, whom I never knew, once wrote to me to say a book of mine had saved her life, a claim which unfortunately proved not to be true.

6 July

I had lunch with Ben Glazebrook yesterday. He greeted me with the news that Constable has lost a contract bringing in a large part of its annual earnings. As a result, he is going to have to reorganise the company, reduce his shareholding, change his life. He was nonetheless philosophical, could see silver linings to the gathering clouds, and without delay switched the conversation to talking about my interests. He urged the publication of the remaining two volumes of my *Collected Works* – making five in all – in this financial year, before the fifth of April 2000, instead of gradually over the next two years. He wished the whole *Collected Works* might be published under his – the Constable – imprint. I was and am in full agreement.

Should I have been, should I be, more worried?

No recluse has ever entertained more guests than me.

8 July

G has taken our dogs to be stripped of their excessive coats for summer wear. Handling four Cairn Terriers in busy Cliffe High Street after finding somewhere to park her car proves her love of dogs in general and ours in particular.

The BBC is putting on a documentary about life and death in communist Russia. It will show that communism in that country, that country alone, tortured to death ten or eleven times as many people as nazism did likewise to Jews and others. Whereas the BBC has been publicising the sins of nazism and the suffering of the Jews for a good half-century, this programme will surely be its first attempt to draw popular attention to the much more heinous sins and crimes of communism, marxism, extreme socialism and the rabid left in power. Why the silence? Answer: the truth has been systematically censored by our homegrown lefties, who still want to turn England red, blood red. Even my books and stories that refer to the horrific record of marxism/socialism have been reviled by critics who cling to their quaint faith in the godliness of Karl Marx and the marxist 'opium of the people'.

10 July

I have been preparing six of my books for reissue, three in volume IV of my *Collected Works* and three more in Volume V, the final one, so as to have them ready for Ben to publish at short notice if he is to lose his Constable imprint. But I only correct the howlers and the misprints that have weighed on my conscience. I cannot put myself in the various shoes I was wearing when I wrote the books: other writers have not done themselves much good with their belated second thoughts.

Our Prime Minister now threatens to imprison anyone who kills a fox, while he pardons and lets out of prison the IRA's killers of human beings.

11 July

Watched one and a quarter hours of the three hour docudrama *Gulag*, screened last night by the BBC. All the blame for all the casualties of the Russian communist Terror is put on Stalin. This must be to mollify the worshippers of Marx and Lenin, who were at least as, and arguably more, responsible. The bodies of the many millions of victims of the Terror were hidden, so the communists knew they were doing wrong.

12 July

Watched the rest of *Gulag*. Both true and moving, the final statement of the woman of Norilsk in Siberia: 'All our suffering was for nothing.'

Gulag, the TV programme, reminds me of Dieter Tressler. Regrettably, I have never used the autobiographical papers he gave me. But my memory is still fairly reliable, and brevity may be tactful – there have been so many books about terrible individual fates. Is Dieter dead or alive? None of us knows. If the latter, I send him congratulations and love from all the surviving members of my family.

13 July

Dieter's War: my half-sisters Anne and June met him in Austria in the late thirties. He was the son of a famous Austrian actor called Tressler, and was a gentle, fey, romantic and athletic youth. He loved flying and was proud of his pilot's licence. He fell in love with a girl in my sisters' party and dropped red roses on her from an aeroplane.

My sisters invited him to stay at Lyegrove, our home, and he spent ten days or a fortnight with us in the summer of 1937 and again in 1938. He yodelled; he could lift my three sisters, my brother and me simultaneously; he made us a marvellous house in a tree; he climbed a drainpipe and did acrobatics at the top; and in the disused quarry where we swam in spring water he dived off a towering cliff. No wonder we all loved him.

After the war he told me what happened next. The nazis called him up into the Luftwaffe; but he was not prepared to drop bombs on his English friends and decided to seek asylum in Switzerland. He deserted his post, a capital offence, and fled Germany by way of the high mountains at night. All went well until he either missed his footing in the dark or was caught in an avalanche, tumbled downhill and lost consciousness. When he came to he was nearer the Swiss border than he expected to be, only about five yards from it, but he had broken bones, he could not move although he could hear the guards and their dogs, and was duly arrested and condemned to death.

His parents got to know of his plight. They were acquainted with Frau Goering, Emmy Goering, and appealed to her to use her influence in order to save Dieter's life. They were successful up to a point. His sentence was commuted, instead of facing the firing squad he was enrolled in the company of real and so-called criminals who were forced to walk across minefields ahead of the German army. He survived to be captured by the Russians and sentenced to fifteen years in the Siberian concentration camps.

Again, somehow, he survived, returned to Austria and in time contacted my sister Anne. I met him in her house in the sixties and he spoke about his experiences. He was recognisable, his fine physique had served him well, but he said his digestion was ruined by starvation and rotten food. He had done better than most of the other victims of communist justice because he could play tunes on a home-made whistle and draw portraits of his gaolers. He had also won favours by helping to stack the stiffly frozen corpses of his companions as if they had been lengths of wood – they were chucked into mass graves when the weather allowed.

In comparison with the pre-war Dieter with his Viennese temperament, fun-loving, sentimental, irrepressible and charming, he seemed a broken man. He had become a sort of mystic and perhaps a seer – part of him was withdrawn and out of reach. The changes in him were not only understandable, but surprisingly minor in view of all he had been through.

The last we heard of or from him, news he communicated to my sister June, was that he had married a woman much younger than he was.

15 July

Off to Chichester to see Jonathan Cecil acting the part of the Reverend Canon Chasuble in *The Importance of Being Earnest*.

16 July

Jonathan has mastered the art of projecting his own eccentricity. He is now as funny on stage as he always was off it.

17 July

Being my age is like fighting in the trenches in the 1914 war. Friends 'catch one' in the performance of their duties, friends who put their heads above the parapet are 'asking for it', friends are constantly getting wounded and stretchered back to a casualty station, or are shell-shocked by all the bad news and turn into nervous wrecks or take to drink, or fall down and die almost as one is talking to them.

I suppose I should be impervious by now, especially because so many of my friends were older than me. Often it was my books that made friends of us. And how flattering it was to be on friendly terms with them, particularly with the writers and artists, and to be able to turn to them for guidance! The other side of the medal was that I lost them too soon, too soon from my point of view, and sometimes feel I have been in mourning for most of my life.

I had written *Morning* by the time I was in my mid-twenties, and Arthur Koestler thought I was too young to rush into print. I protested that I was not rushing, having been writing full-time and flat out for six or seven years. Belatedly I see his point – I knew nothing of the darker side of life. Yet the books of youth have a quality that age cannot supply.

How brave our ill friends are!

18 July

Another hot blue morning. It is already eleven o'clock and I have done no literary work to speak of – what a change! I used to feel guilty and/or resentful to lose or be robbed of five minutes of my daily five hours of writing.

I have a hankering to tell a love story – a long-short story without cynicism.

Marina Picasso states in an interview that her grandfather Pablo was a hateful monster who wreaked havoc on his rich and miserable extended family. And the other day some know-all told G that Evelyn Waugh died of disappointment, because he thought no one liked his books. Two unsurprising stories!

20 July

Our friend Judy Brittain staying, and going with G to *Rodelinda* this evening. We discussed the Don Juans of our acquaintance, a subject of unfailing interest. She said so cleverly that they fall into two categories: flash mice or flash rats. But I have known Don Juans who were not at all flash. One was a middle-aged stage manager with greying wiry hair and a misleadingly desiccated appearance – he was not rich, handsome, young or smart, but either he said, or others said it, that he never took a ride on a bus without stepping off with a woman in tow. Another Don Juan I know is so small that he must creep into the beds of women without their really knowing he is there and what he is doing to them – I suppose he would be a flash mouse, though not noticeably flashy. All that is certain in this field of study is that men can and do fail to spot the Don Juans in their midst. Tall, dark and handsome may not win the prize – think of all the beauties with their hideous lovers and husbands!

21 July

How did I ever have time to write proper books?

22 July

Not long ago I wrote an essay which I hoped would make another Harlequin book. It was about society, High Society or what is believed in some quarters to be the Society that is High. But the subject was like quicksand – I sank whichever way I turned. The truth is that, although there is a sort of High Society which is secret, exclusive, almost indefinable but certainly indestructible, there are many other societies, cliques, clubs, associations and so on, regarded as the highest of the high by those who yearn to be ushered through the relevant portals and by those already seated at the top tables.

Discreet people never discuss their nearest and dearest publicly. Nevertheless I feel compelled to record that G retired from the Board of Directors of Glyndebourne Productions Ltd yesterday, after serving for thirty-two years, during which period the original level of excellence of its productions has been maintained, and the beloved but rickety old opera house was replaced by the splendid and immediately beloved new one.

23 July

Following on from the above, yesterday we were at the dress rehearsal of Smetana's *The Bartered Bride*, a new production. Glyndebourne has succeeded in making an evening of delights out of an opera that can be as dull as ditchwater.

29 July

Where have the intervening days gone?

Another of my unfulfilled ambitions was to make a collection of comparisons such as 'dull as ditchwater', which have become part of the vernacular. One that I particularly like might be peculiar to Gloucestershire, where I was brought up and first heard it: 'as easy as feeding strawberries to a donkey'. They are apt to have hidden depths. In *Morning* I used the following, 'as easy as falling off a log'. The lady who translated the book into French never understood the ambiguity of the English and I failed to explain it either to her or to my own satisfaction. But now to try again: it is easy to fall off a log, indeed difficult not to fall off, but the fall may land you in a far from easy predicament, hurt you, break a bone, cripple you. The 'easy' meaning is encapsulated within a cautionary tale – the phrase warns that what is easy is not necessarily safe.

31 July

The wives of philanderers find contentment in having their husbands confined to quarters by illness and at last under their thumbs.

Chimney Sweeps, Gardeners' Garters, God's Grace, Mousetail, Smuts, Yorkshire Fog – what are they? Varieties of herbage.

2 August

A modern tragedy, which is as old as the hills: two young people fall in love. She is a strictly brought up virgin who works as a receptionist at an auction house. He is older, not a virgin, a smooth-talking salesman in a smart antique shop. They want each other badly – and she half-believes that sex is now the done thing, while he mumbles persuasive vows and undertakings. They are preoccupied by their sexual communings and experiments – she can think of nothing else. They cross another Rubicon by living together. But after a few months she realises that they have bypassed the authorisation of their love in church. She does not like to mention it, she shrinks from proposing marriage, she waits and hopes, but he says nothing, and she is embarrassed by the tentative inquiries of her family and the advice of her friends. It strikes her that she has given and is giving him her all, and that he has no reason to put the desired ring on her finger and assume a thousand new responsibilities. She loves him too much to leave him, and dare not cease to render any of her services in case he leaves her. She sleeps with and housekeeps for him without joy. She tells him she longs to have a child or children, but instead of taking the hint he groans with horror.

How does it end? She is bound to suggest marriage, and probably to nag him about it. He will then have reason to say they are too unhappy to tie a permanent knot. Her child-bearing years may be running out, his guilt may exacerbate the issue. He is more than likely to run away and marry a girl who has not become his mistress.

The moral of the story is that love is fated unless it is a fair do.

I am sorry to say that the harvest of all my experience, a generalisation proved by few exceptions, is that the twin forces that rule the world are not love and justice, but almost the reverse of those concepts, namely brute force and charm.

5 August

Off to Seaview, IOW, tomorrow for our week-long break. G's aunt had a house there and G's family was invited to stay in summer. She has fond memories of the place, and we have returned to the Seaview Hotel for this week in August for at least ten years. We hope to have the same room and usually get it. We can see and hear the sea fifty yards away at high tide. We walk and watch the dinghy races. At night we are lulled to sleep – with luck – by other holidaymakers eating and drinking and chatting and laughing in the hotel forecourt just below us. Everybody seems to be happy at Seaview.

Anne Higgins stayed with us for two nights and yesterday went to stay with her younger sister June Hutchinson. Anne is eighty. She lives in Marbella, Spain. Last year she fell ill and teetered on the edge of the next world. But she revived, and believes she has been granted a new lease of life by a chic London allergist. Quacks do a good job so long as they inspire confidence.

14 August

Home, home, not on the range, but where complications await.

Read Saul Bellow's *Herzog* on holiday: the whingeing overdone and the brilliance compromised by the showing-off. My best memory of *Herzog* is the following, which with apologies I quote without looking it up in the book: 'The most dangerous people are our leaders.'

15 August

At Seaview, laughing children and kind mothers and fathers made me think of the hearts and lives broken by divorce. Marriage should be made much more attractive financially to contract into, and much more expensive for both parties to contract out of. Women who marry for short-term gain, to wit the alimony, should be penalised, and the state should not subsidise single parenthood. Nothing changes minds and fashions so fast as pleasure or pain in the region of the wallet.

17 August

Sad for Anne Tree, as Michael grows iller daily. Her approach to the prospects and practicalities is selfless, positive and valiant.

18 August

Yesterday's hour-long programme on Channel 4 about the death of Michael Hutchence, a pop singer and the husband or lover of a media person called Paula Yates, was a fascinating insight into the immorality, amorality, perverseness, illogic, and crazed muddle that sections of the media promote nowadays. Hutchence in a hotel room in Australia spent the night drinking wines, spirits and cocktails, took cocaine, Prozac and Valium, and died of masturbating with the aid of asphyxia induced by his belt. The Australian coroner brought in a verdict of suicide, to which Yates was objecting. After revealing the lurid facts of her sex life with Hutchence, which sounded uncommonly like boasting, she explained that for the sake of herself and his child she wished the verdict had not been the discreet one of suicide but the squalid truth of death by wanking with trimmings under the influence of alcohol and legal and illegal drugs.

I have recovered from our holiday.

19 August

Ben Glazebrook and Constable have lost a considerable proportion of their business: what happens next? Ben has invited me to lunch in London to discuss the situation. If he manages to bring out the last two volumes of my *Collected Works*, I will be happy, and I believe that he with his characteristic generosity and integrity will be relieved. But we may end up with three vols of a five-vol edition.

20 August

A beautiful morning, blue sky with a few thin clouds looking like torn-off scraps of cotton wool, warm summery sunshine but autumnal in the shade, and all the people and the flies coming out to play.

21 August

I think more creatively in bed and half-asleep than at other times. I am most likely to solve problems in my work when I am shaving, like the writer Q (Sir Arthur Quiller-Couch). Recent rather unpleasant awakenings could be due to my not writing fiction and not 'living' two lives. In *Evening* I said goodbye to life in the never-never land of fiction. Maybe I was wrong. But a wrong can be righted. There is no law against changes of mind.

22 August

To London tomorrow to give lunch to Richard Tomkins and Miles Huddleston.

24 August

Lunch yesterday was gratifying as well as interesting. Richard told me the second printing of *Evening* was almost sold out. Miles is preparing a biography of James Stern, Jimmy Stern, short story writer and sometime powerful book critic in New York, and has just finished reading thirty years of J's diary, in which he found a mention of me. It refers to the night I spent with the Sterns at Hatch House, Tisbury, Wilts. The visit was no fun: Jimmy got drunk and never stopped nagging Tanya (how did she spell her name?). In the morning after the night before, he eventually emerged from his study to show me a drawing of his 'best friend', the late Brian Howard, notorious homosexual, which made my blood run rather cold. I left with the impression that I was not very welcome, although Jimmy had made more and more of an issue of my not coming down to see and stay with him. Our friendship went from high to low, in that it began with his wonderful letter out of the blue about my *Memoir in the Middle of the Journey*, and ended with the rudest of his increasingly rude letters and my reply that I could no longer continue our correspondence. Why exactly he was cross with me I never knew. He bullied me about not socialising with him more often, but perhaps it was love that he longed for in vain. He suffered from decades of writer's block, and was terribly embittered.

Tanya Stern was German, and before her marriage a physiotherapist in Berlin. Jimmy Stern's father, on being told of his son's matrimonial plans, employed a detective to investigate the fiancée. The detective reported that she was young and pretty and was visited by different men for approximately thirty minutes apiece on every day.

★ ★ ★

Will *Evening* be reprinted again, that is the question. The injustice of the bookshops' right to sell or return books will no doubt muck up our decision. To my knowledge a publisher stopped selling to a chainstore that used to order large quantities of new books and, when the publisher had invested in second printings, would return all the copies it had ordered still in unopened cartons.

27 August

Michael Tree died. He was a gifted draughtsman and painter and an extremely generous man. I only knew him well enough to know there was more to him than I knew. How will Anne manage? She has always lived in a family circle. But I think she will do well as a widow.

Richard Tomkins, self-styled Works Manager, that is to say the Director of Production at Constable who is responsible for my Collected Works, has lent me his copy of *The Children of the Sun* by Maurice Green. I have read one third. The author's subject, in modern jargon the literary glitterati of the twenties and thirties, is amusing; but his method is discouraging for readers. He begins by wading into a quagmire of analysis. His divisions of his 'children' into metaphorical fathers, sons and uncles, into dandies, naïfs, Harlequins, Columbines and Pierrots, hunters and rogues, end in confusion worse confounded by innumerable qualifications – so-and-so is a Harlequin but also a naif with a bit of rogue thrown in and a touch of uncle. I skipped as quickly as I could. But when Green gets down to thumbnail sketches and biographies he is good.

28 August

The Children of the Sun should be called *The Children of the Sewer*. Maurice Green's originals, liberating influences, coruscating talents, dominant personalities, could more accurately be described in the plural of a single inclusive word of four letters. He confirms me in my dim view of writers in general. I hero-worshipped them once upon a time. I stretched every sort of point to forgive Tolstoy his abominable behaviour in his older age. I was merely startled by Dostoevsky losing every penny of family funds by gambling, then beseeching his wife to give him her wedding ring to gamble with. I made allowances for Dickens' harsh treatment of Mrs Dickens, and Hardy for seldom speaking to the second Mrs Hardy, and a large percentage of all writers for their neuroses, psychoses, peccadillos, misdemeanours and offences. Success spoils almost everyone, and literary success seems to be especially reserved for people ready to stop at nothing. Maurice Green's book would justify, if I needed justification, my running a mile from Grub Street and its denizens.

29 August

Those 'children of the sun' were mostly middle class, middle-middle class. Their fathers were publishers or editors or journalists or hack writers, and they were often related, if distantly. A lot of their behaviour was cousinly competition, or sick sibling rivalry. They were snobs and social climbers, and ready to make exhibitions of themselves. They wanted to do better than their dim conventional fathers, while sticking roughly to the paternal lines of work. They also leant to the left. They tried to have it both ways with their capitalist tastes and their communist sympathies. No notice was taken of the crimes against humanity, already bad enough to make normal blood boil or run cold, committed in the USSR.

30 August

Yesterday evening at Glyndebourne was for me and surely many others perhaps the most memorable of countless memorable occasions. First we had the exquisite playing of *The Bartered Bride* overture by the LPO conducted by Jiri Kout, then the performance in the production by Nikolaus Lehnhoff, who must be the best opera producer in the world. It was the last night of the Festival, the audience was as usual well-disposed, recognised a good thing when they heard and saw it, and demanded curtain calls galore. Eventually the curtain rose on an empty stage and Gus Christie, George's second son, who is about to take over the Chairmanship of the opera house, walked on and gave an account of next year's programme. His nervousness did not show, his few words that were not informative were well-chosen, his easy warm yet strong personality came across the footlights, his handsome appearance combined with modesty no doubt had an effect, and he was given a rousing reception by the audience. Gus stepped aside and George entered, composed as ever despite the strain of his devotion to his duties. He spoke with characteristic wit and kept on saying how lucky he had been; but we all know he has made his luck by his own vision, drive, high-class standards, stubbornness and hard work. He was given a prolonged standing ovation, our friend Helen McCarthy, the stage manager, did not bring the curtain down, we all sang *For He's a Jolly Good Fellow*, and the orchestra struck up The Queen according to the Glyndebourne tradition. Men and women of good will and good sense were thanking George and Mary and their family for having kept the flag of excellence and style flying for forty-odd years.

7 September

On 24 August, a fortnight ago, I stopped taking cortisone for polymyalgia, having tapered my dosage almost to nil on doctor's orders. No ill effects, and I feel far better, having lost about half or three quarters of a stone in weight – the false weight, or 'cushion effect', that cortisone is infamous for.

9 September

Lunched yesterday with Mark Bence-Jones at Brooks's. He has written good books – I especially admire *The Twilight of the Ascendancy* – and has been more than kind about mine. He is a generous host, and so learned that he cannot hear a surname without assuming it is linked to some historical event, noble lineage, ancient family, stately home, large estate.

Sentimental politicians of all persuasions have been wailing and gnashing their teeth, if they have any, over the death of Alan Clark, a dreadful man who mocked and sneered at them, and made nothing but mischief.

11 September

High-brow writers who publish porn under pseudonyms are really low-brow. High-class people cannot do low-class things: by acting common and being selfish and impolite you establish your true level. If you do not grace the top drawer, where you tell us you belong, you are fit only for the bottom drawer, the one beneath that which is reserved for the masses, who are not so pretentious.

Martin and Mish Dunne have been staying – a treat for us. They love their dogs almost as much as G loves ours – no one could love them more than she does. Some members of G's family going back for generations have been, and some still are, dog-crazy. But dog-crazy people love the human race too, and are more lovable than dog-haters.

15 September

I was invited to lunch at the Ritz Hotel yesterday. At the table next to ours sat Lady Jay of Paddington, Leader of the Labour Party in the House of Lords, with some young guests – her children by Peter Jay? She was attired in red, no doubt indicating her political inclination, looked very smart, and she and her party drank champagne. I was glad to see that yet another socialist appreciates the flesh-pots.

17 September

A word in the ear of young writers: reveal your politics at your peril. Remember, nothing goes stale quicker than political controversy, and it is never difficult to fall foul of some party politician posing as a literary critic. But you will ignore my advice, at least I hope you will: because the better the writer the more he or she is a moralist, who cannot stand idly by while politicians govern badly, the innocent are maimed or murdered, the intelligentsia applaud, and the majority as usual supports the wrong side.

18 September

Another spy, an academic doctor at Hull University, is unmasked. He is alleged to have worked for the Stasi, the East German KGB, since 1977. I once wrote a play about spying. William Douglas-Home said there were too many spies in it – no audience could follow or believe in the plot; but recent developments suggest there were too few.

20 September

Last night on TV a programme called *The Spying Game* about Robin Pearson, the Senior Lecturer in Economic and Social History at Hull University, made me feel physically sick. He was – and perhaps is – one of the blinkered brainy fools who voted for marxism. He reminded me of those insects who permit another insect to lay an egg in them, and the egg hatches and becomes a grub and devours the insides of its host. His Stasi controllers destroyed him morally and emotionally: whether he noticed or minded is a moot point. He was paid in roundabout ways for endangering other people's lives; forced into thieving; fell in love with a girl given to him and then taken away by the Stasi; his career was governed by the Stasi, he was a puppet on the Stasi string, and too deeply compromised to escape – retreat was blocked by the threat of blackmail – he was no longer human, a soulless mess. As a Polish lady on the programme put it: 'Spies are filthy.' Pearson has now been unmasked, is disgraced, has lost his job and fled the country. On the programme his controllers – and cronies – were so rational and sympathetic, concealing the dire threats implicit in all they did and have done, that it brought home the terrifying expertise of modern totalitarian methods.

21 September

The longest day of each year is 21 June, the shortest 21 December. In another three months the days will begin to lengthen, lighting up the world and ushering in spring. That is my view anyway; G thinks the end of December ushers in winter.

Jonathan Cecil told me about an Edwardian lady who referred to homosexuals by means of the adjective 'musical'. 'He's musical,' she would say – the nicest possible way of putting it.

22 September

Old dogs, like our Meg, get in the way, young ones are clever at keeping out of it.

A short story entitled *Influence*: Jo, a good-looking woman with modern ideas is twenty-eight and unmarried. She is an only child, has loving parents whom she loves warily, holds down an interesting job with prospects, and lives in a flat she is in the process of buying. But her private adult life has been unsatisfactory. As sensitive girls will, she fell in love with an inadequate young drifter to begin with. After three frustrating years of it she extricated herself and in due course yielded to the overtures of a married man at work. It took her another three years to shake off her selfish lover and celebrate her freedom from the opposite sex. More time passed, and one day she shocked herself by being pleased to be pursued in the street by a rough brute.

Her parents were wise and studious, and had learned the hard way to ask no questions and be told no lies. They met their daughter undemandingly, and she kept her secrets. Jo's childhood home was full of framed family photographs. She noticed a new one of a handsome man of thirty or so. Who was he? A colleague of her father. What was he doing on the mantelpiece? Her mother replied that he had become a friend, had returned from a posting abroad and felt a bit lost, had been their guest as they had been his, was a charming chap, and she had not liked to put his unexpected gift of the photo in a bottom drawer. What was his name? Mark Lincoln.

Ten days later Jo noted that the photo was missing and again interrogated her mother. Where was Mark? Put away. Why? His photo aroused too much curiosity. Were they still seeing him? Oh yes. A day or two later a further question was asked on the telephone. Was she ever going to be allowed to meet the mystery man? The answer was: not a good idea, Mark was supposed to be rather a Romeo, even a Bluebeard.

Then Jo insisted on a meeting with Mark: 'To make sure he's a suitable friend for you two,' meaning for her parents. The consequence was that they fell in love at first sight, or almost first sight, married and lived quite happily ever after. The qualification in respect of their courtship, and the temporary hitch, relate to Jo's discovery of a photograph of herself in Mark's wallet. Where had he got it, she inquired, and he replied: 'Your parents gave it to me and in return I gave them my mugshot.'

At a later stage the pair of couples were watching TV together, a programme about arranged marriages in Pakistan. Jo said: 'I think it's horrible, old people fixing up who the young are and are not to marry.' And the others agreed.

25 September

Manners maketh man, yes – and today's manners sometimes seemeth to make boors of both sexes. Old authors always know a thing or two about manners. They have been snubbed by publishers and abused by journalists. Amongst their occupational hazards are the comments of friends and acquaintances. Here are instances culled from my own experience: a lady said to me, 'I've got your book *Morning* on my library list,' approximately forty years after it was published; versions of 'I'm wading through your book' are commonplace; about my social comedy *Gentleman's Gentleman* somebody said 'It's so sad'; on the other hand my tragic story *A Boy with a Bird* was the cause of laughter. Strangers usually ask, 'Do you write under your own name?' indicating that they have never heard of me. Readers of my 'literary' novels often tell me that their favourite authors write whodunits or ripping yarns or soft porn or pop biogs. I gave one of my books to someone, inscribed and signed it, and five years later my next door neighbour rang to tell me that he had been sent the book by a friend of his, who had bought it in a junk shop in Scotland. Still, I am lucky not yet to have suffered the fate of the late Dormer Creston, whose last book written in her eighties was reviewed by Harold Nicolson and called 'promising'.

26 September

Reading Anthony Beevor's *Stalingrad*. The communists in the USSR were far more repressive than the nazis, and for far longer; but when they fought each other they were equally vile. Incidentally, why has no marxist–communist–socialist country, political leader, propagandist, fellow traveller, soldier, secret policeman, executioner or torturer ever owned up and at least apologised?

27 September

Hosts and hostesses who expect their potential guests to accept their invitations and, having accepted, never to chuck, should be given the widest possible berth. They should not be kowtowed to – you should not feel forced to do their bidding when you feel ill or have more important, if not better, things to do. Decent people, civilised people, acknowledge that there is more to people's lives than is common knowledge and respect the privacy of their friends and acquaintances. A case in point is the sufferer from migraine. He or she is usually unwilling to publicise the illness. They can safely socialise only with persons who are fully informed and/or tolerant. The alternatives are either to be entertained while feeling like death or be quarrelled with. For the migraine sufferers, and their concerned partners, social life is a minefield, and the one impossible route through it is to make no long-range commitments of any kind.

This is the eleventh commandment: thou shalt not die of politeness – meaning, do not let politeness be the death of you, do not imperil your life by observation of the social niceties. Remember, for instance, that many people die at funerals, and that the jest of the elderly after they have witnessed the interment, 'It's hardly worth going home,' is another cautionary tale.

28 September

M has much to grumble about. But she grumbled when she had nothing much to grumble about.

The luckiest people grumble most: is it true? Is it not true?

29 September

I dream of fiction. The story I would like to tell is determined to
locate itself in the 1940s, the war years. Every worthwhile writer has
looked back in his books, at the years of his youth, about fifty years
behind the time at which he is writing. I know my preferred
background and atmosphere, and think of a young girl who is simply
nice.

30 September

A skit on the literary life in these politically correct days: a would-
be author writes about his happy youth, his upper-class English God-
fearing happily married and loving parents, their home in the country,
on a farm inherited from ancestors, and his own perfect marriage to
a wife who looks after their children and encourages him in his
work. Result — nothing of his gets published. Yet he ends up famous
and rich: how come? He begins to benefit by writing that he seemed
to remember abuse and beatings by his father, and that he was seduced
by his mother. He keeps on changing his religion: he attacks the
Church of England, switches to Judaism, turns against the Jews, is
converted to Roman Catholicism, satirises the Pope and the Vatican,
is momentarily a Muslim, and then becomes a Buddhist preaching
at Speakers' Corner on Sundays. His next public move is to accuse
his forebears of hard-hearted selfishness, since they accumulated the
capital that reared and educated him. He claims that his great-
grandfather was black — it had been a family secret, but he had
winkled out the truth — and he is therefore a blood- as well as a
soul-brother of the race that he most admires. To get away from the
snobbery of his family, he seldom washes or shaves and looks like a
tramp in photographs. He is strong against all countrified things, the
boredom of living in the country and the stupidity of country folk,
against farmers, animal husbandry and country sports, and describes
the advantages of his new home in a terrace house in the East End,
where his best friends are 'real people', criminals and drug addicts.
He has left his wife, of course, and tears her limb from limb in books
and articles, while boasting about the promiscuity of his sex life. He
also makes copy of his battle to gain greater access to his children,
who, he complains, have been taught by their mother to fear and
hate him. The finishing touches to his great literary reputation are

his announcement that he is bisexual, and is leaving this nasty country to spend his last days in the better climate and the more intellectually stimulating society of Miami, USA.

1 October

Down with the cult of the disgusting! What is the point or the charm of metal studs and rings in lips, tongues, nipples and more private parts? They must get in the way of kisses et cetera, will probably cause cancer, and the idea of a painful and dangerous operation having been performed in probably unhygienic premises is the opposite of romantic. Furthermore, people who take dangerous drugs for pleasure and find joy in a hypodermic needle soon look wrong, smell wrong, and do wrong. To be disgusting is not smart, it is disgusting.

2 October

In my little world not all is gloom and doom. I do not believe I have wasted my life by practising the ancient art of storytelling. I have not lost my faith in the power of the written word, the power for good as well as evil, despite bad books, publishers, journalism and politics. I bow the knee, if rheumatically, before goodness of heart, unselfishness, heroism. I mean to go to church more often, one day, when I am no longer able to offer up my mite of work to the glory of God.

5 October

A nasty great black question mark hangs over the professional prospects of Ben Glazebrook and myself. I have realised that Ben is not going to be able to carry on as before. What is to become of Constable and my friends there? What is to become of Constable's publication of the last two vols of my *Works*? In a bookish context, am I again homeless at my advanced age?

The demon drink crosses my path yet again. My family genes notwithstanding, I have resisted its blandishments to date; but for sixty-odd years I have observed it closely in action, pushing illusions and peddling oblivion. Its votaries are convinced that they can cope with stress better when drunk than sober, can drive better, and are more amusing; that another little drink makes no difference and will do no harm; that they are not addicted to drink and can stop drinking at will; that their unhappy marriages, divorces, sad parents, children and friends, and the fights they get into, are not effects of their alcoholism; and that they are not dying of it.

Syphilis used to be called the English Disease. My guess is that the French called it English in revenge for the male contraceptive being called a 'French letter' in England. Anyway, today the English disease is drunkenness.

7 October

Frosts at night, morning mists rising from the water meadows between us and Newhaven, crisp sunlit days, ever earlier sunsets in red skies.

I am tempted to sponsor an eighth edition of *Morning*. I have sold many copies of my books that ended up in my cellar after their publishers went bust; but they bore the wrong commercial identification, and they are now in short supply. My very own edition could have the right ISBN, making it easier to trace and order. On the other hand, supplying the demands of diligent booksellers and wholesalers would be a development of my cottage industry just when I was thinking of reducing all such commitments.

8 October

Rob, Leslie Robinson, the typographical master-craftsman–artist and the designer of the jackets of my *Works*, also my friend, has sent me a number of mock-ups of possible semi-hard covers of the above-mentioned edition of *Morning*. He thinks it should be a limited and quite luxurious production, whereas my idea was that it should be like a French paperback, and cheap – cheap in price only, I mean and hope.

Spoke to Ben Glazebrook yesterday. He is lunching with me on the 25th.

10 October

Artemis Beevor, née Cooper, daughter of John Julius Norwich who was called Cooper before he inherited his father's title, and granddaughter of Diana Norwich, formerly Cooper, née Manners, whose maiden name might have been Cust since she was acknowledged to be Harry Cust's daughter – Artemis, as I was saying before I wandered into the wilderness of their aliases, has written a book about Elizabeth David, née Gwynne, a member of the landowning family over Eastbourne way, who became the celebrated cook.

The love of Elizabeth David's life, according to her biographer, was Peter Higgins, my late brother-in-law. Peter's marriage to my half-sister Anne was his second and her third. I believe they were happy together, and she looked after him devotedly when he fell ill. Her story bears out the adage about try, try, try again – the third time can be lucky.

Woodrow Wyatt, who was or pretended to be a fan of my books and whose political journalism I admired, has turned out to be treacherous. Of course he was a turncoat, and, although it was honest of him to broadcast his conversion from socialism to capitalism, turncoats are seldom trustworthy. He divulges all available secrets in his diary, and reveals the infidelity of one of his so-called friends, a male acquaintance of mine. This adulterer was afraid of the reaction of his wife to the revelation that she was sharing him with another woman. Luckily he is also a philosopher, and on second thoughts was glad to remember that his wife was almost illiterate, had never read a book in her life and was unlikely to look into Woodrow's, which has no pictures.

16 October

Paid a visit to the Tring Zoological Museum, housing the collections of a scientific Rothschild. The stuffed creatures are amazing – I was struck by the nine-feet tall bears with four-inch claws, and the huge tigers. The fleas in fancy dress are like Dr Johnson's dancing dog, which did not dance well but was remarkable inasmuch as it danced at all. The fleas can only be studied through a magnifying glass. There are two, one wearing man's clothing, the other a woman's dress. They look like nothing on earth, although their garments seem to be knitted – they are in homely knitwear. They were dressed by a Mexican lady long ago, according to a museum note.

18 October

Yes, yes, I agree, the politicians were to blame for what went wrong with this century. But politicians do not have the brightest ideas: the brightest ideas are dreamed up by art. Having just leafed through a Christie's magazine showing the 'modern' pictures for sale, I see clearly that Stalin's gulags and Hitler's concentration camps would have been unthinkable, would scarcely have been possible, without art's obliteration of the human body, its beauty, individuality, ideals and yearnings, blood and nerves. Abstract art made men and women into words or numbers or ciphers. The distortions of art taught the world not to take injuries, people in mortal agony, too seriously. Canvases filled with phony writing mocked culture, crazy collages poked fun at logic, spattered paint gave the go-ahead to anarchy, and bare canvases with or without a coat of paint on them carried nihilism to its dead end. What is the point of abstract sculptures? How future generations will laugh at the hideous lumps of metal littering our public places! The worst 'modern' music – or is it the best? – sounds like choruses from the torture chamber.

20 October

My friend W wanted to give his cousin some financial assistance. But the cousin had socialist sympathies, so W, thinking that he was probably against the hereditary principle, asked if he would be embarrassed to accept money by way of inheritance. The cousin said no.

21 October

Tony Blair puts the blame for everything wrong with this country and this century on 'conservative forces'. Is that a typing error? He must mean 'socialist forces'. Or can he somehow have blanked out the appalling records of the Union of Soviet Socialist Republics and Hitler's National Socialism?

22 October

C J was commissioned by a Russian conductor to write a sort of running commentary on Prokofiev's *Romeo and Juliet* ballet suite, which was to be played in the Royal Albert Hall in a gala in honour of Rudolf Nureyev. Perhaps C J should have smelt a rat – Shakespeare had already done what he was asked to do. The end of the story certainly had a twist. The conductor cancelled the performance in the morning of the day it was to be performed. He had quarrelled with the Russian bass, and flounced out. He – this conductor – was also the sponsor, and is faced with a bill for hire of the hall, for the Royal Philharmonic Orchestra, for participating artists, for C J and the seven thousand or so ticket holders – one million pounds or two or three? What are the odds on his paying up?

24 October

Why buy expensive drugs to make yourself ill? Nature will make you ill for no fee.

26 October

Yesterday I had lunch with Ben Glazebrook. He was like the stag at bay, cornered by the machinations of partners, philosophical in his acceptance of his position, resourcefully planning to extricate himself with a little luck, considering his employees and authors rather than himself, and determined to spare Sara worry. I felt for and admired him. But my future looks bleak: he cannot give the go-ahead for Vols IV and V of my *Collected Works*. I have been suspecting it. I repeated that I would far rather the books came out under the Constable imprint and his control than in any other way. The consolation prize was our agreement that they could be produced by lots of other publishers if the worst came to the worst. Will he succeed in reclaiming something from the wreckage?

27 October

Trollope informed a friend: 'I have written a memoir of my own life and now I feel as though everything were finished and I was ready to go.' In the next six years he wrote fourteen books.

Modern philosophers are not necessarily 'philosophical' in the sense of being wise, kind, privately admirable, and setting the highest standards and the best examples. Bertrand Russell was thought by many to have treated his first wife cruelly and he was certainly unkind to Lady Ottoline Morrell. He was a figure of fun to Rachel Cecil: he came to tea at her childhood home and made passes at her mother under the tea table. Rachel's mother was always scolding him: 'Oh do stop it, Bertie, don't be a bore!' As for Sir Alfred Ayer, meeting him once was more than enough. In my experience he was arrogant, insensitive and rude.

28 October

Iris Murdoch was also a philosopher; but her philosophical cred is marred by the fey strain in her novels and the sudden loss of her grasp of literary reality.

30 October

According to my newspaper Nick Leeson broadcasts the fact that some Dutchmen paid him £60,000 for an hour and a half's talk. Is he lying again, or is the newspaper? He reminds me of the Artful Dodger: he puts all the blame for his crime on the failure of his Barings bosses to catch him. According to that logic, not criminals but the police should be punished for the crimes they have not prevented. His post-penal success story is one of the oldest. The common and not so common people, all the people, have only ever wished to be entertained by monsters.

Times are changing along with the millennium. Homosexuality can now adopt children, it can bathe little boys; has secured its place in the barrack-room; can marry in church, and has many matrimonial rights. Schools will soon be under pressure to teach and preach it. And the age of consent for homosexuals will be lowered to sixteen. The relaxation of tried and tested rules and regulations saddens men who were once pretty boys harried by schoolmasters and lustful youths at boarding schools.

1 November

Morning caused its publisher difficulties because he could not decide whether it was fiction or autobiography. My later books have mostly refused to fit into any precise category or any particular shelf in bookshops – more's the pity, commercially speaking, but thank goodness in other ways. I refuse to be typecast. Lefties call me reactionary, but I was ahead of them in foretelling that communism was a dead letter. Conservative readers shy away from the new-fangled forms of some of my books, *Cautionary Tales for Women*, for example.

2 November

I know the chronology of *The Third Time*, the novel that is still a twinkle in my eye. But will I ever write it? And who will publish it, if not Constable? My friend Vera Brice has both written and spoken to Tweedledum at the Superior Press about my work.

3 November

Is Catherine – Cath – a good name for the heroine of *The Third Time*? Surname: Allen? Another Christian name – Lily? Lily Allen sounds fresh and clean.

4 November

I am too discreet to be a diarist – I cannot bring myself to dish dirt, and deliberately hurt feelings. Alan Clark's caddishness and Woodrow Wyatt's treachery have served their diaries well: monstrosity pays. Parson Woodforde's diary is a list of his dinners, but food must have been his passion and passion is an aid to readability.

5 November

Tonight is Bonfire Night in Lewes. The seventeen Lewes martyrs burned at the stake for their Protestantism will be remembered as well as the failure of the Catholic plot to blow up Parliament. People annually flock into the town from far and wide, the Bonfire Societies march backwards and forwards behind bands from early evening till late at night, there are banners and floats and good-natured anti-popery signs and symbols, then final flurries of fireworks which drive our dogs half-mad. The celebrations deserve support if only because the spoilsports work harder and harder at denying people a bit of fun: the BBC tries to compare Lewes to Northern Ireland, and the cries of bigots, prudes and prigs are that it is politically incorrect, provocative, barbaric, dangerous, orgiastic, noisy, and usually coincides with bad weather. I shall therefore go along to see the sights. Charities get a lot of money from the event.

6 November

Tweedledum of the Superior Press has shown interest in my work and wants to see samples of anything I have written with a London setting; so this morning – without asking questions, for instance why the London connection? – I sent him a letter, a copy of Vol II of my *Works* containing three books including *The Best of Three* which has eight out of its fifteen stories linked to London, and a TS of *Harlequinade*.

8 November

Idea for a short book of manners entitled *How to Grow Old Gracefully*. Here are a few random rules that should be followed by men: keep yourself clean; get your clothes cleaned as often as possible; do not wear rags; invest in new sober-looking garments; no down-at-heel shoes; do not let your hair grow long; buy a magnifying shaving mirror; only grow a beard in special circumstances and when you can have it properly trimmed; beware dandruff; go to the dentist; never say 'It will see me out' or 'I have bought my last overcoat/air ticket/car'; remain aware of your posture; never stoop or shuffle; never hurry; never drink too much or take drugs that change your personality; try not to complain; do not become a monologuist; sympathise with others if possible; be your age!

Ben seems to have opted for going in with Nick Robinson of Robinson Publishers; but I have not spoken to him for some time now.

9 November

A good few of my tips for the older man also apply to women of a certain age, but I would add the following: forget about the passage of time while you remember to exchange your old charms for new ones; yesterday's naughtiness and sulks and pouts will charm no one, and you will have to work harder in order to be popular; steer clear of fashionable clothes; dress to suit your shape; wear trousers with discretion; never even think of shorts; never run anywhere if you can help it; never have a face-lift on the cheap; dye your hair if you must with caution – you will probably regret it anyway; interest yourself in something other than the opposite sex; retain your femininity whatever your sexual orientation; laugh at life however tempting it may be to cry; carry on loving.

Spoke to Ben at last. He has had too many worries to keep everybody informed. He now has hopes of rescue and survival.

10 November

'The hero of my tale ... is truth,' Tolstoy wrote in *Sevastopol*. I have laid claim to a similar aim in my work. The ethics of this century show clearly the 'beauty' – Tolstoy's word – of truth.

11 November

In private life truth without tact can be unbearable. But in all human relationships, not to mention our relations with animals, lies are hell. Nowadays the matrimonial vows are lies in a large percentage of cases. Egalitarianism is both a popular political cry and a whopper: men always were, are still, and will always be born unequal, and, I hasten to add in the present pedantic climate of opinion, women ditto. Socialism in its charitable, unselfish, anti-capitalist guise is a confidence trick – socialists are as keen to feather their nests as everyone else, and preach that we must do as they say, not as they do. Communism invented organs of repression that were professionally committed to 'brainwash' truth into untruths.

The trouble with truth is that it can be perverted by faith.

13 November

I love our ambiguous language, and ambiguity has figured in various ways in my work. In two books, *Hope Cottage* and *Money Matters*, the narrator of each is disappointed not to have written the book he had in mind, not to have written any book, while his regrets actually add up to one. His notes for the book he had planned are a complete but different book, and the story of his failure is a success inasmuch as it is in print and published – a point often missed.

14 November

I spend more time watching television than reading. When I was young I read a lot and wrote slowly, later on I began to write a lot and read less. But the admission that I am no longer an avid reader is not another proclamation that the end is nigh for literature. On the contrary, although I watch nonsense on TV which does not affect my work or influence me, I take up a good book with relief. For me the moving image has never been a match for the allure of the written word and its effect on the imagination, and I believe the same must apply to others now and in future.

16 November

The relationships of siblings in their later years are fraught with an accumulation of difficulties. Overlaying the problems of their shared childhoods are the differences of their adult experience, the different interests, the different friends. I knew in my bones that my dear brother and I liked talking to each other on the telephone better than meeting. With my darling sister Rose I had to pretend to be somebody that I no longer was.

17 November

About *Evening*, I fear it has been another casualty – to an extent – of the tribulations of Constable.

18 November

A call from Ben, warning that he was sending me a Press Release by fax. The fax announced the merger of Constable with Robinson Publishing, the creation of Nick Robinson, Jim Lees-Milne's great-nephew. I rang Ben after reading the fax, saying, 'I believe I must congratulate you'. He explained that the merger was a rescue operation inasmuch as Nick was moving his whole operation into the Constable premises next month and thus taking over the extremely expensive lease and rental, which otherwise would have ruined Ben and/or bankrupted the company. Murray and Methuen had both rejected a deal because they did not want to move house or help with Ben's rent. He was realistic about the 'clash of cultures' between Constable, an old-style publisher, and Robinson Publishing, a more commercial operation. He said that one of his priorities would be to clear the way for the publication of Vols IV and V of my *Works*, and that he hoped there would be no objections. He would be the Chairman of Constable and Robinson Ltd with a small shareholding and reduced responsibilities. He felt vastly relieved, he said.

This signals a change for me as well as for Constable. What I was waiting for, one of the things I was waiting for, has come to me, as they say in China. It looks as if I may not need to look elsewhere for a publisher willing to complete the edition of my life work (or nearly my life work). A feeling of anti-climax is mainly my response.

Oddly enough, I have never worried much about finding myself without a publisher. I wrote *Memoir in the Middle of the Journey* while pretty sure that Jock Murray would hate its unusual form and reject it, and *Eleanor* after Sinclair-Stevenson Ltd shut up shop and I had no idea where or when it would be published.

I suppose the news from Constable should remove one of the reasons for my marking time in this journal; but I have been bitten too often by publishers not to be shy.

20 November

Cherie Blair aged forty-five is having another baby. Tony Blair or one of his spokesmen has said it was 'unexpected': like the consequences of his political initiatives and acts.

22 November

Covent Garden Opera House has spent some of the money we and others donated to its refurbishment on abolishing the entrance in Floral Street and the staircase that led to the old Royal/Directors'

Box and, I think, to one of the balconies. This was done so that all the people must enter in the same way, the egalitarian way, according to some senior spokesperson. How inconvenient! How babyish! But the management continues to charge elitist prices for seats to make up for frittering our money away.

23 November

At least I have served a novelist's apprenticeship inasmuch as my life has included feast and famine, narrow squeaks, good times and hard times, beds of roses and a palliasse in sundry barrack-rooms for private soldiers, some success and my share of the other – in short, I have inside information about most classes and conditions of existence. When I began to write professionally, one or two people urged me to work my way round the world so as to acquire copy for my stories. My advisers got me wrong. If my writings specialise in anything, I would say it was the female heart.

Nothing from Tweedledum. Why not private publication from now on?

24 November

My *Morning* began as a short story. I plotted almost every sentence of *Tug-of-War*, and spontaneity suffered in consequence. I did not know how *His Christmas Box*, *The Social Comedy*, *Money Matters* and *Evening* ended until I had written everything except the final pages. I announced that *Evening* was my 'last' book largely because I could not again face the strain of composing impromptu, so to speak.

26 November

To cut is half the battle of writing. To have the nerve to cross out, to be hard-hearted enough to part company with your favourite bits, and regret nothing, is half the art as well as the battle. There is no remedy to compare with a cut – rewriting is unprofessional and inserting afterthoughts is often a mistake.

Good writers do not make good critics of other writers' books. You are one thing or the other. Tolstoy told Chekhov he was a failure.

Great critics are rarer than great writers, they have to be more generous.

If you love literature, never read biographies of your dearest authors written in the modern style, that is at enormous length, omitting no personal detail, and without a trace of affection. Great writers are easy to debunk, in the first place they are bound to be strange, and in the second the effort of creating a masterpiece drives most of them mad. Margot Oxford's paradox, 'Genius is closely allied to sanity,' is true in that books of genius display qualities of perception and practical skill that are pre-eminently sane, but misleading in that to preserve the emotional, mental and physical balance required throughout the composition of such work is to strain resources intolerably in most cases. Shakespeare, was he again the greatest exception?

27 November

I became a professional writer not when I began to write for far too many hours a day, nor when I was having a few one-act plays performed on London mini-stages, nor when I set to work on *Morning*, nor even long after that, but when it was much easier for me to write than talk, when I found out exactly what I had been thinking by writing it down, and was not incurably ashamed of what I had written.

Professionalism is also defined by whenever a writer learns not to take risks. A pro stops before he is exhausted, because he is aware that to take a wrong turning in a piece of work may well be irremediable. A pro knows intuitively how long a book or story or chapter should be, and does not ramble on and cause himself future headaches. A pro has found not only his 'voice', the 'tone' of his writing, the way he can communicate with his readers, he has also found, metaphorically and metaphysically, in his facility for using words and making sentences, a kind of home.

How to exclude ego from a diary? My egoistic answer is that I cannot answer the question. There is another I in the above: please accept my apologies. Yet yours truly would have been glad to get such tips about writing when he was beginning.

28 November

Just over three weeks to the shortest day of the year, hurrah!

The upside of having four Cairn Terriers outweighs the downside; but the downside in the case of Meg begins to outweigh the upside. Meg is fourteen and a half. She now has most of the disabilities that her age suggests, and I personally think her time has come – I mean time for a last trip to the vet. It would be merciful since she now loses her way in our garden and is likely to come to harm one day. Moreover she is blind and we have a lily pool. But occasionally the sweeter side of her nature reasserts itself, and physically she retains her beauty.

Tomorrow to London for lunch with the Glazebrooks.

30 November

Nothing decided. The occasion, our lunch, was very enjoyable, but Ben was unable to say much about the prospects for Vols IV and V – they are largely dependent on Nick Robinson now.

My distant cousin and namesake rang up the night before last. He is one of the four Julian Fanes alive at the present time. He says he is almost blind – he is also deaf. When he asked me what my wife used to be called, he reinterpreted Gilly Swire as Golly Squires.

1 December

It is high time I stopped writing about writing. Listening to those fashionable pseuds gassing about 'doing' their 'art', or rather trying not to listen to them on arts programmes, puts me off.

I shrink from becoming my own publisher so late in the day. With a little regret, I record what John Crook said to me yesterday evening. He had shown me the Harlequin Edition copies of *The Harrison Archive* produced by himself, text, end papers, binding, everything, and I had signed them on the limitation page, and we were talking over the possibility of our uniting to publish *Harlequinade* and other unwritten books of mine. Referring to the prospect of the marketing and distribution of such books, he said: 'The problem is, we're only interested in trying to create a work of art.'

2 December

Off to Brighton to meet my old friend Val May for lunch and afterwards to a matinée of his production of *The Importance of Being Earnest* at the Theatre Royal. G has never met Val. I have not seen a play directed by him for between forty and fifty years. Yet he and I and a few others shared our youthful aspirations, and he directed my first play, a one-acter entitled *Something Dangerous*: it was about a girl evangelist, genuine or a fraud, torn between sacred and profane love, a melodrama which Val fashioned into a minor success. He went on to direct hundreds of plays here and on Broadway, and is now semi-retired, but exactly as he was in the old days, unspoilt and diffident.

3 December

G and Val took to each other, and we and the rest of his audience loved his version of Wilde's play, which was labelled foolish and ephemeral by Bernard Shaw a hundred years ago. Val said afterwards that the danger for all involved in staging it is that if the mood or communicative force of a performance is lost there is nothing to hang on to, really no characterisation or even human interest – it is all about blowing bubbles and keeping them in the air. I hope I am not misquoting him. He was complimentary about my work, and amazed by its virtual boycott by the literary establishment that occurred in the middle of my career. He is not much of a reader, except for reading plays, he never was a book reader, but he did read my *Social Comedy*, thought highly of it, and repeated yesterday that it would make a good film, in fact was ready-made for filming. Why was it not in paperback? He pointed out that lip-service is paid by all the arts buffs to the search for quality, quality writing, quality entertainment, yet they ignore my books, the early ones of which were praised to the skies.

6 December

My godson, a successful media consultant, tells me that no best-selling author would think of signing a contract unless £500,000 was guaranteed for 'marketing', to be spent on advertising or hyping the book in question. If true, how literary!

7 December

This morning I rang Tweedledum. Anti-climax number one, the telephone was not answered for ages; anti-climax two, Tweedledum was in New York. Luckily Vera Brice had given me the name of another Superior Press bigwig, Tweedledee, and I was put through to him. He advised me not to wait for Tweedledum to make up his mind. Still more anti-climactic was his warning that if or when Tweedledum had read my book he would still want others' opinions. No no no – I feel I cannot go back to the proprietor of a publishing house who lacks the confidence or the right to back his own judgment. On the strength or weakness of the above I studied my list of Vera's candidates and picked out Stuart Proffitt, now working at Penguin, and cracked up to be a fine publisher. I rang Penguin. At least someone answered the telephone promptly. But I was then put through to yet another answerphone, on which in no doubt a gloomy tone of voice I left my telephone number. The publishing business has gone downhill since I was involved in it. We were hungrier than today's publishers seem to be, and would not have dared to risk any loss of custom.

9 December

To London tomorrow to lunch with my two British Library ladies, who some years ago accepted the bequest of my archive.

11 December

Lunch yesterday with the Curator of MSS at the BL, Ann Payne, and the Curator of Modern Literary MSS, Sally Brown. The meetings of our trio have rarity value, since they only happen once a year. We seem to resume exactly where we left off twelve months previously. As always they were full of interesting information about the literary scene in general and morale in museums in particular. Apparently the Government, and specifically the misnamed Department of Culture, have infiltrated representatives of its 'thought police' into museums, who insist on political correctness. Everywhere, the egalitarian levelling is without exception downwards – soon the 'people' will have nothing to admire.

12 December

I have been so busy with practical matters and concern about Vols IV and V that I have hardly spared a thought for *The Third Time*. I would say that my thoughtlessness is the ideal method of plotting and planning a book – it leaves all to the unconscious. Whether or not I am right remains to be seen.

What are Buckies, Chinaman's Hats, Fool's-caps, Piddocks, Quahogs, Tritons, Volutes? Answer: sea shells.

15 December

At Covent Garden Opera for *Falstaff* yesterday evening. The music was as good as ever and the singing fine throughout, but I disliked the production – actually I could not understand chunks of it, and find that I admire Graham Vick and his colleagues less and less.

The refurbished opera house is a vast curate's egg. The best bits from this customer's point of view are the Floral Hall, especially when nearly empty, some of the outlying passages despite low ceilings, and the mercifully unaltered-in-looks auditorium. The bad or worse bits are the heaviness of the main entrance doors, the rather cheerless floorboards that replace the carpet in the stalls, the swirl of chill air-conditioning in Row L on stage left, and unsatisfactory architectural changes to the old Crush Bar. The gents' toilet is a success. I saw no signs of the People's Palace of Blair's vapourings; on the contrary, elitism seemed rather more rampant – our tickets were more expensive, not cheaper.

Our operatic evening was a great treat, setting aside the art and the politics, and we are truly grateful.

16 December

We are going to have a Thai lunch with John and Diana Crook to celebrate the completion of the Harlequin Edition. The first of the fifteen little books was signed by me and published in July 1995, and the fifteenth in December 1999 – the Edition has been roughly three and a half years in the making. John became more expert at printing and binding the books as he went along – they were manufactured from scratch by himself alone in his attic. The layout of text, the quality of marbled end-papers, not to mention the combinations of coloured papers we chose for each title, grew at once more refined and more striking. And the numbers of copies he could produce – between fifteen and thirty – were so small that the whole edition, always a rare item, has now been whittled down to four or five saleable sets.

Still no word from Tweedledum, to whom I wrote on 6 November. Publishers' time differs from our idea of time. Ben Glazebrook's manners are exceptionally good by all standards and perhaps unique in his profession. Jock Murray redeemed many of his failings in my estimation by the courtesy of his letters.

A wild night of wind and rain last night; but we thanked God again for the roof over our heads, and I was comforted by my memories of a book I read as a boy, *At the Back of the North Wind*, which describes sleeping in a hay loft over a stable for carthorses. The wind blew and buffeted in the story, but the young hero is snug and cosy up there in the hay, warmed by the breathing of the great horses below, and lulled to sleep by the movements of their hooves on the straw and cobbles, and their companionable equine equivalent of snores.

18 December

How to write about love nowadays? Nearly all the sexual frontiers have been crossed by writers through the ages and in our century. I cannot help feeling that even pent-up voyeurs have had enough of hackneyed sex scenes in books, and actors and actresses heaving and groaning in cinemas and in our homes on TV. All love stories are different, however small the difference, but sex boils down to being roughly the same. Bad writers and cheap film makers may make money by ignoring that fact of life – artists can no longer do so, they have to find other ways of redefining romanticism.

The latest cinematic fashion is that the woman undresses the man –

she does it with the expertise of a prostitute although she may be acting the part of a teenage virgin, whereas in real life most people know that male clothing is nearly as mysterious as female, buttons often refuse to go through buttonholes, ties get knotted, zips catch in shirt-tails, in pants and even in penises, and trousers cannot be pulled over shoes. The more natural proceeding, that the man undresses the woman, is apparently old hat. Lovers in films seldom get into bed: the climate in Hollywood is warmer than the climate in Carlisle or Inverness; and towels, such an important adjunct to adultery, are conspicuously absent. Film lovers sleep entangled together, post-coitally: not an insomniac, not a restless writher, let alone a thunderous snorer, amongst them.

19 December

Sensuality has a hard time of it in the busy world of today. Most men, what with work in the money mill, TV, sport and possibly paternity, have time only for the quickest of sexual fixes. The art of seduction, in modern lingo 'foreplay', is confined to the Australian model: 'Brace yourself, Sheila!' But quick fixes quickly become boring in a book, except maybe for schoolchildren of all ages. Courtship, not consummation, is the real stuff of love stories, and, in a sense, of fiction in general. The best books now have to have recourse to the secret language, the intimate signals, that arouse – and possibly please – sophisticated readers. Film directors will have to try to be more subtle and present the dramas enacted by eyes; the sexual capabilities of lips and smiles; the power to excite of the movements of hands; and remember that the removal of a necktie or a woman's rings or earrings or spectacles, can be more of a thrill than seeing paid performers doing sexual gym in the altogether.

Neurosis has a field day with sex. The unpredictability of neurotics drives their lovers round one bend or another. Neurotics are too keen on sex or too averse to it, or often both. They are apt to enslave their partners by means of the aphrodisiac of their sudden changes of heart, and the effect on their other bodily organs. Their love-making is the more intense because they fear it may be the last time, because it is additionally fired by desperation, guilt and contrition – they are trying to make up for all the trouble they have caused. They are dangerous people, they as it were carry a fatal infection, and their partners, although they may say adieu and retreat and flee, can easily find that those individualistic kisses and nights of wistful passion are irreplaceable.

Love need not be consummated to be consuming. Chateaubriand is supposed never to have possessed Madame Recamier, although they were lovers for years and she spent so much time on a *chaise longue*. She is supposed to have said that if she had given all of herself to him she would have lost him, meaning that as he was or had been a potent womaniser she kept on pleasing him by offering something different. The love-life of French sophisticates is not a firm foundation for generalisations about sex or no sex. Yet in cold climates the same phenomenon is recorded. Hazlitt in his intriguing *Liber Amoris* describes his enslavement by a chit of a girl he scarcely touched. And I know of representatives of both sexes who hang on to normal healthy lovers in spite of ruling out fun and games.

20 December

The 'emancipation' of women gets two cheers. The third cheer is held back because 'emancipation' suggests love has been unshackled, that love is at last free, and free love is one of the benefits won by the revolt of the fair sex. H.G. Wells preached and practised it, and men have been giving tongue ever since. But, even while women run countries and are at liberty to sleep around, bear illegitimate babies, and join men's clubs, the emotional and physiological conditions of their lives, and in innumerable cases their material and financial welfare, are exactly the same as they always have been; and to think otherwise is asking for trouble.

21 December

The Church of England is under a three-pronged attack, first and foremost from the enemy within, who have censored the poetry in the Bible, and introduced absurd and embarrassing practices into its services; secondly from its homosexual priests, the consequent publicity, and the muddle about it all at the top; and thirdly from the spoilt population of this affluent country, and the facile and shallow cynicism of its media people who pull long noses at any person or institution unlikely to answer back.

To call the spirit of the age iconoclastic would be to dignify what is more like street wit and anarchy. Respect for virtue is a dead or dying letter – and what is sacred? Blasphemy is a new line in music-hall patter. Our Queen is mocked for serving her people with lifelong and selfless devotion, and republicans bare their teeth at her while – in my lifetime – presidential despots, tyrants, homicidal maniacs, sadists, embezzlers, thieves and lunatics, not to mention the warmongers, the alcoholics, the satyrs, rule other countries and usually escape punishment for their crimes.

A young man of my acquaintance, well-favoured and clever, was repeatedly either pushed out or walked out of good jobs, deserted lovely and loving girlfriends or was given his marching orders, switched sides politically, changed his mind, came to grief and seemed incapable of mending or seeing the need to mend his ways. A friend of his and mine explained that he 'had a little problem with authority' – a brilliant and charitable description of square pegs, rebels without a cause, members of the awkward squad, and class warriors – the worst people and sometimes the best.

23 December

Rejection slip – actually a peculiar and even illiterate letter – written on behalf of Tweedledum probably by an office boy being cared for in the community of the Superior Press.

24 December

It is Christmas Eve, and a second letter arrived from the Superior Press today, translating the first into English. Tweedledum has taken about six weeks to tell me that he has no room in his list for my work. Yet, via Vera Brice, he invited me to submit that work.

★ ★ ★

Cooking tomorrow instead of writing – we shall be in the kitchen, preparing to feed my sister June, husband Jeremy and son Christopher. Happy Christmas everyone!

26 December

We went to church yesterday morning. The officiating priest read the

Communion Service well, but his explanation of the Nativity managed to translate a mystery into an enigma. Anyway, I gave thanks for my many blessings, not least for the one – G – who knelt beside me.

27 December

It would be against the odds that Eng. Lit. will do much in a world-beating way in the foreseeable future. Our glory days ended half a century ago, our language is showing signs of decrepitude, and we are no longer a united kingdom. Great books are written as a rule in nations where conditions prevail that are the exact opposite of ours.

Doubtless – probably – possibly – maybe! After all, the millennium is just round the corner, the fate of prophets is often to be proved wrong, and temperamentally I need to strike a positive note. There is no telling, nor foretelling, what good writers will write. There are flowers of autumn as well as of spring. There is even good work that has emerged from the ends of centuries, when civilisations are apt to break up and break down.

30 December

Subject for a novel: a girl of good family rebels against parents, siblings, home, school, and feels lost and angry. She gravitates to a psychiatrist, who hears her out over a year or two of sessions, then tells her to make peace with the world. This is not what she wanted to hear, so she goes to another psychiatrist, and another and another. At last she finds one who satisfies her: his message is that she is right and everybody else is wrong, she must vent her anger on all the people she is angry with, express her hatreds, get all the bile out of her system. How does the story end? It would be poetic justice if the girl turned on her evil genius and exposed him in a book or newspaper.

31 December

The writer Malcolm Bradbury is urging fellow-writers to forsake their computers and take up the pencil instead, so perhaps I have been at the cutting edge of literary technology all along without knowing it.

We will be celebrating the birth of Jesus and the beginning of Christianity tonight. The two Christian millennia are a blink of the eye of time. But religion has existed as long as we have, and all religions unite in defending us from death.

I wish I was a better Christian – I owe Christianity a bigger debt than I have repaid, though I have tried to stand up for it in my books. It helped me through many crises in my life, and I hope it will do so in the days ahead.

1 January 2000

We saw the old year out and the new millennium in at Glyndebourne. It is not possible to thank the Christie family adequately for all the enjoyment they have given us and a good few million others. There was a party on the stage for the permanent company and friends of the Christies. In the enormous stage area tables for ten were arranged under spectacular lighting, spotlit pools of light for each table. The tables were beautifully laid around central vases filled with white paper chrysanthemums, trailing ivy and theatrical golden spikes – the chrysanthemums were those used on the stage sets of *Pelléas and Mélisande* and *The Bartered Bride*. There were a couple of large TV screens which would show the ceremonies in London at midnight. The schedule was tight: we had to sit down to dinner and finish eating on various dots. All was good, all went smoothly, and the generosity over wines and liquid refreshments was lavish. Then we had speeches and a cabaret performed by the stars of international opera. When they stopped, our attention switched to the TV screens, and eventually the clock for a second or two showed '00'. Cheers from everywhere – G was with me and we embraced. Kisses and good wishes were exchanged generally – Auld Lang Syne was being sung on the telly – and the high decibel band for dancing struck up. It was time for us to leave, and we said as many goodbyes as possible and drove home through the deserted and peaceful streets of Lewes to find we had not been burgled.

EXTRA TIME

2001

1 January 2001

Where was I?

Oh yes – a whole year has passed – and after a night disturbed by fireworks – last one heard between 2 and 3 a.m. – I am trying to remember all the loose ends left dangling by my 1999 diary.

2 January

Our hometown Lewes has a Chinese-style passion for fireworks. Any excuse is a good excuse for my neighbours to let off a few. Not only the dogs of Lewes have had enough of sights and sounds that mimic war.

To recap: Ben Glazebrook's company Constable merged with Robinson Books – Constable and Robinson Ltd was created. But Nick Robinson ruled out the publication of fiction – no more proper novels – which meant that the last two volumes of my *Collected Works* were disallowed and would not get into print.

However, Ben urged me to be patient. And in the first six months of last year, 2000, he was pleased to report increasingly close co-operation between Constable and Robinson. At last, after an interruption of about fifteen months, Ben obtained Nick Robinson's agreement to honour my contracts and complete the edition. The two books in question are now in the final stages of production and are due out in June of this year, thanks be and much to my relief.

12 January

Ten days have passed since my last entry. We went to Venice to celebrate our silver wedding, where I was attacked by vertigo. Venice was the up, we had spent our honeymoon there, my giddiness and nausea were the down. But how lucky we are to have been in Venice, and how lucky I am to be able to stand up straight, courtesy of some little white pills and the NHS!

Venice was flooded repeatedly during our four-day visit. Dinner on the last night of our stay was served by waiters in waders – they had to wade through a flooded area to reach the kitchen.

To carry on from where I left off ten days ago: last year I managed to publish personally the 8th edition of *Morning*. It was originally launched by John Murray in 1956. Nearly fifty years later it still sells in small quantities. To keep it alive, and looking better than in any of its previous incarnations, had been an ambition of mine for months. Leslie Robinson and Vera Brice, the latter presiding over the Production Department of Harper Collins, designed the 8th edition. The imprint used, St George's Press, derives from the company of the same name which I helped to found and, in time, voluntarily to wind up – St George's Press is also the name of my cottage industry of selling back numbers of my books. At last the finished article, two hundred and fifty numbered copies signed by the author, in a superior jacketed paperback format much admired by connoisseurs, burst upon the wide world last September.

The tally so far is that I retain just under two hundred copies, which suits me quite well, taking the long-term view. The exercise has been successful in my own estimation – not too many downs in the context. But I had never before published anything of my own, and now I am in a position to join in the chorus of advisers against doing it yourself. Here again I was lucky – my text was not vandalised by uncorrected errors like Proust's, nor was I conned or robbed as colleagues of mine have been. The fact remains that the slog involved, and the risks and responsibilities incurred, are incommensurate with the rewards in my own case and, I suspect, in the great majority of cases.

The next slices of my literary life are typical of all my recent experience. In 1999, while writing *Marking Time*, I itched to stop keeping a diary and to go back to fiction. Eventually I did so, brought forth the novella I had been gestating, *The Third Time*, and immediately wished to, and then did, write two more novellas, *The First Nail* and *The Last Straw*. Each was forty-odd thousand words in length, as against sixty to eighty thousand for a full-length modern novel, and I hoped to get them published separately, making three short books – after all, nobody nowadays is supposed to be able to concentrate on anything for more than minutes.

13 January

Ben Glazebrook read *The Third Time* and approved of it, but, as was established following the merger of Constable with Robinson, he was no longer in a position to publish fiction. After many sheltered years with St George's Press and Hamish Hamilton Ltd and Constable, I was on my own in the literary jungle, armed with nothing more than advice from friends that some of the wild beasts might be kinder than others. I contacted six publishers: with one exception they behaved atrociously. My letters were not answered, my telephone calls were ignored, the publishers misled me or lied, had no manners, were as contrary as spoilt children, venal yet missing the point of remunerative offers, knew nothing and, again by my standards, had closed minds and no imagination. If there should ever be a genuine study of the decadence of English literature in the second half of the twentieth century, students would find most of the information required by looking at the majority not of writers but of publishers. The lone exception to the above, while I was searching for someone to publish me, rejected *The Third Time* with grace and regrets, and for reasons beyond his control.

At that point I gave up – I had neither the time nor the inclination to be treated like dirt. Despite the strain and stress I would do the job myself. Again, my friendly experts gathered round and supplied suggestions and estimates. The best suggestion was to do the three books in paperback with black titles on red covers, and sell them either separately or in a semi-transparent plastic box. But the cost of a production of that sort was prohibitive. And however the books were produced, the problem of distribution remained – they would have to be marketed, not buried in my cellar. Two distributors were recommended to me: one never responded to my inquiry, which might have put money in his pocket, the other was so extraordinarily pessimistic and defeatist that I was pleased to say to him, 'No, thanks'.

In the middle of all this, late last autumn, the proofs of Volumes IV and V of my *Collected Works* arrived. Proof-reading approximately half a million words was both a distraction and satisfactory.

But when the 10 kg of printed matter had been posted back to Constable I was confronted by the same problem. What was to become of my possibly final, and unusually fecund, year's work? The long up of the joys of creation began to deteriorate into the down of fearing that the destination of my three stories might be my bottom drawer or wastepaper basket.

I mentioned my difficulty to yet another friend, who asked why I had not spoken to the Book Guild.

Suffice it to add for the present that I am now waiting to clinch a contract for the publication in a single volume of my three *Tales of Love and War* by the Book Guild of Lewes.

14 January

Last night on the four main earth-bound channels of television, as I zapped from one to the other as quickly as I could, I was disgusted by relentless references to excrement. Not only the adult morons of today's entertainment industry are attracted verbally to faeces and sewage, the lumpen-intelligentsia follow the fashion. A theatrical producer at the top of his particular tree, while producing a high comedy written by a famous foreign playwright and translated by a friend of mine, inserted rude words in the text and introduced farting into the action.

15 January

Here is a list of Queen Victoria's descendants who have surprising nicknames: 'Affie', Duke of Edinburgh and Coburg, d 1900; 'Liko', Prince Henry of Battenberg, d 1896; 'Ernie', Grand Duke of Hesse, d 1937; 'Alicky', Tsarina of Russia, murdered 1918; 'Mossy', Princess of Hesse, d 1941; 'Nando', King of Rumania, d 1927; 'Ducky', Grand Duchess of Hesse, d 1936.

18 January

I cannot say I am sorry that Auberon Waugh is dead. The hoary adage about not speaking ill of the departed is absurd – can one not say that Adolf Hitler was a devil? Waugh carried on a vendetta against me and my work for many years. I have no idea why, I never met or had words with him or wrote to him. Some would suggest that he thought my writing so bad that he wished to censor it out of existence; but I have published at least four times as many books as he did, have had a five volume collected edition of my books published while still alive, and his sister Harriet Waugh wrote a charming review of my *Happy Endings*. I think he must have been as crazy as his father, though much less gifted. Long ago Patsy Grigg reported to me that she had met Waugh at some dinner party and remonstrated with him for denigrating me in different ways, to which he replied: 'A lot of people say the same thing, and the more they say it the more I shall denigrate' – or words to that effect. More recently he got himself invited to stay at Badminton, where he sat next to my sister-in-law at dinner. The next morning my sister-in-law rang to ask me: 'What on earth have you done to Auberon Waugh?' – a question referring to his public diatribe against me. In the distant past he reviewed one or two of my books in an extremely patronising way, but I did not object to being called 'a silly boy' in spite of my seniority. Again, he showed his scorn or his spite by commissioning a duke with no literary credentials to write a review of my book about my mother for his magazine. Evelyn Waugh and son did not like competitors: Evelyn at once snubbed his contemporary writers and indulged his psychopathic snobbery by claiming that the drunken ramblings of aristocratic Henry Green's autobiography was the best of books. Auberon Waugh's obituarists have written that he was a generous friend. Be that as it may, he was a mean self-appointed enemy.

Met Carol Biss at the Book Guild yesterday morning. The publication of my *Tales of Love and War* is now in the bag, barring a signature on the contract. Hurrah! And hurrah not least for having found an impressive managing director of a publishing house located some five hundred yards from my study.

20 January

I owe my last literary harbour and haven to Miles Jebb, our friend, the author and editor, and now, following the death of his father, Lord Gladwyn.

Six weeks ago I was on the verge of throwing in the towel in the sense of consigning my three novellas to perdition. Then Miles told me that George and Jane Nissen had acquired The Book Guild. The reputation of Jane Nissen swung it for me: without delay I rang her up, and now I am about to become a Book Guild author. Jane Nissen was in charge of the Children's Books at Hamish Hamilton while I was part-published by the same firm. Everybody spoke well of her and admired her record as a publisher. I once submitted a children's story for her consideration, and received a letter rejecting it that caused more pleasure than pain. As soon as Miles mentioned the Nissens' name, I was confident that an enterprise in which Jane was involved could not be bad.

Contracts are due to be signed in three days. Thank you, Miles! Here's hoping the story has a happy ending.

Reading a most interesting book, *Explaining Hitler* by Ron Rosenbaum. It is wonderfully researched, well written, and has taught me much that I did not know, despite my interest in the subject. Rosenbaum quotes from *The Portage to San Cristobal of A.H.* by George Steiner. I imagine that Steiner was aware that his two letters of the alphabet, which refer to Adolf Hitler, were used to describe the anus in the English vernacular of my youth, and were regularly applied to raw recruits in the army by sergeant-majors.

21 January

I presume to think I can understand why the Jews have created an industry of research into why they were 'chosen' to be sacrificed in the Holocaust. But could it be that they are pushing their 'explanations' of Hitler to Byzantine extremes? He was wicked, he was evil, and evil does not need to be argued over, the facts describe it, common sense recognises it, and perhaps in an ultimate definition it is what is inexplicable.

Liberal opinion denies the existence of evil. Liberal opinions are the

Achilles heel of Jewry in the twentieth century. Karl Marx, born a Jew, reheated the Christian potage and served it up with liberal trimmings, class war leading to heaven on earth – no need to die in order to get into the marxist heaven. Jews fell for it: they played a large part in the October Revolution and in Leninism and even Stalinism, and were mostly liquidated for their pains. They have run with the hare of capitalism and hunted with the hounds of socialism in Western democracies ever since.

The paragraph above reminds me of my late brother-in-law, the concert pianist Franz Osborn. He was a card-carrying communist in Germany, where his family had lived for generations, but fled in the nick of time, reached England as a refugee, and belatedly became the most right-wing of conservatives. Arthur Koestler ditto – he was a communist activist in his native Germany, also in Spain, and became an arch-conservative in England. They were two of the many who worshipped the God that failed.

Liberals believe people called evil are misunderstood. They cannot stomach the idea of original sin. They cling to their faith in the notion that human beings will always behave themselves, given the chance. The consequences have been that liberal optimism, gullibility, naivety opened the door for the tyrants. Is liberalism on guard against an always possible revolt against fallible democratic governance and the rise of evil politicians promising to get rid of criminals and make the trains run on time? Is it – hell!

★ ★ ★

The banner headline of *Dog World* (7.4.2000), WHIPPET MURDERS, referred to the murdered mother and daughter who bred whippets.

22 January

Eileen Short died. She was our daily lady for several years long ago. We became friends and kept our friendship going. She was a spinster, plain, overweight, clever, cheerful and ribald. She was not known by many, and will soon be forgotten except by a few. But she was a heroine. She was a heroine of unselfishness. She had a dotty brother, who was put in an institution when his and Eileen's parents died. He was unhappy there, so Eileen said she would look after him in the family home. She did so for twenty-seven years, during which he went madder than usual at full moons and was apt to use violence against her. He clung to her, he was always able to beg her not to return him to the institution, and she never complained and never abandoned him.

24 January

This afternoon I am due to sign a contract with the Book Guild for my thirty-seventh book. The BG has treated me from the word go with exceptional respect and courtesy.

A pet parrot was ill. Its owner took it to a vet who specialised in parrots' ailments. The waiting-room was full of other parrots and their owners. All the parrots were doing their tricks: one sang 'I Did it My Way', another 'Greensleeves', a third kept on saying 'Pretty boy', a fourth 'Bugger off', a fifth imitated the ring of a telephone, a sixth wolf-whistled.

27 January

We do not travel much. G seems to have been everywhere and I am a stick-in-the-mud, like my mother. She laughed at travellers bringing home more or less nasty infections, and hard-line stories of hours of waiting for planes and trains, of traffic jams, missed connections, stolen luggage and unexpected weather. Very late in life she agreed to go and stay with friends in Holland. She was accompanied by a much younger and stronger female acquaintance. On the second night of the visit the young and strong acquaintance suddenly died. My mother was confirmed in her view that it was better to stay put.

A sunny day – what is the world coming to? We have been rained on for weeks. The water meadows between us and Newhaven are flooded. I hope my long-suffering neighbours and friends who live in Cliffe and Malling – parts of Lewes – have not had more mucky water in their homes. The birds are unaware of the plight of our town. They have been singing since before Christmas. I love song-birds, and hate to see so many magpies and even jays spying out the nests soon to provide them with hot dinners.

30 January

Neither a borrower nor a raconteur be.

1 February

G found the diary she had kept when she was about ten years old. It was such a slim volume that only one ruled line was provided for each daily entry. Her writing was therefore limited to the briefest record of the outstanding event of each day. These examples of two-day sequences certainly convey an impression of time flying: here is one, 'Stayed in bed ... Went shopping', or again, 'A (her brother Adrian Swire) went to school ... A's school burned down'.

I have been acquainted with two women who share the distinction of living with husbands but paying with their own money for their own food. The absurdities and the miseries of the war of the sexes will never be fully chronicled or known.

2 February

'Mistress' has become a taboo word. A woman living in sin with a man is a 'lover' now – no discrimination between her and her opposite number. And homosexual partners are both 'lovers'. 'Lover' comes in handy in a different context. The vernacular uses it in negative sentences: 'I'm not a lover of Banoffee Pie ... I can't say I'm a lover of poisonous snakes.'

3 February

My preparations for going abroad on holiday in six days are pathetic. My pleasantry to the effect that I might as well be going to the next world is hardly an exaggeration.

4 February

I cannot claim that sociability is my second nature. Most practitioners of arts have difficulty with social rites and obligations. Although my family tree is decorated with amateur writers, I never met a professional artist until I was nineteen years old. He was Edward Seago, the painter, whose secretary I became for six months half a century ago. In those days Ted Seago guarded his privacy fiercely and fairly successfully. But later I think he was appalled by the high price of fame, and was driven demented by having to put in personal appearances, and by intrusive admirers and fans. He quarrelled with people who had bought his pictures – he was always prepared to hurt feelings in order to be free to get on with his work.

Ted Seago died in his early sixties. He was born with a heart condition, but died of cancer. It was another of the ironies that must have been written in his stars.

He was the younger of his parents' two children. His elder brother John was the favourite, and Ted was the weakling, who cost the family a fortune in doctors' bills. But John ended up as an impecunious bore, while Ted gritted his teeth and supported his philistine father and malicious mother for many years.

Ted sold his first picture aged sixteen, and not long afterwards, as soon as he could scratch a living, resisted all parental pressure and left home. He acquired technical wizardry, and became extraordinarily prolific. That he was patronised or ignored by the aesthetes, critics and crooks who ran the modern art market during his lifetime, distressed and then embittered him. But he had won his immortality.

5 February

Ted Seago, owing to his productivity, painted some pictures that were better than others, or, vice versa, some that were less good. He had a tendency to hark back to sentimental rustic scenes of a bygone age, and often accused himself of having a picture-postcard mentality. Actually, as a rule, his pictorial imagination was romantic and refined, especially so in his native Norfolk studies. But I was young when I worked for him, did not take the range of his work into consideration and was grudging in my praise of his hay carts in the sunset and ploughing with horses in a flock of seagulls. Now I regret my error, having learnt that artists worthy of the name need and merit encouragement.

Ted's father was a coal-merchant and smallholder. I would classify him as a yeoman. Ted's mother was or thought herself a cut above: when Mr Seago wrote her letters during his courtship, she returned them with the grammar and spelling corrected in red ink. A remarkable artist was an unlikely consequence of their pairing. Are all artists changelings?

Another painter taught me a lesson about the artist's life. A friend of mine wrote to Augustus John begging him for a picture to be sold in aid of some charity and to attend the auction in person. He wrote back to refuse. He stated that he had no pictures to spare and never turned up at society dos. He added that his sister Gwen had ruined herself by giving away her pictures, and wrecked her work and her health by responding to every appeal for help.

26 February

Just back from our fortnight's holiday in France. We flew to and from Nice: the flight lasts about two hours whereas any other form of transport would take much longer. Flying is convenient from the temporal point of view, but is thoroughly inconvenient otherwise. Big airports always seem to be miles away from one's point of departure, delays are apparently inevitable and too long however short, muddle is customary, discomfort is par for the course, and then there is the fear of getting and being airborne. Modern travel is supposed to be better in all respects than it used to be, but whether or not it is safer and more dependable than it was in the eighteenth century is a moot point.

★ ★ ★

On our holiday I read two books by Kingsley Amis. One, *The Green Man*, is a conventional ghost story but quite clever, the other, *The Riverside Villas Murder*, is ridiculously far-fetched. The prose of both is workaday, but in *The Green Man* it is packed with cynicism, in the *Murder* it falls apart at the seams. *The Green Man* was first published in 1969, the other book four years later. What a decline! Was it due to drink? The personality of the writer that emerges from both books is disagreeable and despairing.

I was shocked to see that C.P. Snow, my friend Charles Snow, whose weakness it was to think he was or soon would be the king of the literary castle, heaps fulsome praise on that potboiler *The Riverside Villas Murder*.

[69]

28 February

My unhappy country – now a foot and mouth epidemic and ruination faced by many of those who feed us!

1 March

This March has come in like the most mangy and miserable of lions – uniformly grey sky and snowy drizzle, another rail crash, news bad – so for pity's sake let it go out like a lamb happier than those being killed and burned along with other livestock on the countrywide funeral pyres (science's high-tech remedy for the foot and mouth disease).

★   ★   ★

While on holiday I jotted down ideas for entries in my diary. I did likewise when I was writing fiction. But such ideas have never been any use to me. On the contrary, they turn out to be red herrings. In my own opinion my best work has been a spontaneous record of a train of thought shunted along on a daily basis. The suggestions of my holiday persona feel like interference by a stranger.

Here are a few of the delightful names of the pioneers of jazz: Cannonball Adderley, Big Bill Broonzy, Wayman Carver, Ornette Coleman, Dusko Goykovitch, Huddie Ledbetter, Fate Marable, Miff Mole, Dudu Pukwana, Pinetop Smith.

2 March

Two newcomers into the rude vernacular: first, the Americanism 'Wow!', an exclamation signifying surprise, also pain or pleasure, sorrow or joy, fear or any feeling thought to be indescribable by means of the spoken word; and secondly 'There you go', meaning 'Here you are … Eat your dinner … I've done what you asked me to do' etc. The latter is friendly, but, like 'Wow!', so imprecise as to resemble a neigh or a grunt.

On the other hand, a faint sign of hope worthy of a 'Wow!' and a 'There you go': the daughter of a carpenter friend of ours walked out of her job at a bank because of the filthy language of the bank manager. More employees should follow her example. The people who work in the media should all refuse to peddle swear-words and smut. Actresses should not imitate copulation – they should not be blackmailed to do so. Journalists should clamber out of the gutter, and self-styled artists should not be encouraged to disgrace art. Pigs should learn to fly.

4 March

A true statistic for a change: no less than ten members of our circle of acquaintances are more or less involved with criminals in and out of prison. Is it idealism? Is it slumming? Does do-gooding do any good? Undoubtedly women have a dangerously soft spot for criminals.

5 March

A shorn head used to be a mark of shame meted out to wrongdoers. Nowadays, some people choose to cut off their hair for more or less good reasons. But skulls are seldom nice to look at, and as a fashion accessory are a flop, also in bad taste because of the link with illness.

6 March

Alan Ross died while we were on holiday. He was gifted and gallant. He ran the London Magazine for years on a mysterious shoestring, and published one of my stories. The LM was the last respectable literary magazine, and may continue to be so. Alan lent it some of his own quirky character. His quirkiness was exemplified by the 'art' photographs he chose to publish in many issues: as a rule they were extremely banal – of shoppers queuing for a bus, or a schoolboy in the middle distance – and the reproduction was 'grainy' almost to the point of invisibility.

The unpalatable truth for egalitarians is that you have to get about in smart society, and mix with the wealthy, in order to obtain the backing for idealistic ventures in support of art. Capitalism is the 'only begetter' of the best art. God bless the patrons! Alan was a class act, as they say nowadays, in both the editorial and the fund-raising contexts.

Egalitarianism promotes insubordination.

7 March

I would like to write in praise of my wife. Many a diary has done GBH to wives: for instances, John Osborne's with its repeated references to the wife he called Adolf, and Alan Clark's with his boasts of having betrayed Jane, and Jim Lees-Milne's which blames Alvilde for standing in the way of his homosexual affairs. The trouble is that writing is a means of getting something out of your system, and that is exactly the opposite of what I was thinking of in relation to G. The most I dare to put on paper is that her unselfishness knows no bounds: which might as well be written in invisible ink since not many people will appreciate the dimensions of the compliment.

★　★　★

John Crook is coming to teach us how to use our computer this afternoon. The three questions that arise are – will it be any good for me, will G let it replace her beloved typewriter, and will we ever master it? I could never do creative work on a computer – the appearance of my hand-written pages, the age-old act of making my mark on a receptive medium, are an essential part of the process. I speak for myself – but again with thanks to Malcolm Bradbury for having publicly argued that computers are the enemy of art.

9 March

I woke in the night, was convinced it was morning and struggled not to fall asleep again. It must have been two o'clock. I realised my mistake round about three, failed to readjust and get back to sleep, and seemed to become a compendium of every ailment in the medical dictionary (of which we do not possess a copy).

One night I dreamt of the unsavoury title of a book which I hope has not been written and never will be: *Feet in Hot Weather, The Odorific Conditions known to Podology.*

10 March

Talking of fools, BBC 2 rushed in yesterday evening with a programme about class. A narrator claimed that the end of World War II at long last gave merit its chance and ushered in the rule of a brand new meritocracy.

What rot! Most of the hereditary peers in the House of Lords were and are descended from meritocrats. The Establishment was, is and will be meritocratic. The class system in England defeats analysis, and certainly defeated BBC 2. Its mystery is its charm and its strength. The upper class – aristocracy by another name – is indestructible and timeless. High society during the French Revolution differed from the high society it was destroying by nothing but its cast of characters. Napoleon could not wait to reign as emperor, supported by those whom he ennobled. Lenin and Stalin were tsars, and both were more imperious and terrible than Ivan. And meritocrats nearly always do their level best to pass on their privileges to their offspring in a universal and natural manner.

A clever friend of my youth identified the disability of the English proletariat to speak English, and its cause, as early as 1945. They speak without closing their mouths, and either adenoids or laziness or both complete the formation of 'peasantalk'. Thus they say 'fi' and chi' for fish and chips. 'Ho' equals hullo, and of course 'Hi' suits them to a t. Here are up-to-date translations of a few common phrases: 'Wa dri'?' = Want a drink? 'Wi you ma me?' = Will you marry me? 'E ma bi' = He's my baby. 'I yad nutt i' = I had enough of it. 'Bi'nd good ri t'ba rish' = Goodbye and good riddance to bad rubbish.

11 March

Pigeon-holing is not exclusively reserved for pigeons. People never have stopped, and never will, cramming their fellows into races and classes, into psychological straitjackets, and divisions reserved for sheep and goats. To discriminate is just about the first function of being. Later, it often poses a political threat. But in between it can be socially entertaining. Isaiah Berlin had a pigeon-hole for those who experience mental events and those who experience none. David and Rachel Cecil invented a category of 'leprechauns', who live in worlds of their own.

12 March

My bookshelves are full of signed copies of good books that are dodos. What became of P Anthony Spalding? He produced *A Reader's Handbook to Proust*, an essential reference book for as long as *A La Recherche* is read; but his fascinating *In the Margin, Extracts from a*

Bookman's Notebook, published probably privately round about 1960, caused a stir amongst the cognoscenti and has sunk without a trace. The novels of C.P. Snow are out of print, I believe. L.P. Hartley's masterpiece *The Boat* is unobtainable. Does anyone read the poetry of the painter David Jones, once admired although nobody could make head or tail of it? Are T.S. Eliot's prose musings read nowadays, and is the courageous vivacity of Joyce Cary's fiction another victim of time? Better to write for fun, to amuse ourselves, than for will-o'-the-wisps like posterity, fame, success or money!

13 March

We live in a country decaying, disunited, nearly bankrupt, and governed by leaders who like to pose disastrously as Good Samaritans. Where would be a better place to live?

14 March

My *Tales of Love and War* has arrived, copy-edited and marked up, and I must try to concentrate on it.

24 March

For ten days I have been finally revising the typescript of my *Tales*. I worked according to my wont, that is hard, and as a result was exhausted. The occupational hazard of old age is to think it is capable.

Another mistake in the losing battle with time was exemplified by a deaf old boy who came to tea with us. He apologised for his deafness, but said he never wore his four-thousand-pound deaf aid, he could not abide the thing, he could not get used to it, and thought it did not improve his hearing. Result – he was a menace. He could hear nothing, demanded repeat performances of our every pleasantry, strained our vocal cords, and obviously should have stayed at home. My sister Anne and lots of friends learn to manage their aids – often supplied by the NHS – discreetly, and are not noticeable doornails.

I have never liked revising my books. It is such a strain to bottle up the creative impulse and hand over to the critical faculty.

25 March

A sad story: Aggie married Bert, a postman. They were plain people in every sense, and had no children – she was disgusted by sex and his sex drive was minimal. They rubbed along in a dim and dull way until they were each getting on for fifty. Then their friend and neighbour Tom, a widower who owned the other half of their semi-detached property, resigned from his job in local government, went to live with his daughter in another town, and rented out his house. Tom's tenant was a dashing young man, handsome and black-haired, Desmond by name. Aggie fancied Desmond – it had never happened to her before. She spoke to him if she could, spied on him, treasured his smiles, wove daydreams round his fine figure. He drove an open-top red sports car, and one Saturday afternoon in summer he brought a blonde woman home. Aggie happened to be in her bedroom at the time, therefore looked down on the couple through her net curtains. They were talking and laughing at something, Desmond and that woman, and she leant across and stuffed her hand through the waistband of his trousers. A few moments later she withdrew her hand, they both got out of the car and hurried into the house.

This scene, witnessed by Aggie, led to her writing to Tom to complain of his tenant. Desmond was keeping bad company, she told Tom, and bringing their shared premises into disrepute. She did not leave it at that. Ignoring the attempts of poor old Tom and his daughter to placate her, she bombarded them with complaints about Desmond's garbage, loud music, late hours, and especially his female visitors who were clearly prostitutes and the disgusting noises that penetrated party walls.

She vented her spleen on Desmond himself, but in sneaky ways. She poured weed killer on his front lawn at night, and blamed vandals. She scratched his car with a nail. She blackguarded him in local shops. At weekends she rang him from phone boxes in hopes of interrupting sexual intercourse. And she persuaded Bert to pinch his mail from the sorting office, so that she could steam open the envelopes and read the letters – Bert did it to stop her nagging him to death.

Eventually Desmond moved out, whether or not because of Aggie's activities.

She was stricken. She shed bitter tears by the bucketful. She could not sleep or eat, and banished Bert from their bedroom. At last he took her almost by force to see their doctor. The doctor gave her a few pills to counteract the symptoms of the change of life and promised that she would soon be right as rain.

Reading a biography of F. Scott Fitzgerald by a certain André le Vot. In accordance with the biographical fashion, it is too long and detailed; but the story survives its treatment. FSF must be the most extreme modern example of the classic syndrome of genius and idiocy unified in one person. Zelda, his wife, exemplifies another type, and was possibly the model of the neurotic Southern Belles who figure in the plays of Tennessee Williams. Her dicing with death is breathtaking. His stupidity and alcoholism likewise.

26 March

FSF was an alcoholic, Zelda drank too much. Drink, and no doubt harder drugs, make and break talented people. Van Gogh explained to his brother that he could not have used the colour yellow as he had done if he had not been drunk. Malcolm Lowry owed his *Under the Volcano* to his alcoholic experience; the same applies to Patrick Hamilton's *Hangover Square* and Charles Jackson's *The Lost Weekend* – but there are too many examples to list. Insensibility, self-induced and chronic, is apparently as inspirational as sensibility. Whatever is closely related to death – religion, love, politics, war, and natural and unnatural illness – always inspires. Zelda went mad and died in a fire at a sanatorium.

Back in touch with Emmanuel College at Cambridge. I wrote to my friend and former Master of the College, Derek Brewer, professor and poet, some weeks ago to say that the edition of my *Collected Works* would be completed in the summer and I was thinking of donating a set of the five volumes to Emmanuel. He advised me to speak to the new full-time Emmanuel librarian, Dr Helen Carron.

I did so last week, and gave her the briefest possible history lesson, as follows. My forebears founded and endowed Emmanuel College, from which Harvard University sprang. Consequently, about a decade ago, I offered to bequeath my Archive to it, plus bequest. The then Master, Derek Brewer, accepted the offer and metaphorically welcomed me with open arms. But Derek retired, and a new master, Norman St John Stevas, ennobled in the guise of Lord St John, took over. I soon noticed a lack of interest in me and mine; and Norman was markedly uncommunicative.

At length I wrote to him to say I felt neglected and wondered whether Emmanuel still wanted my Archive. Answer came there none: I waited for a few months and then approached the British Library, offering the same deal. It was accepted with alacrity and enthusiasm. When Norman eventually wrote to the effect that the College longed to receive my bequest, I could reply that he had missed the boat, the BL would be the recipient.

Dr Carron assured me that Emmanuel would be pleased to have a copy of my *Collected Works*. I then mentioned my condition, since I was twice shy of giving to the ungrateful. Could I have an introduction to the Harvard Library? Intriguing to see what happens next.

29 March

The astronomers, scientists and damn nearly everybody else are dying to know if there is intelligent life on another planet. The much more pressing question is whether there is intelligent life on ours.

30 March

Old people always fall over. I took my second tumble last night. I was carrying our faithful old dog Dulcie down brick steps on to our garden lawn. It had been raining as usual, my feet slipped from under me, and I crashed down, but apparently my left hand took most of the strain. That hand and particularly the left wrist are more or less painful, though no bones seem to be broken. Otherwise, a grazed right elbow, nothing else so far – I have been lucky. But there are the unpredictable effects of shock to look forward to.

Incidentally, the shock for Dulcie must have been as bad or even worse than it was for me. She was flung from the arms of the master who had always previously been kind and gentle. After my fall, while still prostrate on the steps, I was pleased to see her squatting to relieve herself in a flowerbed some six inches from my face.

31 March

Left hand and wrist swollen, but no longer so painful. Possibly due to shock I slept yesterday morning, again in the afternoon, and some nine hours last night.

Nearing the end of the Scott Fitzgerald biography at last. His latter days were terrible. He had been loved and envied, rich and famous, then he could not afford to eat, was a hopeless wino, a fighting drunk, and his fine books were out of print. He had great dignity yet could behave in the most undignified and intolerable ways.

One of the many interesting things in the story of his life is the nastiness of Ernest Hemingway. I know the Hemingway type, and that it is to be avoided, if possible. Ernest competed meanly with Scott, and showed malice towards him. Ernest was all for masculinity, masculine activities and sports, and the courage of brave men, but he was a bitch at heart. He despised and condemned Scott for doing his best to destroy himself, yet in due course he committed suicide.

Beautiful writing is difficult to define, but unmistakable to those who have the eye and ear to be moved by it. The eye is dazzled by sentences that carry neatness, precision, individuality and charm to astral levels. The ear can hear the melodious and haunting rhythm of their cadences. The psyche is seduced as if by a siren's song which beckons us not against rocks but into a new and better world.

The letter of the alphabet most closely linked with love is v, v for Venus and venereal, vulva and vagina.

1 April

Not feeling up to much today, is it shock or hypochondria?

3 April

My reaction to falling flat on my back on brick steps was to go to sleep – I have had hours and hours of sleep in the last few days and nights. Think I am quite normal today, but wonder if others would agree.

4 April

Not so normal yesterday as I liked to think I was. Vitality ran out, stamina proved to be in short supply. Blood pressure must have sunk through the floor.

6 April

Received a letter from Dr Carron, Librarian at Emmanuel College. She thanked me for the copy of *A Reader's Choice* I had sent her – it is Diana Crook's anthology of excerpts from my books. Dr C. wrote to say she had included it in an exhibition of books etc that bear upon the founding of Emmanuel – I was in with my forefathers. She also informed me that she had forwarded the other copy of *A Reader's Choice* that I had sent her to the Widener Library, part of the Harvard Library: which is just about all I had hoped for.

The Last Illusion, a story I have in mind, which will probably remain there, would or could go like this: a young woman called Jane with literary leanings aspires to become a professional writer. She sets about making her wish come true by seeking the advice of established authors and critics and commentators. The letters she writes them are flattering, she declares that she has regarded their writings as positively godlike, that she longs to become their disciple or, in terms of authorship, their protégée, and she encloses a revealing photograph of her nubile charms. For the next six or seven years she services over-sexed scribes and media men in their studies and offices. At the end of that busy period she produces a slim volume: it is reviewed glowingly and widely – which of her important lovers would dare to displease a girl who has dirty stories to tell and sell? Jane's book sales, then her appearances on TV, at first in literary programmes, next in chat shows, game shows, advertisements for lipstick, make her famous or at any rate notorious. But she is no slacker, her pen and her person are harder at it than ever. In the next twenty-odd years she runs through generations of useful lovers and publishes a few blockbusters based upon her wide experience of the opposite sex. Alas, the change of life pumps her up to three times the size she had been when she was pretty and powerful. And she can write nothing – once upon a time her men put in stints of post-coital creative editorial work on her books. She is afraid to go out, and stays at home to cry in front of the mirror. She is lonely, she has never needed to marry, and now she would not lower herself so far as to wed the types that pity and propose to her. But years pass, her courage revives, and she takes up her pen again. She writes letters to her old friends to ask for advice about the autobiography she is contemplating. Immediately she is not only remembered but in demand, propositioned this time round to serve on quangos, committees, prize juries, supply forewords and compile anthologies, and eventually to receive prizes and honours for her lifelong dedication to the cause of literature. She never writes her autobiography – it is superfluous to requirements, she enjoys the honourable niche she has carved for herself in the world of letters and art. She takes to public speaking, gives talks to PEN and at out-of-the-way universities. The burden of her message to writers in general and the young ones in particular is that they must make their mark by talent and nothing else.

An heroic journalist called Minette Marin writes in *The Daily Telegraph* today that 'allowing women into something is usually a sign of institutional decline. That has been the way with the Church of England, men's clubs, MI5 and the armed services'. Where is the hero or heroine who will include in Minette's list many of the jobs associated with literature?

9 April

A story called *Dreams* could be shorter than short. A woman divorces her husband, who is a charming rogue, and marries a second husband whom she cannot fault. She claims to be perfectly happy; but in her dreams she still loves her first husband and is sorry that she got rid of him.

Reading Montherlant's *The Bachelors* (*Les Celibataires*), a great book by a great writer. What a joy to read something so good, what a relief to be reminded that great writing exists! The translation by my friendly acquaintance Peter Quennell seems to be worthy of the original.

12 April

Easter approaches.

I was extremely religious between the ages of twelve and fourteen when – and because – I was unhappy at school. Often since then, but intermittently, God has been my friend in need – my need, not His. Nowadays my prayers include apologies.

In various books I have written about the sort of religion I subscribe to. The funerals of atheists must be responsible for many conversions to belief in a god of some kind. Science answers none of the riddles of the universe so far. My bet is that God will stay well ahead of the scientists.

13 April, Good Friday

Strange that Good Friday should fall on a Friday the thirteenth.

This is the weekend that retells one of the seven great stories, the story of *resurrection*, death and resurrection of Jesus, and of redemption. On lower levels it is also the story of rags to riches, of Cinderella, and the story I have told in most or even all of my writings. But, although I am not ashamed of having tried to cheer people up, I am well aware that the story of resurrection, not the tenet of Christian faith but the story in a general sense, can be inverted – millions, billions, the casualties of the twentieth century, would deny the possibility of endings happy in a personal mundane form. Older age specialises in appreciation of the negative sides of the six other great stories: absence of *love*, not so much *conflict* as surrender, not so much *recognition* as blindness, a reluctance to discover anything by means of *exploration*, no *faith*, and not enough *generosity*.

I write my diary in Extra Time, two words borrowed from the rules of football, referring to the period of play after two teams have finished their game without one scoring more than the other. The particular relevance of the phrase to my circumstances is that I am writing here and now after the game of my life's work was or seemed to be done. When I wrote *Evening*, someone asked: 'What about *Night?*' When I told someone about *Extra Time*, I was asked: 'Is *Injury Time* next?'

15 April

Before I gave a talk the other day the gentleman who introduced me told the following story. He said his name was Walter Allen, and he recently attended the graduation ceremony at a university where his son had studied. His son warned him that car parking would be a problem, but on the day he arrived early and noticed an empty space in a car park close to the place of assembly. He drove towards it and was stopped by an attendant, who asked his name. He supplied it, and was waved into the aforesaid space politely. He then met his son, took his seat, and watched the long-drawn-out business of the awards of degrees. Eventually the man in charge of the proceedings made an announcement. He apologised on behalf of the guest of honour, the eminent academic Professor Walter Allen, who was hoping soon to arrive and deliver his address as planned – he had been looking for somewhere to park his car for the last hour and a half.

17 April

Religion equals choice. You can choose to be religious or irreligious. You can choose to be married in church, you can have a downbeat atheist's funeral. Your life, your private life, is dependent on choosing, on the exercise of free will. It is all your own fault, apart from the workings of nature, the whims of politicians, and accidents.

20 April

Finished copies of the two last volumes of the *Collected Works* arrived this morning, and make everything worthwhile. By everything, I mean all that has happened between Ben's tentative proposal over lunch six or seven years ago and the sight of the five vols in my study. The problems of finance were solved. The design of the dustjackets by Leslie Robinson and Vera Brice is perfect. Ben survived the assaults on his company and rescued it with assistance from Robinson Publishing. Both Ben and I withstood attacks on our health. Of course there are things that could be better, there always are, especially in the writing of the fifteen separate books included in the five vols; but it is too late to worry, and whatever happens to my work once it is available to readers is really not my business. A huge thank you to the talented people who contributed to the venture, and supported me as I stumbled towards the finishing line of what often seemed a marathon too far.

24 April

One of my see-saw days yesterday. In the morning I worked well, and in the afternoon we went to a nursery garden and found and bought the few plants we were looking for. The sun shone, it was a balmy spring day with blossom and birdsong. After tea we went to Seaford for a walk beside the calm sea, and later I rang my sister

Anne in Spain. She sounded mortally ill. She ended by thanking me for having always been kind to her – a sad signal. She has wished in vain to die ever since she lost her husband Peter Higgins.

25 April

Rang Anne this a.m. She sounded bright and belligerent. I had almost buried her.

27 April

What are Aristotle's Lantern, Cobbler, Corkwing, Father-lasher, Medusa, Pogge, Shanny and White Cat?

Answer, creatures of the watery world.

Aristotle's Lantern is part of the sea urchin. Cobbler is a fish of the sea-scorpion family, and a Father-lasher and a Pogge are others. A Corkwing is a fish called wrasse. A Medusa is a jellyfish. A Shanny is a blenny, and a blenny is like a stickleback. A White Cat is a nasty-looking worm.

Arts are easily lost. Draughtsmanship went to the dogs in the last century: is there a revival? The writing of fine English prose is history: I generalise, but compare the sentences of two best-selling authors, Sir Walter Scott and Ian Fleming, in order to see what I mean. William Douglas-Home explained to me that all the prose in his plays had a distinctive rhythm, but that usually the directors of his plays and most of the actors failed to grasp it. No contemporary literary critic to my knowledge has ever commented perceptively on a writer's prose, and I would guess that no more than one in a thousand members of the public could tell the difference between journalese and an elegant sentence. The New English Bible is the sin against the Holy Ghost in this context.

28 April

Tolstoy thought that a person's appearance, whether it was considered good-looking or bad-looking by people in general and by himself or herself in particular, and especially if it did or did not find favour with the opposite sex, formed that person's character, outlook, opinions, fortunes, happiness, and might actually make history in one way or another.

Alas, the savage spinsters, growing old ungracefully, with nothing to boast about except their quarrels, so sharp that they continue to cut themselves, biting every hand that would feed them, and amazed that they have been condemned to die alone and largely of their loneliness!

Some spinsters lead the happiest of lives, thanks to their characters.

29 April

Tomorrow to London to lunch with my nephew, the jeweller Harry Fane, my brother's second son. He and his elder brother are getting more interested in our family history. I have nothing against Fanes, but feel myself more in tune with my mother's family. A strange episode occurred some fifty years ago. I was at home, at Lyegrove in Gloucestershire, had been chopping wood on a winter's afternoon, and was walking back to the house through the gathering dusk. On entering the house I found my mother and her sister, my aunt Laura Lovat, in distress. Apparently they had been drawing the curtains, saw me in the drive, and were afraid that I was the ghost of their father, the Lord Ribblesdale painted by Sargent. They thought I looked like him. Certainly I share his ascetic tastes and love of literature.

Before jotting down the above I referred to the Extinct Peerages section of the 1956 Burke's *Peerage, Baronetage and Knightage*. The entry under Ribblesdale, my grandfather, omitted the eldest of his three daughters. She was Barbara Wilson, Wilson being her married name, who wrote several excellent books, including the highly praised *Dear Youth*. Such is life and death for writers.

1 May

Riots expected today in London. The rioters are rioting against those who pay the taxes that provide the money that pays the dole that enables them to riot on a working weekday.

A story describing one couple's attempts to plumb the mysteries of the marriage of another couple, and the mistakes they inevitably make.

2 May

The novelist who writes a diary cannot pretend to be someone else – there are no closets to hide in, the motley must be set aside, birthday suits are the order of the day. He or she is under pressure to use the first person singular in an unaccustomed manner. Consequently I feel honour bound to confess that both my parents were, in today's jargon, toffs. I belong in the class pigeonhole reserved for fairly modern English writers together with the Sitwells, Siegfried Sassoon, George Orwell, Byron, Shelley and Walter Scott. Similar foreign types are Dante, Goethe, Pushkin, Tolstoy and nearly all the great writers of Russia's Marvellous Decade. I believe my work has sometimes been sneered at for non-literary reasons, just as, in the good old days, Byron sneered at Keats for being plebeian.

3 May

Apparently the riot in London cost about twenty million pounds worth of damage. The Civil Liberties brigade is arguing that the police should have allowed the hooligans to do more.

6 May

Domestic sins, crimes and misdemeanours, what are they? I mean not GBH or illegal activities, but those traits of personality and those habits which are difficult to live with. Husbands who lunch at home are supposed to be providing cause for divorce. A bully can be intolerable, likewise a drunkard, a gambler, a spendthrift, a bore, or a sharp-tongued or plaintive spouse. An oppressive father, a proprietorial mother, uncaring parents, parents who divorce, all play havoc with young lives.

On a more personal level some people are allergic to dirty minds, fingernails, tricks. My wise old friend Violet Schiff thought that flippancy was a great mistake. Teasing that hurts is definitely a no no. And watch the face of the partner of a raconteur, who is listening to the same story for the umpteenth time!

In my opinion unresponsiveness is deadly. It is the antonym of charm. It is charmless; you cannot communicate with it; nothing excuses it – absent-mindedness, other preoccupations; it is the worst of bad manners; it is a killer. The powerful and impatient, the insensitive and inconsiderate, the clever-clever and the stupid-stupid may think that they get away with not bothering to respond: they are wrong, they are loathed and not forgiven.

The cruelty of innumerable episodes of the cull of livestock, unhealthy and healthy, to cure the national herd of foot and mouth, has elicited not a squeak of protest from the RSPCA, the animal rights terrorists, the anti-vivisectionists, the anti-fox hunting mob, the ignorant animal lovers who finance these organisations, the millionaires who pay for illegal violence against law-abiding scientists and sportsmen, and above all the media.

7 May

Hard cheese for atheists! In the 1962 edition of Roget's *Thesaurus* thirty-eight column inches approx. (960 mm) are devoted to the names of Gods, of the Divinities of various religions in various countries in the various ages. Unbelief and doubt, on the other hand, get four inches (100 mm), and irreligion another four inches.

8 May

The election for 7 June to be announced today. God help us all!

On a summer's day two Chelsea Pensioners rested on a seat in the King's Road, watching the girls in miniskirts and flimsy dresses go by. One Pensioner said to the other in a wheezy old voice, 'You remember that stuff they put in our tea when we were in the army – bromide, they called it – to stop us feeling fruity? Well, I'm afraid it's starting to work.'

9 May

When I was a boy my favourite birds were falcons and hawks. Then I graduated to liking owls best. Now my favourites are swallows and especially swifts.

Swifts are mysterious and romantic. They fly beautifully, know their way across the world, and their cries are summery and sound joyful.

Not well today.

12 May

My indisposition which was mildly gastric has turned into shingles.

Unknown words that describe a fool: calf, tony, Tom Noddy, moonraker, sawney, beetle-head, numps.

13 May

Human inconsistency has a field day during a political election. Some self-made millionaires, the odd lottery winner, and persons dependent on capitalism from birth, also those who would starve if the rich got poorer, and social snobs fighting tooth and nail for status, are proud to proclaim that they will vote for socialism, which aims to redistribute wealth and do away with class distinctions.

16 May

When the body hurts, mind has a job to overrule matter. But heroes managed it, Keats, Proust, Denton Welch. And creative work is better for you than nothing.

17 May

Sam Goldwyn, the Hollywood mogul, is said to have said: 'Nobody ever lost money by underestimating the taste and intelligence of the public.' This is clearly the advice followed by the popular media in my alien country.

This evening the Glyndebourne Festival opens with *Fidelio*.

18 May

Again *Fidelio* moved me, because of Beethoven, Simon Rattle and good singers. The producer, Deborah Warner, is quite contrary. She is contrary to abolish the season of the year, spring, referred to in the libretto; not noticeably to release the prisoners into the fresh air, the open air, which they gratefully sing about; and to dress the prisoners, their gaoler and the prison governor in identical modern attire, which makes the story difficult to follow – actually, I believe the governor's clothes are even more slovenly than those of his 'servant', the gaoler.

In Act II she places the action not in a prison 'vault' but in a huge unconfined space – no walls or ceiling; and finally she drops snowflakes on the entire company of thinly clad 'Spaniards'.

I do not forget that I am lucky to have had the chance to discuss the work of Miss Warner.

21 May

Shingles not an aid to keeping a diary.

Reading a thriller by the best-selling American author James Hall, whose writing has been highly praised internationally. My estimate is that versions of the word 'fuck' occur at least one thousand times in its three hundred-odd pages.

22 May

'Ask no favours, lose no friends': if that is not already a proverb, it ought to become one.

Britten's *Midsummer Night's Dream*, Peter Hall's production thereof, revived in memory of its designer John Bury, equals another enchanted Glyndebourne evening.

25 May

My seventy-fourth birthday.

Luckily for me I am like my mother, who took no notice of anniversaries or the passage of time. I rather think she died of a ninetieth birthday party my brother gave for her – it suddenly reminded her of how old she was and that it would be impolite to keep death waiting.

★   ★   ★

I have turned against paperback books belatedly. They began well, but have become the repository of all the trash masquerading as literature. There are many more bad books than good books in paperback. Their boast is that they are cheap – they should be ashamed of how cheap most of them are. And they fall apart and the paper they are written on turns yellow and decays.

26 May

For that matter, following on from the intolerant entry above, I marvel that the majority of writers should be willing to cede control over their work to the kind of middlemen and middlewomen I have come across. The literary agents known to me and my friends were apt to take no trouble if there seemed to be no money in a book. Moreover they were judge and jury in respect of work submitted to them, although usually without discernible literary qualifications. Unconstrained by responsibility, they must have sealed the fate of innumerable writers.

Again, a very few exceptions have proved the rule to me that publishers are a low form of life. I allow that they must take financial risks, and no doubt have wives and children to feed, but do they need to be disobliging, both sheeplike and reckless, and to play fast and loose with authors' hearts, souls and interests? Publishing was meant to be the profession of gentlemen once upon a time.

There is an alternative to putting all your artistic eggs into the baskets proffered by agents and publishers. You can retain a smaller or larger share of the process of publication of your work. That means expenditure of money in cash or loss of money in contractual form. Money is difficult but not impossible to raise – I speak from experience. I became a publisher myself in order to get my books published as I wished, and my investment in the business was virtually nil, neither I nor my two colleagues, Carlo Ardito and Michael Hatwell, invested a penny in it (see my book *How to Publish Yourself*).

27 May

Night thoughts on yesterday's entry: I must issue a warning about writers employed by publishing houses – they are most unlikely to appreciate or be well-disposed to other writers' work – the story of Andre Gide's rejection of Proust's *Swann's Way* for the worst reasons is typical.

28 May

Down with the Kennel Club! It sets the standards for the various breeds of dogs, and appoints the judges for Crufts, and the consequences are the crippled hindquarters of German Shepherd Dogs; dogs blinded by their drooping upper eyelids; other dogs with drooping and inflamed lower eyelids; Bulldogs with such big heads that they cannot reproduce naturally; Poodles with foxy muzzles; Pugs and Pekingese with such short noses that they are incapable of breathing properly, and so on ad nauseam. But the Kennel Club will have to mend its ways – foreign dogs that are better looking than English ones are now able to compete here.

2 June

A story called *The Man Who Cared for Women*. The father dies young, and the son takes care of his mother. He feels for her in her widowhood, shoulders her burdens, protects and cheers her as best he can and devotes himself to her welfare. But when he is seventeen she remarries, and her second husband is an architect who gets a job in Saudi Arabia and drags her off to live there. The boy is bereft and bewildered – how can his mother opt to take the sort of risks from which he has shielded her? Some years pass, and he finds Miss Right. She is charming and suffering from her parents' divorce. He promises her security, that he will look after her always, and she promises never to desert him. They marry and are happy. But then she becomes pregnant. He worries about her day and night, and dreads the dangers of parturition. The birth is far worse than he anticipated – he is driven half mad by her protracted agony and rages against her doctors, the baby and even herself. And she does not survive and his daughter dies. He has been doubly deserted, deserted yet again, and decides that women are not to be trusted – all his care of them is in vain. Many more years pass, and he marries once more, doubts notwithstanding. She is much younger than he is – he can guide her through life; and she is poorer – he can provide for her. She is a career girl in a small way and is grateful for his support. But as a result of her marriage and her new-found confidence she wins promotion and works twice as hard in a more responsible job. She comes home exhausted on weekday evenings and spends weekends in bed with migraines. He urges her to rest, see a doctor, look for less stressful employment, and begins to be cross with her for not heeding his advice. His nagging, as she calls it, is a bone of contention between them. In the course of a terminal row he accuses her of being masochistic and of not letting him save her from herself; whereupon she retorts that he has never really cared for her or, she suspects, for anyone else, all he cares about is to stop people upsetting his own peace of mind.

Election notes: two socialist households in our street advertise their political sympathies with posters. The houses they have recently bought cost in the region of £500,000.

6 June

Adults to seven-year-old boy: 'Do you like your school? ... Are you happy at school? ... Have you got lots of school friends? ... Is the work hard at your school?'

Seven-year-old boy under his breath: 'School, school, school – I know enough!'

Character is worth more than cleverness in the longer term.

10 June

If you want to know how painful it can be to put on a soft cotton shirt, get shingles.

20 June

Brave artists, Tom Stoppard, for example, are beginning to speak out against the meaningless messes of what claims to be 'conceptual art'.

The stuff that is on show in some of the great London galleries is bad enough, but go into the country, into the new towns, and see the abortions presuming and presumed to be art that have been commissioned by councillors and clerks of the works!

22 June

The proof of the dust jacket for *Tales of Love and War* is pretty, but bears no relation whatsoever to the text of the book. It must contravene the Trade Descriptions Act.

23 June

I have never written about the famous people I have known, setting aside the four subjects of my *Best Friends*. This diary is not exactly autobiographical, nor a scandal sheet, nor a gallery of thumbnail sketches – and may therefore be less amusing than it could have been. But now, rightly or wrongly, I feel obliged to throw my own flicker of light on history before it is too late.

26 June

The Book Guild is proving to be the most obliging of all my publishers. Because that dust jacket of my *Tales of Love and War* has no connection with the stories in the book but is otherwise eye-catching, Janet Wrench immediately suggests getting another design from a different artist.

27 June

As I was saying or writing, this seems to be the place for my memories of the mighty. Winston Churchill was a small man, surprisingly so, not least because his ducal cousins of younger generations were and are bean-poles. He must have suffered from his small stature, height being considered the prerequisite of gentility in some snobbish quarters. He looked to me like a clever version of a mixture of Mr Pickwick and Jorrocks. I met him only once – he was old, in the pink of health, forceful and with some magnetism. I saw no sign of his social boorishness – my mother once walked out of a luncheon party because she had been seated next to him and he refused to speak to her.

Anthony Eden was a friend of friends of mine, as a result I was included in two Sunday lunches at his last home in the country. They were memorable in different ways. The first convinced me that he was the most charming man I had met – and I have not changed my mind since then. He was outstandingly handsome, and intelligent and responsive – he had the sensibility of an artist, no doubt inherited partly from his father who painted well. And he was more than polite to me because of a strange link between us: my grandfather Lord Ribblesdale and his father Sir William Eden, the bad-tempered subject of *The Tribulations of a Baronet* written by his son and heir Timothy, both rented suites of rooms in Rosa Lewis' notorious Cavendish Hotel in Jermyn Street – between them they gave Rosa her start as an eccentric hotelier. However, my second lunch verged on the disastrous. Another guest, a politician, was late and Anthony Eden over-reacted – his chronic ill health asserted itself, he was impatient and cross. His wife Clarissa behaved admirably and calmed him down as best she could; but at lunch he was provoked into trying to justify the Suez fiasco that ended his political career. It was a disillusionment for me. He died soon afterwards. He was created Earl of Avon and had every kind of decoration, including an MC for valour.

Harold Macmillan was genial and wanted to know what I thought about things when I was too young to have thoughts about anything – I might have been nineteen when I met him. He was reputed to be a very good shot and an expert billiards player. Although he was considered by some to be too easy-going and lax as Prime Minister, after retiring on the grounds of ill-health he took up the reins again at his family publishing business and reorganised it ruthlessly.

Hugh Gaitskell, an academic and socialist who led the Labour Party, betrayed his political principles and probably his wife by succumbing to the wiles of an aristocratic society hostess, married thirdly at the relevant period to Ian Fleming, the creator of James Bond. Anne Fleming gave parties in her elegant house in Victoria Square, to one of which I was invited. Gaitskell was not included; but, in accordance with the rumours, he joined us after fighting under the red flag in the House of Commons, shared Anne's chair at the head of her luxurious dining-table and drank coffee out of her coffee cup.

When I met Prime Minister Margaret Thatcher, she startled as well as pleased me by saying she had a soft spot for Fanes. She explained that she had been at school with a girl who asked her out to tea at her home near Grantham: the girl was my distant cousin, a member of the Fane family of Fulbeck, Lincolnshire, and her home was Fulbeck Hall. Mrs Thatcher, as she then was, Lady Thatcher as she is, said she thought Fulbeck Hall marvellous and that she had never forgotten the kindness of its owners. Margaret Thatcher rose far above the prejudices of male chauvinists and snobs, of jealous feminists and women, and was an exceptionally good English politician with common sense and an admirable character. Her husband Denis had perfect manners and tact.

28 June

Those historical literary cliques amaze me. I cannot believe that Thomas Mann in Hollywood benefited from reading aloud his work in progress to Einstein, Chaplin and other luminaries. Editorial assistance usually tolls the knell for real writing. Creative writers talk too much at their peril. A literary vocation requires you to be alone, search your heart in solitude, and never lay your life-work before outsiders or the public until it is complete, unchangeable, and proof against critics and meddlers.

Drink looms large in my memories of artists – other drugs too, probably, but mainly drink. Harold Nicolson and Vita Sackville-West were never sober when I met them, Leslie Hartley died of drink, Evelyn Waugh likewise by all accounts, John Betjeman over-indulged, Philip Toynbee was an alcoholic – the list could be endless.

Harold and Vita and John Betjeman were true friends of my work. Harold had a red face and a moustache and could have been in command of a regiment, judging by his looks; but his heart was soft, not martial, his temperament was all tenderness and generosity, and he was the most modest of men, considering his achievements. When I thanked him for his help in getting my first book Morning published, he said something to the effect that his greatest pleasure was to promote the work of young writers more talented than he himself was.

The Nicolsons exemplified the potentially successful union of male and female homosexuals. Vita was a manly figure with big hands and feet, Harold's hands were small and his feet looked tiny in his suede shoes. She was enchanting when sober and a bully when drunk, and Harold was willing to be bullied – he let her wreck both his diplomatic and political careers. They were an odd couple, she the haughty aristocrat and poet, he the journeyman born and bred. They stuck together largely by living apart – he was in London during the week, and at Sissinghurst at weekends they occupied different houses. They also stuck together by post, by their correspondence, and apparently by their tolerance of each other's sexual proclivities.

My friend Cynthia Asquith told me a story that illustrates Vita's masculine ideology. Simon, Cynthia's son, said to Ben Nicolson, Vita's son, 'My mother complains that I drink too much and have too many women,' to which Ben replied, 'My mother complains that I don't drink enough and don't have enough women.'

29 June

John Betjeman is indescribable – he was a mild case of the multi-personality syndrome. He was a road-hog, the most competitive of drivers; yet extraordinarily generous to young hopefuls in his own field. He was convivial, yet reserved and hid behind his jokes and laughter. He was loveable, but tested the patience of those who loved him with his demands for service and attention. He was part teddy bear part tyrant. I was very fond of him – he was not only kind to me, he understood everything.

In connection with the Nicolsons I think of the Pope-Hennessy brothers, yet can find no record of either of them in any of my reference books. They were the arch-intellectuals of the cultural scene in my youth, John the authority on painting and architecture, the big cheese in the world of museums, and James the social favourite who combined scholarship with dining out, the biographer par excellence, and now their work is superseded, they are dead, buried, forgotten, and I apologise to their shades if I have misspelt their name.

John was the most superior, apparently arrogant, unapproachable and awkward of social presences. He looked down his nose and deigned scarcely to speak to anyone outside his precious circle. I tried to read a book of his the other day, *Aspects of Provence*, which I hoped would be more accessible than he had ever been and than I imagined his tomes on art were. It was hopeless, academic beyond bearing, history run riot, a leaden touch throughout and no encouragement to anyone to go anywhere in that delightful region of France.

James was a close friend of Harold and Vita, and perhaps John was too. They all had art and their sexual orientations in common. But James deteriorated rapidly and painfully until he was murdered. He looked Malayan – there had surely been a slip-up in his forebears' consular activities in the Far East. He had swimmy black eyes, a brown complexion and inky black hair. He had a high-pitched laugh and exuded hints of his perverse interests. He overspent, was always in financial trouble, dunned his friends, did everything to excess, including drinking, and squandered his remarkable literary gifts. Publishers were not encouraged to advance money on books he neglected to write. His rakishness was the death of him, he invited criminals into his house and they tied him up and gagged him too tight.

The Pope-Hennessy brothers had a formidable mother, Dame Una

Pope-Hennessy, a noted blue stocking. I never met her, but gossip suggests that neither of her boys would have dared to look at another woman while she was alive even if they had wanted to.

30 June

I met T.S. Eliot at tea with Violet Schiff. She told him that I wanted to be a writer and he said it was a very difficult career. He spoke the truth, but discouragingly. Some years later, Jock Murray suggested that Tom Eliot should decide whether or not he was to publish my book, *A Letter*. I asked for Violet's opinion. She replied: 'Don't agree, don't do it – Tom's never had anything nice to say about any living author.' For the record, it was John Betjeman who made up Jock's mind with his enthusiastic foreword.

Eliot looked to me more like a bank manager than a poet (he had worked in a bank). He was very low-toned. He smoked cigarettes in a gloomy way. At the time he lived with an Oxford don, John Hayward, who was dying of MS. By all accounts he cheered up when he remarried. He was never flush with money, but his least serious work made posthumous millions via Andrew Lloyd-Webber's musical, *Cats*.

Belatedly, I sympathise with T.S. Eliot for having to meet me. No doubt he was sick of being expected to encourage would-be writers, and had learnt from experience to be non-committal. Years later I myself was bullied by an old friend to see an aspiring scribbler, son of a friend of my friend. I not only could not spare the time to see this youth, but also had no practical advice to offer, was sure that every writer has to work things out for himself, and nervous of treading on toes and giving offence. However, eventually I knuckled under and the aspirant accepted an invitation to come to tea. He was large and he was silent. As a result I talked more than I wanted to, and regretted the whole stupid business. The youth turned into a journalist and gave my popular book *Gentleman's Gentleman* a vengeful review.

Cyril Connolly's *Enemies of Promise* is a tragic book. Those enemies were too much for Cyril, who had seemed to be cut out to write more than a few patchy books. His editorship of *Horizon* was not the sort of achievement he had surely hoped for. Writers imperil their creative faculty by knowing too much about literature. They show they have run out of creative steam when they write about the art of writing.

I met E.M. Forster once. It was at Cambridge, we were having drinks before lunch with Patrick Wilkinson and his wife – I remember no other guests. He was a dingy little old man in a three-piece suit sitting in an armchair by the fire. He wore woolly bedroom slippers and never opened his mouth – signs of his genius?

Forster's book *Howards End* came in for a waggish criticism: 'Howards beginning is better than *Howards End.*'

Sacheverell Sitwell was more fun than pompous Osbert. When I met him he asked me: 'Have you written any good books lately?'

Hostesses cannot count on gratitude for the dinners and treats they dish out. Dickens mocked the Veneerings and Proust mocked the Verdurins for their generous entertainments. Nearly all the writers who skulked in comfort and safety at Garsington during World War I attacked their hostess, Lady Ottoline Morell, in their books. D.H. Lawrence, the most mixed-up of mixed-up kids, that hell of a genius, understood some things but misunderstood most, and thought his foul treatment of Lady Ottoline would not affect their friendship. He got the wife he deserved, Frieda, a German he-woman who was dead-set on making him and everybody else miserable. Aldous Huxley was another snake in Lady Ottoline's grass – and, as some wit said in a different context, there was not a lot of grass.

The upper crust that accepted Laura Corrigan's bribes from Cartier to attend her functions jeered at her for being American and rich, and the guests of Lady Cunard also bit the hand that had fed them. The best of many jokes at the expense of Lady Colefax was that she lured people to her table by telling them they would meet the Unknown Soldier.

7 July

The late Donald Dewar has put the cat amongst the socialist pigeons by leaving two million pounds – he was supposed to be an ascetic puritan, undeviatingly red, but had invested in privatised utilities while in government and opposing their creation.

At a dinner party in Hong Kong a lady asked her Chinese neighbour: 'Do you ever eat brown rice?'

The gentleman replied: 'Brown rice is for poor people.'

'But brown rice is full of vitamins.'

'I get my vitamins in a bottle,' he said.

8 July

There is an eighth Age of Man, the Age of Indignity, and, medically speaking, I am in it.

Pills in bottles are a reminder that I rattle. I am grateful for, and embarrassed by, the largesse of my medical advisers. I call myself the Phantom of the Pharmacy. How on earth can my country afford me?

So-called tycoons, loveable or not, captains of industry, men of power, the big employers, the wealth creators, should be knelt down to or at least looked up to by poor folk and old folk and all beneficiaries of the Welfare State. Egalitarians are inclined to call them fat cats and parasites: where do they think the money lashed out on the NHS, and our innumerable benefits of one sort and another, come from?

The facts of the matter are that people are soon spoilt, they take gifts for granted, gratitude is a wasting asset, and privileges turn into rights.

12 July

Beware of doctors with bad secretarial back-up!

The bandwagon rolls towards the legalisation of cannabis. I believe Baudelaire rather than Lib-Labs. Baudelaire described his own experience in *Les Paradis Artificiels*. He said that cannabis affects and eventually destroys the will, the will-power that enables us to perform our existential duties. Cannabis causes physical and mental listlessness, and Baudelaire bitterly regretted that he became its slave.

14 July

List of foibles and faults that affect sober intelligent persons in their latter years:

1. Unstoppable verbosity;
2. A determination to be the centre of attention, relentless drive for selfish ends, sulking if crossed;
3. Megalomania that stops just short of madness, characterised by boasting, no interest in anyone else's existence, and extreme irritability;
4. Religious mania, which persuades some people to think they have a private line to God and need to obey none of the laws laid down in the Holy Bible or the rules of social life;
5. Irrational attitude to money, penny-pinching in well-heeled ladies who are convinced they are ruined, while men squirm on the horns of a dilemma – will they die before they have enjoyed spending their capital, or will they live after they have spent it?
6. Fund-raising *sans frontières*, that is with no holds barred, a substitute for the give and take, or take and give, of the competitive sexual exchanges of yore;
7. Foolhardiness, exhibited by blind drivers of ninety, and by superannuated yachtsmen, potholers, mountaineers and parachutists who have to be rescued by brave men at great risk.

15 July

No public sympathy in the country for policemen who kill people threatening to kill them and others, and no sympathy for policemen who do not stop madmen and murderers killing people: that is democracy in action, and why leadership differs from it.

18 July

Yesterday I was informed of the results of the tests I have been undergoing. Thank God, they were okay. Tomorrow we will be told how G's treatment is or is not working. Our hearts go out to everyone else waiting for the results of tests, and to everyone who has waited.

A scene sticks in my memory. At the hospital, in the changing room to which I returned after my tests, a young woman sat in one of the chairs, bowing her head low over a magazine. She wore another of the white dressing-gowns of towelling, and was obviously about to be summoned for an x-ray examination of some kind. She did not look up when I entered the room, she remained in the same rigidly bowed and rather unnatural position. I did not believe she was reading the magazine, and, rightly or wrongly, imagined she was afraid and sorrowful. She was very young, perhaps thirty, and I was so sorry for her.

19 July

G's treatment is working, but slowly. She rises above it.

21 July

Reverting once more to the effects of seniority on certain citizens, I refer to the increasingly common case of the hyperactive pensioner. Nowadays, old people sign on for package tours offering dawn starts to sight-seeing expeditions, a fortnight of bus rides, walking, swimming, games, evenings of seven-course dinners, then dancing into the small hours. Night flights on chartered aeroplanes to faraway places seem to deter nobody over sixty-five. In Eventide Homes, single old men have to lock their doors at night against harassment by their lusty female counterparts. The coupling of the ancients of days is now possible with the aid of science and no doubt leads to further expenditure of effort.

Excess on top of excesses, as usual, is reserved for 'higher' society. No debutante is so social as the bejewelled biddy who breaks and enters into every party. Cocktails here, dinner there, a ball until you are swept out with the detritus, luncheon somewhere else on the next day, and anything but a quiet evening at home – these are the preferred conditions of existence for unreconstructed flibbertigibbets. Tiredness is no excuse, satiety is simply not on the menu, ill health alters nothing, distance is no bar to a good time, 'pace' is the best of last words – and people who disagree are spoilsports.

22 July

Belas Knap and Soldier's Grave are prehistoric burial barrows located in the Cotswolds. Clifford Chambers is a Cotswold village, and Whispering Knights is the remains of a circle of stones. Egypt Mills at Nailsworth made cloth. Bliss Gate is near the Wyre Forest. Sweet surprising English names, not yet 'modernised'.

Story entitled *The Poor Philanthropist*: John was honest and poor for the first half of his life. He had been an orphan at twenty and was now pushing thirty-one, he stacked the shelves in a supermarket, dwelt in a remote lodging house, ate food past its sell-by date and rejected the idea of a wife whom he could not support. But then he had a flutter on the Lottery and won millions. He married Jane, a check-out girl aged forty, who was nicknamed Plain Jane. He liked her because she was as disadvantaged as he had been, and he was proud to wave his magic wand over her destiny. They bought a house in town and another in the country. She went shopping, he gave some of his money away or tried to. His relations, who had not been kind to him when he was poor, were nasty to him because he was rich. His gifts were either mingy and mean or distributed unfairly, they said, and their thanks were qualified by envy. He gave money to his friends, and they took umbrage: they could manage quite well without his patronage, and some made it clear that they were not for sale. Public charities were different in that they held out hot hands for more and still more, but caused suspicions to cross his mind: why did charities spend so much of the money on glossy brochures, extravagant adverts and administration? Further disillusionment was in store for him. Plain Jane sued him for divorce and the law enabled her to get away with half his remaining capital. Honest John told everybody that he had no money left, which was not completely true. But he almost felt sorry for himself and was inclined to mutter under his breath, 'Poor me!'

23 July

A brief history of my acquaintanceship with female beauty is comparable to a minefield. I shall start with the harmless past and end at a safe distance from the present. David Cecil told me he treasured memories of my mother in a filmy ball-dress of butterfly blue, and of his own sister Mary, later Duchess of Devonshire, waltzing at a ball: he commented on their airs of distinction and high spirits as well as their beautiful youth, and considered that they were the stars of his generation. He was also an admirer of Diana Cooper, who once upon a time must have deserved the praise lavished on her looks. But when I knew Diana, from the late fifties onwards, I could not admire that pale chilly countenance and deadpan expression. Vita Sackville-West as debutante was admired by my mother, who said she looked like a gipsy girl. Sad to think of

Vita in the breeches and boots of her older age with her bucolic complexion, as it is to be reminded that my friend Cynthia Asquith, with not a trace of beauty, had formerly been one of the pair of 'moon goddesses', the other being Diana Cooper.

My Aunt Laura Lovat also lost her looks too early: in her youth she had deserved the nickname Lady Love-at-first-sight.

Joan Moore, the pianist, Countess of Drogheda, differed from the professional beauties, for she had other interests, her musicianship and career in concert halls, and her exhaustive reading and knowledge of literature. Her beauty, which no doubt cut both ways in relation to her life as an artist, was reinforced by her intelligence, and because it expressed the sympathetic warmth of her nature.

Beautiful womanhood does not necessarily denote a *femme fatale*. The fatal female has physical magnetism combined with a contrary and even perverse nature and a ruthless streak. An example was Patricia Douglas, later de Bendern, then Hornak, a relation of Oscar Wilde's undoing, Lord Alfred Douglas. Pat was not even very pretty, she had and retained into middle age a school-girlish face and figure, yet she was unusually and perhaps involuntarily seductive.

I dare to say no more.

Lord Alfred Douglas lived and died in Brighton. In his latter years he accepted an invitation to lunch with some friends, who all agreed not to mention the scandal of his youth. But the relevant name slipped out, Lord Alfred heard it, and announced in a loud voice: 'I used to be thick with Oscar Wilde.'

24 July

The *homme fatal* also exists. It might be that a *femme fatale* is only subjugated by an *homme fatal*; but in my view such poetic justice is unlikely. The men and women referred to either have a special gift for identifying willing fatalities, or their attractions are reserved for masochists. I cannot imagine two fatal people getting together.

Don Juan is not always *fatal*. Womanisers can be bad or relatively good for women.

31 July

Putting to bed *Tales of Love and War* – meaning, that I have chosen the better of two roughs of the dust jacket, checked that my corrections of the proofs have been corrected, and given the text one last reading.

In the world of my work there are two warning lights. One stops me rewriting what I have written. I may know it is faulty, but, at the same time, that I can do no better, and if I fiddle with it I shall compound old faults and introduce new ones. The second light comes on when I am correcting work – it is the signal of satiety. It tells me I have done enough and had enough of proof-reading or whatever, and must call a halt and give up.

What an eye-opener it was for me when Leslie Hartley confessed that he did not revise his work! That was before I had heard of the weird ways in which some books get written. Ghosts lurk in many a bookshelf, and the fingerprints of editors are left on books. How much of Ian Fleming's work was done by William Plomer, poet and his publisher? Is it true that large parts of Bertolt Brecht's plays were written by the actress/actresses who would act in them? Sarah Bernhardt undoubtedly wrote most of the surviving version of Dumas' *La Dame aux Camélias*. Literary wives, literary secretaries, are often handed first drafts of books of which the authors wash their hands – Ursula Codrington, who typed for Leslie Hartley, chose and supplied 'his' adjectives.

Back to the subject of beauty: at a ball at the start of a London 'season' of long ago somebody asked Sir Edward Marsh, Winston Churchill's unwed private secretary, 'Well, Eddie, who are the beauties this year?' to which Sir Edward replied, 'I think he's rather beautiful.'

4 August

In art, the shocking card has now been played too often. Modernism equals reheated sensationalism. Sexual perversion is yesterday's mashed potato. Iconoclasm is just pulling a long nose at your superiors. The look-at-me specialists are ten a penny. Nihilism has been seen to mean what it says – nothing. The way forward? Read Hamlet's speech to the players.

5 August

Some years ago Sir Martyn Beckett MC asked John Grigg to give the address at his funeral. John agreed, and the other day went to visit Martyn in hospital where he lay terminally ill. Martyn greeted John thus: 'You're on!'

6 August

Thetis Blacker, the painter and our friend, sent me a mail order catalogue issued by OKA which markets household furnishings. It arrived by post, and she referred me to page 28, an illustration of a small standing bookcase, and to one of the books filling the shelves – my book *Gentleman's Gentleman* in its first edition. What a delightful start to the morning! Perhaps only Thetis would have thought of studying that catalogue with a magnifying glass, spotting one out of thirty or forty books, and passing on the result of her research to gratify an old author.

8 August

That delightful subject, female beauty: my negative suggestion would be that it is recognisable only by being impossible to describe. Women blessed or cursed with it are also indescribable because they operate on a level different from the rest of us – different laws, values, preoccupations, aims, fears and practicalities govern their existence.

The career of Helen of Troy, whose face launched the thousand ships bearing soldiers to fight the Trojan War, is anti-climactic. She began by marrying Menelaus, left her husband for Paris, when Paris was slain in 'her' war she married his brother Deiphobus, then had him killed by her first husband Menelaus, with whom she settled down and lived quietly in the country until death carried her off.

9 August

I am mistaken for somebody else with Shakespearean regularity. My worst case occurred at Glyndebourne a few years ago. A young woman approached and enfolded me in an unsolicited embrace, saying how wonderful it was to see me after so long. I made the mistake of signifying agreement, and the following conversation ensued.

'Oh we did have such fun in the old days!'

'We did indeed!'

'I'll never forget the tennis matches.'

'Same here.'

'Is your mother still alive?'

'I'm afraid not.'

'What a shame! I never will forget her underarm serve, nor her home-made lemonade.'

'Did she make lemonade?' I queried, cudgelling my brains as to whom I was talking.

'She certainly did – fancy you forgetting that! But how are you?' She regarded me with some anxiety, clearly thinking I was going Alzheimer's way. 'Are you all right?'

'I'm fine, and I don't need to ask how you are, I can see you're flourishing.'

'Thank you. I'm married and the mother of two.'

'Well done!'

'Are you married?'

'I am.'

'Oh do introduce me to your wife!'

'I can't – she's not with me at the moment – I don't know where she is.'

A shadow flitted across the face of my interlocutor – my answer had been on the hysterical side, I suppose, since I did not know her name and could not have introduced her.

'Aren't we lucky to be at Glyndebourne this evening?' she inquired with traces of doubt.

'Aren't we just!'

'Did you come all the way from Hampshire? You are still living in the ancient family pile, aren't you?'

'Hampshire?' I ventured to say. 'No, I've never lived in Hampshire, I was brought up in Gloucestershire.'

'Who are you then?'

I told her.

'Well, really!' she exclaimed and stalked off in high dudgeon.

11 August

In my youth I enjoyed doing lots of things which I now struggle to refrain from telling young people not to do.

At last I have come across a book that I cannot believe I will ever want to read: Duncan, I.K., *A Guide to the Study of Lichens* (T. Buncle, Arbroath, 1959).

12 August

Sunday, the Sabbath, the day of rest, and as usual I wish I had not read my newspaper.

Tomorrow we leave for our week of summer holiday, and hope it will cheer but not inebriate, as the Scots say about tea.

21 August

Happy children beside the sea, happy families by the English sea, charm, amuse and revive hope. The inevitable 'but' refers to all the obesity on view. It was tragic to see those fat and fated young persons waddling to and from the ice cream shop.

Read Harold Acton's *More Memories of an Aesthete* with enjoyment. I met him once after he had given a splendid lecture – I forget the subject, but not his delivery, which was urbane and amusing: as is his book.

★   ★   ★

Acton describes in detail a holiday he spent with his friend Evelyn Waugh. It reveals in terms not altogether friendly Waugh's behaviour, the contrariness, the brutishness replete with bullying, the half-crazed impersonation of an eighteenth century aristo by the son of a middle-class twentieth-century publisher. Genius, especially the literary sort, is apt to go with bad character and unpleasant personality, often with madness too. Waugh proved his genius with *Brideshead Revisited*.

24 August

Something called The Artwave takes place in Lewes this evening. It seems to be partly rustic carnival and partly late-night shopping. No doubt it will all end in boozing.

26 August

Reading Anthony Powell's *The Kindly Ones*, part of his *Music of Time* series of novels. His prose reminds me of a steamroller cracking nuts;

yet it instils a sense of security because of its good manners and implied promise that nothing too shocking is in store for the reader. I met the Powells once – they were very nice. He fagged for David Cecil at Eton (ran David's errands and toasted his muffins for tea), and they kept up in later life. David enjoyed Anthony's company more than his books, although he went in fear of the curries with which the Powells were apt to regale their guests. At my meeting with them, Anthony said he had seemed to spend his days of work at *The Times Literary Supplement* packing up books to be sent to me to review.

27 August

In the Glyndebourne Festival just ended, my favourite opera was Janacek's *The Makropulos Case*. I loathed it when I first heard it, and other performances simply went over my head. But I learned to love it, and to love more and more the music, especially the overture and the final ten or fifteen minutes. Moreover, now, the libretto makes sense to me, and I see why Janacek chose to set it to music.

28 August

I quote from memory Harold Acton who was quoting a Chinese sage: 'Happiness is only possible by exclusive absorption in art.' But how hard it is to try to live exclusively for art!

29 August

Anthony Powell has invented a whole social system which, in literary terms, is comparable to Burke's *Peerage, Baronetage and Knightage* coupled with *Who's Who*. Less flatteringly, it is like those genealogical pages which we do not understand and tend to skip at the beginning of old-time fiction. Another comparison springs to mind: when he launches into yet another disquisition about heredity, relationships, and who was or had been or hoped to be married to whom, and children legitimate and illegitimate and cousins and halves and steps, I am reminded of a schoolmaster of mine who knew the national railway time-table by heart and loved to be asked how one could travel from Llandudno to Perth via Bognor Regis.

Here are words that I find difficult to spell: stye (in the eye – rarely sty); riveting; coquettish; eighth; coypus (S. American rodents); cocoon; coccyx (bone at base of spine); plied (past tense of ply); barre (rail used by ballet dancers); zoophyte (animal that looks like a plant); viscountcy; tappet (part of combustion engine); sapphire; lay-bys; irreplaceable.

31 August

To London yesterday to lunch with John and Patsy Grigg: he is in his seventy-eighth year and said that he could just about see the end of the fourth hefty volume of his life of Lloyd George – and there is yet another volume to come.

1 September

The fair sex should stop me feeling that I ought to write a sequel to *Cautionary Tales for Women*. Consider Agnes, a career-girl, a banker on the way up, efficient and not ugly, who fell in love with Martin, an accountant, mathematically strong but rather a wimp in other respects. She was twenty-six, he was twenty-four; she had loved no other man as she loved Martin from the word go; he was taken aback and perturbed by the passion he had inspired. But at the Christmas 'office' party, encouraged by John Barleycorn, he allowed himself to be seduced – ironically, in the bank vault reserved for Security Deposits. Agnes was soon happy to find herself pregnant, and, taking it for granted that the father of her child would do the honourable thing, hurried to tell him the good news. With outpourings of gratitude, with promises that she would take care of everything, himself not least, and with her vision of their perfect little family unit, she swept him to the altar. And she was as good as her word: she bore him two healthy children, ran a comfortable home, arranged her life so that she could continue to work at the bank and contribute a second income to family funds, denied her husband nothing, and was not forgiven by her friends for having such an enviable marriage. Martin's announcement that he was in love with someone else hit her hard. But she recovered some sort of composure and discussed the matter sympathetically. She referred to mid-life crises. She said she would not object to a spot of discreet adultery. She let him talk about his mistress, a twenty-year-old aspiring model called Polly. She also did her rather shocking best to exhaust him sexually. He then told her that Polly was going to study modelling and acting in America for six months, and when she returned he intended to set divorce proceedings in train. He would stay put for that period, he continued, and continue to cohabit, especially as he had new social responsibilities connected with his work and would require Agnes' assistance. She agreed, she submitted, she was sure he would change his mind. In the ensuing months Agnes worked her fingers to the bone for Martin – and not only her fingers, for they still slept in the marital bed. She cooked delicious dinners in order to advance his career, and ate dinners that she often found unpalatable to please him. She was ready for anything he suggested, never moody, never challenging. And she never asked what had become of his intentions – he could not be so horrible as to spurn her after all, she imagined. But one day he asked her to help him to pack his things. What had he said, what did he mean? She laughed in disbelief, told him he could not do it, prophesied that if he did he would rue the day, and so on. Hoping to frighten him somehow, she actually did do some of his packing. He walked out on her with his suitcases, some of which she carried to his car, and her optimistic suggestion when he pecked her cheek in response to her clinging hug, 'See you soon', was not quite the end of the story. They divorced. Polly married a different man. Martin's second marriage was to a different woman. Agnes was left alone to reflect that love as one-sided as hers is a mistake.

2 September

Passion and lust are natural. Passion and lust know no boundaries. Without religion and fear of the fires of hell, passion and lust can and do become criminal.

Tales of Love and War is scheduled for publication in the second half of January 2002, a time when, I was once encouraged incorrectly, so few books get published that critics are willing to review the telephone directory.

4 September

Feminism – is it proactive flirting and a short cut to becoming a damsel in distress? The fair sex is also the weaker one, and muscles do not believe in equality. Very few women are able to overpower their husbands or lovers – physically, I mean. Women of a certain age with children, living in poor circumstances, have no realistic alternative to getting beaten up by their worse halves. Cruel men can frighten lots of women into not leaving them. Girls, beware! Love does not have to be, it should not be, a white-knuckle ride. Take cross references if possible before you 'behave like a man', commit yourself or agree to marry. Sex, exclusive sex, is no substitute for sympathy, comprehensive sympathy; and no sex, or too little, is another danger signal.

The excuses of men echo down the years. Women's accounts of men's violence are always 'grossly exaggerated'. Women 'bruise themselves', are 'frightful whingers', are 'romancers, neurotics, psychological cases, liars, out to make trouble, bloodsuckers and bitches'. Men claim they were 'only teasing', that their wretched partners 'have no sense of humour', that they themselves are actually the victims of the relationship and are scared stiff of frail creatures with black eyes and broken bones. How are you to react to those solemn promises that offenders 'did not mean it ... had not known it would be taken so hard ... would never do it again ... would be different, good, kind, gentle, sweet in future', and the accompanying pleas and prayers to be given a second or a last chance, to be reinstated in order to create more misery? Are you strong enough to say 'No, thanks – forget it – get lost – goodbye'?

Do not imagine that such dilemmas, such disasters, happen only to other people, you well-brought-up middle-class girl with hopes and ideals! Wife-beaters abound. Everywhere sadists either have sought out or are seeking masochists. I know popular members of the establishment whose recreation is to torment and torture their wives.

7 September

Byron's Diary beckons. *The Third Time* tempted me to interrupt my first journal, *Marking Time*. I wonder if history is repeating itself. The attractions of the Byron book would be the mystery and the deception.

A new game could rival Happy Families – it would be called Unsuitable Appointments and also be played with cards – the method of play undecided as yet. For example, in my lifetime in the Kingdom that was United, we have elected Scotsmen to govern England and a terrorist to educate children in Ireland. Our Arts Council is run by a gentleman also responsible for service stations on motorways. We have republicans swearing allegiance to our Queen, egalitarians queueing up to be lordships and ladyships, money-mad socialists, and pacifists in charge of armies. Not long ago a curmudgeon who had hurt the feelings of most of his compatriots was put in charge of race relations. We have sportsmen who are renowned more for their unsportsmanlike behaviour than their skill. And the personage summoned to organise entertainment in Tony Blair's Dome was a lawyer.

8 September

The new Lewes library will not be built. The plan has been scrapped because local government is four million pounds poorer than it should have been. We are not meant to dish out blame just yet. The Conservatives have not run the Town or County Councils for several years.

9 September

I am going to set aside my journal for the time being, and see if I can squeeze a short book out of my idea for *Byron's Diary*.

7 November

Between the last entry and this one, an example of man's inhumanity, ranking with the great horrors of history, has occurred. On September 11, in an attack of undeclared war, several thousand civilians of mixed nationalities were killed in minutes. The murders were committed in the name of the Muslim religion. So far the international leaders of the Muslim community have not publicly disassociated themselves from the act.

My lifetime was overshadowed by the cruelty of Marxism and Nazism in action, and I foresee my life ending in the course of another long, horrible and ultimately pointless period of conflict.

I think of the saying of an unsophisticated friend of ours: the best we can do at such times, at all times, is to keep our own little corners bright.

Incidentally, I have written the first draft of *Byron's Diary* in thirty-eight days for better or worse.

12 November

A Sussex gardener spoke to us of the Americans having trouble with 'that there Andrex' – he meant anthrax, not lavatory paper.

My second draft of *Byron's Diary* is now complete. The third and last will not take long. Writing seems easier after Gerard Noel's praise of my *Collected Works* in the *Catholic Herald*.

13 November

Cecil Beaton continued to bring out diaries long after he should have stopped. He lent my sister June the diary that described his 'love affair' with Greta Garbo – he asked her to read it and tell him if he could or should publish it. June was uncertain and passed it on to me. My verdict was that of course he should not publish but that of course he would – and he did. The diary showed that he courted Garbo more for publicity purposes than for love, and what a go-getter he was.

Jim Lees-Milne's amusing and reckless diaries are still being published posthumously. I suspect that he is ill-served by his executors and editors. On the other hand the more recent ones seem to warn women against marriages of his type, which resembled Harold and Vita's. Alvilde was the daughter of a general, but even she with her militant disposition complained of Jim's extra-marital activities. One day both Lees-Milnes were invited to lunch somewhere. Jim chucked, Alvilde went alone. When she arrived, her hostess said how sorry she was that Jim was otherwise engaged with his nephew. To which Alvilde replied: 'They're always his nephews.'

20 November

I have finished *Byron's Diary*. It must be about the twenty-fifth book of mine, including the Harlequin mini-books, that Diana Crook has typed faultlessly for me, correcting draft after draft. Her work has complemented mine in other ways – she is my archivist, and the archival system she invented has been approved and even copied by the British Library. Her comments on my texts have never been destructive, while her suggestions have always been wise and often improved my writings. She is my colleague, and I set great store by her opinions.

21 November

I have advance copies of *Tales of Love and War*. My friends at the Book Guild of Lewes have done an excellent job so far, but I wonder whether they can distribute it even as well as Constable did with other books of mine – that is to say, I do not expect to sell many copies.

24 November

A book which I shall not write could be amusing and would be topical – title: *Human Consistency – A Lost Cause.*

Here is an example: in the *Observer's Book of Wild Animals of the British Isles*, the revised edition published in 1958, the two expert authors open the entry on the fox with the following sentence: 'It is safe to say that ... the fox would have been placed long ago on the list of extinct British animals, but for its careful preservation by the various "hunts".' Now, almost fifty years later, the sentimentalists and the inverted snobs want to outlaw hunting with dogs – they object to the 'cruelty' of the sport of 'hunting'. No doubt the politics of ignorance will get its law on to the Statute Book. As a result the anti-hunting brigade will kill off many highly developed breeds of hounds, fox, stag, otter hounds, 'natural' as distinct from racing greyhounds, beagles and so on, will decimate the horse population and probably cause the fox's extinction.

26 November

Less than a month to go until the shortest day of the year, 21 December, after which days lengthen and spring comes in.

27 November

True diaries are records of events. True diarists are recorders, they are not led on by the discoveries, surprises and excitement of creative writing unless they are liars.

I feel a bit flat in a literary sense after tearing through *Byron's Diary*. I used to write slowly, now I have joined the speed merchants. I am amazed by the number of books I have written – after my first I was almost convinced that I would never write another.

The genesis of *War and Peace* occupied thirteen years, from 1856 to 1869. Tolstoy claimed that he put his whole heart and soul into his book – a proceeding Byron warned against, advising writers always to hold something back and keep a secret or two. Byron might have been proved right, for in my opinion Tolstoy never recovered mentally from the huge creative effort. I am not comparing myself with Tolstoy, far from it, but do know that keeping control of long books is terribly difficult and a terrible strain: computers may seem to be a solution, but in fact beget a whole range of new problems. Tolstoy himself thought it had been a bad idea to embark on *Anna Karenina*, another heavy tome, immediately after *War and Peace*. He loathed it, got stuck in the middle, had to force himself to complete it, and found fault with it to his dying day. Parts of *Resurrection* written in his old age are excellent, so are the stories of his even older age, but the two marathons, *War and Peace* and *Anna Karenina*, seem to have robbed him of common sense and compassion for persons, if not for people.

Dostoevsky's books show genius and often his epilepsy and mental instability as well. *Crime and Punishment* is disturbing not only because it is an ingenious murder story; and *The Brothers Karamazov* casts a sinister and unhealthy spell. One of the many divisions by which humanity in general and readers in particular can be described is that some people are born to love Tolstoy's 'straightforward' books and others to prefer Dostoevsky's 'psychological' ones.

1 December

In receipt of the umpteenth piece of evidence attesting to the unfailing capacity of members of my extended family, even the most distant of my relations, to live beyond their means.

2 December

My grandfather on my father's side went bust, my great-grandfather on my mother's side ditto – he also committed suicide. My father died aged fifty-five in financial distress. One cousin of his had to 'cut down a tree in order to buy a bottle of gin', as the family put it, and he and another cousin handed over to their heirs estates that were bankrupt. The widow of yet another cousin of my father's generation inherited a fortune and ran through it, and her daughter frittered away her own fortune in the course of a short life.

My brother papered the walls of a dining-room in one house he lived in with prints of the grander residences our forebears had built, inherited, dwelt in, and been forced to sell, including Apethorpe in Northamptonshire and Mereworth Castle in Kent.

5 December

What are these: Ancient Wife, Cock Paddle, Colin, Father Lasher, Longnose, Miller's Dog, Sweet Lips? Answer: sea creatures.

Harold Pinter has publicly tried to moderate his speech urging people to attack America delivered a day or two before the Muslim extremists did so. The speech was meant to thank an Italian University for presenting him with an award of some description.

6 December

My friend Anne Tree, upon whom part of the perennial political mantle worn by the Cecil family, her maternal forebears, seems to have fallen, said yesterday that our country was now out of control. I agree, and hope we may be proved wrong.

I have tried for years to ignore reviews of my books, not always successfully. Reviewers seldom review my work nowadays – I am old, no longer news, and have steered clear of the literary rat race in London. Appreciative notices are nice nonetheless, as nice as the other sort are nasty and somehow unforgettable.

7 December

The best and most intelligent English review I have received was of *Money Matters*, written by Adam An-tAthair-Síoraí and published in *Icarus*, the journal of Mensa. The best and most intelligent review of my work in general and my *Collected Works* in particular was written by the author and editor Gerard Noel and appeared in *The Catholic Herald*. Both *Money Matters* and my *Collected Works* were ignored by the 'national' newspapers.

8 December

I see no ships, only hardships – Cockney saying.

9 December

G approves in the main of *Byron's Diary* – which is most satisfactory for me.

Beautiful cold weather, not comfortable for people with bad circulations.

10 December

Yesterday the Turner Prize was awarded to an empty room with lights that go on and off at five second intervals – the judges were also intentionally or unintentionally making a comment on Philistia, the Great Britain of yore. Another such comment was their choice of prize-giver, the American pop and film star Madonna, who in a short speech upset millions of people watching on TV. I repeat that nothing succeeds like offence.

With thanks to our friend and neighbour Tony Shephard, here are a few uncommon examples of Cockney rhyming slang: Jeremiah = fire; Gawd forbids = kids; Cain and Abel = table; daft and barmy = army; royal soup and gravy = navy; frog and toad = road; Donald Duck = luck; taters in the mould = cold; Piccadilly Percys = mercies; Jim Skinner = dinner; Forsyte Saga = lager; jam tart = heart.

Reading *The Faustian Bargain* by Jonathan Petropoulos, the story of the German artists and middlemen of the arts who lent their support to the nazi regime. Could they have done otherwise? I wish that many had not made fortunes, got off scot-free after the war, and hung on to their money.

11 December

Books I just want to look at, and maybe read, I borrow from David Jarman's membership library located a hundred and fifty yards from our home. It occupies approximately two rooms, financially must hang on a shoestring, and is an admirable enterprise really run on a combination of David's charm, taste and reassuring love of books.

A grim statistic, culled from the Bookseller publication *Who Owns Whom, 1998*: Random Century, the English subsidiary of Random House USA, owned at the time twenty-two different publishing imprints. Since 1998, the German group Bertelsmann has bought Random Century, therefore its eleven imprints (1998 tally) have to be added to Random Century's twenty-two – Bertelsmann must now own thirty-three of the better-known imprints operating as British publishers. What percentage of the whole publishing industry in this country does that add up to? Is it almost a monopoly? No question that it is a monolithic bureaucracy – not a very clever development, when everybody who knows anything about the literary life is convinced that only individuals, who love the printed word and have a nose for talent and quality, have ever been good at publishing.

12 December

We are feeding our garden birds in this cold weather. They are not active while it is dark – owls and nightjars must be the exceptions proving the rule that most birds cannot see to fly and to land on twigs until the sun has risen. Avian meal-times seem to be as strict as they were in middle-class Victorian households – eating at anti-social hours is not always the done thing. Starlings have muscled in on the food we provide for smaller birds, and now a grey squirrel is bagging the biggest share – the bird world is not so different from ours.

13 December

The murderer of six-year-old 'Mary Sunshine' has been condemned to spend his whole life in prison – he is a pervert who sexually assaulted and killed a little girl, and, if ever given the chance, would be expected to strike again.

For the Sunshine family, the private tragedy grinds on; nationally, the comedy begins. The judge has no power to imprison Cain, the murderer, until he dies – he merely makes a recommendation to the Government that Cain should never be released. Therefore Home Secretaries in the plural are going to have to decide whether or not to keep Cain in prison after he has served his life sentence of a decade or so. If no liberal Home Secretary sets Cain free, he will join five or six other monsters who have become virtually political prisoners – I know of no law of lifelong imprisonment at the disposal of the judiciary. Everybody wants to sweep Cain and other murderers under the carpet, but nobody wants to pay for their comfortable living conditions until they die. There is an extraordinary conspiracy to censor the words that begin with the letters C and P. You can curse and swear to your heart's content on the stage, you can turn plays, films and TV linguistically into a barrackroom, you can spew out sedition publicly and blaspheme to your heart's content, but it is not done to say even in an undertone 'capital punishment'. I not only do say or rather write those words here, but I also challenge the anti-death-penalty mob to tell me what is the point and the use of keeping Cain and his ilk alive and in cages like pets at enormous expense for ever. Please do not con me with the story that you are against the shedding of blood, because you are a vegan and a pacifist: do you never wear leather, and refuse all medical assistance linked to the death of your fellow creatures when you are ill? Please remember, and own up, that you live on death, however strict your regime – carnivores and herbivores, birds and sea creatures, we all kill to eat, and hypocrisy cuts no ice with common sense. Cain should die – honesty would rule that it is good to be rid of bad rubbish – and in an overpopulated and increasingly violent world the death penalty will soon be forced on politics. It is already happening in an underhand way: Blair has pledged to hand over Bin Laden or any of his criminal gang, should they be apprehended by our troops, to the USA, which has promised to try them by drumhead courts and polish them off if necessary. Why are all our brave journalists, who criticise the defenceless Royal Family and the Church of England, so craven in respect of this issue? What are all the young Turks in the media, who can be rude to almost everyone, doing about the injustice of the law, which has freed murderers to kill children and others? Do-gooders believe we are all guilty of crime in general – I believe we are guilty of not making certain in the most cost-effective way that incorrigible murderers will lose their lives for taking life and can never do it again.

14 December

The successful redistributor of wealth is not a phoney political doctrine, but, practically and historically, sex. Cinderellas, Galateas, chorus girls transformed into duchesses, pretty faces that launch ships, and sundry other lucky sex-objects prove my point.

15 December

Times change, to coin a phrase: two young footballers, overpaid, under-educated, with records of violence and drunken brawling, are not sent to prison for helping nearly to kill an Asian youth, just as two hundred years ago upper-class hooligans would not have been imprisoned for a similar offence. Now the upper-class hooligan would be made an example of, while the thuggish entertainer is above the laws of the land.

16 December

The face of Osama bin Laden spills beans, I believe. His eyes are all very well, but his mouth is a disaster. It is the mouth of a clown, he has the blubbery lips of certain fish, they are joke lips of equal dimensions top and bottom made of rubber, and they contradict his eyes. He is dysplastic, he may well suffer from dysplasia in other parts of his anatomy, have a strong torso and rickety legs for all I know, or thin ankles and non-matching fat feet. *The Varieties of Human Physique* by W.H. Sheldon of Harvard University describes dysplasia thus: 'the aspect of disharmony between different regions of the same physique'. Sheldon's companion volume to the above, *Varieties of Human Temperament*, links physical and temperamental combinations and draws his various conclusions. Here are my own deductions from first-hand study of the dysplastic syndrome. The 'disharmony' accounts for personalities not fully integrated, for people who look sensitive but behave insensitively, or vice versa, for clever people with stupid streaks, or pacifists who fight for peace, or, in a catch-all couple of words, the inconsistent. Dysplasia seems to go with an inability to connect cause and effect — they are the charitable sadists and rough masochists, they are the loving husbands with downtrodden nervous wrecks of wives, or the loving wives who henpeck their hubbies, the fond and oppressive fathers, the sweet Oedipal sons, the phallic mothers, the vengeful daughters, and many others who carry their innate contradictions to measurable and even clinical lengths.

17 December

The whole story of a new novella, plus the title, came to me in the small hours of this morning during half an hour of wakefulness in bed. It will be called *Duress*, if it ever gets written.

Acquaintances and even my friends are apt to be unimaginative in respect of the life I lead and the lives of professional working people in general. Strangely, lovers of art seem to have the foggiest ideas of how art is created in practical terms – perhaps they also badgered Michelangelo to take time off from painting the ceiling of the Sistine Chapel and stay for the weekend and draw something nice in their Visitors Books. Social life is goodbye to art, and socialites can never or will never understand that the majority of artists and for that matter pros of every description, including craftsmen and artisans, need peace and quiet in which to prepare to do, and recover from, their work. A minority of exceptions burn their candles at both ends, and as a rule die of it.

Unusual artists with strong constitutions may be able to work and play almost simultaneously. But for Pushkin exiled to the depths of the country, Tolstoy snowed up at Yasnaya Polyana, Solzhenitsyn hiding from the secret police, Proust alone with his asthma in a cork-lined noiseless room, and for all the famous failures, for examples Vermeer and van Gogh, obscurity was the mother and father of their wonderful work.

An original expression of a widow's grief: 'I am sad that I no longer have to put down the seat of the lavatory.'

20 December

Sex without seriousness is nothing to write home about. True love on both sides, modesty on the female, confidence tempered with respect on the male, and shared awareness of the parameters of sin – these are the ingredients of the most powerful of aphrodisiacs in the human pharmacopoeia. Permissiveness and promiscuity equal wet blankets as well as sheets.

I now have two novellas in mind, *Duress* and *The Stepmother*. I hope to have the strength to write them, beginning perhaps after our holiday in February.

21 December

The shortest day of the year, praise be!

22 December

The Commissioners of Irish Lights bear a romantic name, but only look after lighthouses.

23 December

A few evenings ago we watched a programme on TV about Russian churches, their architecture, decoration, services and congregations. It was in all respects beautiful − snow lent further enchantment to the outdoor scenes, and we were spared a pretentious and distracting commentary. The members of the congregations were of both sexes and every age, and their faces as they watched and listened to the celebration of Christian rites seemed to glow with faith. I thought of the horrors they had lived through, of the seventy years of the communist experiment in Russia, of the blood, tears, bereavements, grief of their last century which was worse than ours, and gained understanding of their joy to be free to worship a deity who offered them not despotism, but consolation and hope.

Very bright cold weather continues − I await global warming in vain.

24 December

Regrettably, Scrooge-like feelings about children of all ages who do not thank for Christmas presents.

John Grigg extremely ill. He has been my friend for sixty years. A brilliant man, and a good one − rare combination! He is blessed with the happiest of marriages.

26 December

A peaceful Christmas Day – counted my blessings – worried about those less lucky – in the evening Sky TV showed a fine Italian production of Verdi's *Falstaff* – such a relief to see a great opera not defaced by the cheeky midgets who peddle 'contemporary' versions and 'relevance'.

Falstaff was first staged in 1893. Verdi was then eighty, according to my calculations, so must have been writing his last opera in his later seventies. The work sparkles with vivacity, humour, compassion and gentle morality, and has not only delighted audiences for more than a century, it also offers a glimmer of hope to septuagenarian practitioners of other arts, the writer of this diary, for example.

27 December

The other day I said to G, 'This year has been awful, so violent and sad – I'll be glad to see the back of it,' and G replied, 'You say that every year.'

28 December

Someone's theory is that the occupational hazard of the English upper class is melancholia. If true, that would explain the widespread weakness for the bottle of that class of person.

But drunkenness is more egalitarian than any radical philosophy or revolutionary action. It may be the second great leveller, poverty being the first.

How can poorer people afford to get drunk? How can richer people – a couple of alcoholics can drink up to twenty thousand pounds p.a., and much more if they are hospitable?

It is a mistake to judge alcoholics by the common or garden criteria. They have renounced 'normality' knowingly or unknowingly, they have left happiness and health far behind, and seek nothing but the relief of the next drink and the bitter joy of a loss of control of their lives.

29 December

Snow fell overnight, we awoke to a white world.

We have been discussing the phenomenon of J.K. Rowling, the girl who has written the Harry Potter books which have sold almost as well as the Bible. I saw her for a moment on TV and liked her, and G saw her for longer and thought she was a genuine vocational writer. She is now famous for ever and rich beyond the dreams of avarice; but more by accident than design, for she could not have aimed to make so stupendous a success and confine herself in a gilded literary cage. No book of hers not about Harry Potter will please her fans. A different sort of book will be meat to all the hungry carnivores of Grub Street, the critics and journalists, the poor hacks, the competitive female authors, the miffed publishers, the envious agents, the big battalions massed behind the green flag of jealousy. Any difference from the Harry Potter books will disappoint thousands of millions – not an inspiring prospect for a proper author always hoping to write a better book one day!

30 December

Last night a TV programme on John Betjeman in the *Reputations* series. It was pretty good, if somewhat pre-digested for his young admirers. Tastefully, it omitted much that I and other close friends know, while dropping occasional hints suggestive of a slightly different story: John's morning 'glass of champagne', for instance. G thought the programme failed to convey John's charm; but I was sorry that it left out his kindness to younger writers. Somebody expressed a hope that he would be judged by his work – a fitting epitaph for many fine artists.

Elizabeth Cavendish is too sensitive and sensible ever to discuss her relationship with John. Anyway, she has her niche in history, and deserves it.

31 December

One of Margaret Thatcher's brilliant insights was her talk of the 'courage of 3 a.m.' She meant it is braver to be brave in the small hours of the morning than at other times. Recently I have formed the bad habit of waking punctually at 3, therefore can quite agree with her. Worries seem to line up to assault you at that hour, adrenalin rushes in or out to repulse them, fear combined with exertion affects the rhythm of the heart, and only dawn promises rescue and relief. What would we do, what could we do, without morning?

George Christie of Glyndebourne has been made a Companion of Honour – one of the better things done by the government.

New Year's Day 2002

John Grigg died yesterday. His childhood home and ours were two miles distant across the fields. His mother Joan became my mother's friend when they nursed together in World War I. His grandmother, Lady Islington, mother of Joan, a beauty and a noted wit, was also my mother's friend. John's father, Ned Grigg, DSO, and with many other letters after his name, was a sweet benevolent grand old man in my memory, but never won over his mother-in-law Anne Islington, who insisted on calling him Grog. John was the eldest of three Grigg children and the same age as my brother David. Tormarton Court in Gloucestershire was a gracious manor house in a Cotswold style, and the Griggs lived there in considerable comfort. But the interests of the older Grigg generation were political and cultural, whereas my mother was more interested in the decorative arts and gardening, and my father in sport; and although my half-sister June made friends with John, there was no immediate meeting of minds between John and my brother. The latter took grave exception in his eleventh year or thereabouts to three harmless manifestations of John's personality: he said 'See you anon' instead of goodbye, he wore a French beret instead of an English cap, and he was discovered reading a leather-bound copy of Charlotte Brontë's *Villette*. The intolerance of the youth of David, who became a markedly tolerant adult, chose to think that John was attempting to pull intellectual rank by behaving so strangely by his standards, and John compounded his offences in David's eyes by speaking French fluently.

John and David were firm friends later on, but John's support of my literary leanings and my sympathy with his enthusiasms drew us closer together. I remember an early speech of his – it must have been just after the war. He was already a political activist, impatient to stir people up and change things, and he created a forum for lectures and discussion – it bore some blood-curdling name, the 1949 Club, I think, and met in the Church Hall at Tormarton. I went with my mother to one of his rousing efforts, in which he criticised the whole system of government of the country, made learned historical points, bashed into the Establishment, and called for a brand-new better world. His audience consisted of his mother and mine and myself, a few other neighbourly gents and ladies in the front row, and otherwise the residents of the village of Tormarton, most of whom worked for the Griggs in various capacities. In response to the exhortations of the speaker, and when he finished and sat down, the cries that rang out took the form of either 'Hear hear, darling!' or in rich Gloucestershire accents, 'That's it, Master John ... You give it to them hot and strong, Master John ... Well said, Master John!'

In line with his attempt to revolutionise the clodhoppers of Tormarton and its environs, one day he invited me to write a piece that could be spoken or performed in the village church. He called for controversy, and I obliged to the extent of daring to produce a playlet about the wise and unwise virgins. John surprised me by thinking it too tame, I resisted his urgings to make it scandalous, and that was the end of that.

His notorious article about the monarchy was motivated by the spirit of his 1949 Club, that is by a somewhat blinkered high idealism and without malice. Taken in conjunction with his renunciation of the hereditary peerage of Altrincham conferred on his father, it put paid to his attempts to become a professional politician and launched his distinguished career as journalist, critic, historian and biographer.

John could be said to have been born with a silver spoon in his mouth, but he suffered with never a word of public complaint from lifelong ill health, from the eccentricity of his mother, and from problems created by his siblings. He was lucky to have been so intelligent and articulate, and such a fluent writer, but in my opinion he should not have done or had to do a lot of work unworthy of his talents. He was lucky to have been so charming, popular, hospitable, generous, but those delightful qualities are not especially conducive to literary composition. His only unqualified piece of luck was his marriage to Patsy and their family life.

He inherited some of the contentious inclinations of his forebears. Yet he was courtesy personified. In sixty-plus years of close friendship with him, I never knew or heard of him doing a mean or disreputable thing. He was at least as brave as his father, and his sense of humour was at least as keen and jolly as his grandmother Anne Islington's. He was the most modest of heroes, and I am honoured to remember that once upon a time, when we were both churning out books, we thought of calling ourselves the Gloucestershire Group.

2 January

Someone said to G: 'I don't like opera, I don't like opera singers, I don't like the way their mouths are always open.'

The euro is launched. Will pounds be replaced by euros? Blair promises a referendum on the issue. My guess is that the vote would go against it in the unlikely event of Blair keeping his promise. That the euro will find itself in trouble must be a sure thing. It may or may not be scrapped. If it survives, if Europe becomes one country, expect the process to be complete and successful in not less than a hundred and fifty years.

For sixteen days there has been no collection of refuse in Lewes.

5 January

Refuse was collected today, as Mr Pooter would write or should have written in his *Diary of a Nobody*.

Reading Nabokov on Gogol. I am impressed by both writers – I had known little about Nabokov, had only read *Lolita* which I thought rather awful, and although I much enjoyed Gogol's *Dead Souls* and *The Government Inspector* I had read nothing about Gogol himself. Nabokov in this blessedly and unfashionably short biography is excellent, loves his subject, communicates his enthusiasm for Gogol's writings, brings all to life with the grand sweep of his intelligence, impatient dismissal of trivialities, bold comparisons and muscular compassion. He presents us with two Gogols, an irresponsible crazy paranoid escapist and dreamer, and a soaring genius above and beyond mundane analysis, a surrealist who makes sense, a comic tragedian and tragic comedian almost tortured to death by doctors.

6 January

Our Prime Minister patronises the people of India by telling them that he is 'a force for good' and implying that they are not so. Where are his manners, where are his wits? No one can talk to the proud sophisticated satirical people of India like that. Blair will be laughed to scorn by Indians for dressing up like Nehru and not minding his own business.

11 January

PLR, the Public Lending Right, is an author's entitlement to a fee for each of his or her books borrowed from Public Libraries. This was a governmental concession fought for and won by Bridget Brophy and Maureen Duffy some decades ago. The present rate paid to an author for each loan is 2.67p – and the number of loans is calculated by averages and ready reckoning. If I should ever sink so low as to belong to a Trade Union, I would describe the 2.67p as 'derisive', and take strike action. Public Libraries were no doubt a good thing once upon a time, but these days they rip off authors and ruin the book trade. I would have earned a living wage for the last fifty years if my books had not been lent nationally to readers.

12 January

A further word of advice to young writers: do not give your books to members of your family, start by not giving them as you mean to go on, for your siblings and other relations will either not read them, or read and criticise them too harshly and for non-literary reasons. A gift of even one book to a family member can be a costly mistake, for you will then be expected to buy books for all the other members, who will reward you with still more lack of appreciation. In my opinion the best way to preserve your peace of mind, although your publisher's publicity people might not agree, is to disappear shortly before Publication Day and remain in limbo for a few months. After that sort of lapse of time your family will have forgotten your book – it probably never understood your literary leanings and will be pleased to think again that you are a bit of an idler and a parasite.

13 January

I quote from Nabokov's book about Gogol, the great Russian writer: 'When the critic Pogodin's wife died and the man was frantic with grief, this is what Gogol wrote to him: "Jesus Christ will help you to become a gentleman, which you are neither by education nor inclination – she [your wife] is speaking through me." '

14 January

Thinking of the range of ways to 'sandbag' a man and drag him to the altar. The woman who became the first wife of Sydney Schiff, Violet's husband, pretended to sleep or faint while they were together in some lonely wilderness and at the same time enabled him to make love to her. When she 'awoke' or recovered, or when the deed was done, she accused him of having taken advantage of her – to put it mildly – and exerted enough pressure to ring the wedding bells. Sometimes the family and happy home life of a young man or woman can exercise the seductive influence that he or she lacks. Again, money can compensate for almost every physical, mental and social imperfection. Schoolgirls are told to be good if they are neither beautiful nor clever; but cynicism would advise them not to be too good if or when they want a man – availability, used with discretion, can overcome most male objections to romance.

The verb 'to sandbag' in the context above means to knock someone senseless. It was used in Edwardian times in the matrimonial connection because 'sandbagging' not only robs a potential husband of his senses, it has the added advantage of leaving no mark on the victim.

Sydney Schiff's *nom de plume* was Stephen Hudson. He tells the tale of his first marriage in his series of autobiographical novels, *A True Story*, which fell by the wayside long ago. He also translated *Time Regained*, the last volume of his friend Proust's masterpiece.

Violet, wife of Sydney Schiff/Stephen Hudson, was my friend when she was in her eighties and I was in my twenties. The friends of my youth nearly all died in the distant past. The names of those who first encouraged me to follow the star of letters are like the roll-call of the fallen after the battle of Agincourt in Shakespeare's *Henry V*: Dorian Williams, Mr Chilcot, J.D. Upcott, A.R.D. Watkins, schoolmasters; Patrick Wilkinson, Cambridge academic; John Wyse, actor. My father died before I had heard the call to be a writer, and my mother was tolerant and supportive of my unremunerative literary beginnings. As for my parents-in-law, my work is deeply indebted to them for providing me with G. G's mother Juliet and father Jock Swire raised four outstanding children, and have had equally remarkable grandchildren. Jock Swire brought hope to Hong Kong after its wartime occupation by the Japanese and played a leading part in the drama of its revival, survival and success against all the odds.

16 January

Bullies in state schools are now to be taught elsewhere and stigmatised for life – a cruel punishment devised by liberals who will not teach a child a lesson by physical chastisement followed by forgiveness.

22 January

Publication Day for *Tales of Love and War*.

23 January

An impressive, long yet concise, and appreciative letter from our friend Pamela Wedgwood, *nom de plume* Pamela Tudor-Craig, about *Tales of Love and War*. She makes an interesting point re the great losses of marriageable men during World War I: as a result women outnumbered the opposite sex by such a large percentage that they were almost forced into the arms of husbands old enough to be their fathers – she quotes the example of her own mother.

24 January

The Book Guild has measured up to my expectations. The majority of London publishers should come to Lewes to learn how to do their jobs properly. Amazing that, after my half a century of professional authorship, I should find a publishing company providing the highest level of service to its authors within ten minutes' walk of my home!

This description of a good sleeper was new to me: 'She could sleep on a clothes line.'

25 January

I quote from *A Need to Testify* by Iris Origo: 'Lytton Strachey ... considered biography "the most delicate and humane of all branches of the art of writing".' Biography is all very well, but which English biographies have stood the test of time, apart from Boswell's *Johnson*? 'Definitive' is not an adjective to be trusted; 'ephemeral' is a truer definition of the biographical genre. I would suggest that Gibbon's view squashes Strachey flat: 'A cloud of critics, of compilers, of commentators, darkened the face of learning; and the decline of genius was soon followed by the corruption of taste.'

Strachey did not participate in the 1914 war, whether because he was as unfit as he looks in photographs or because he was a conscientious objector. While the fighting was at its fiercest and the lists of casualties lengthened, he wrote an account of his apparently unrequited passion for his postman – the late John Wells, actor, teacher, humorist, recited it in mincing accents as a party piece. In Strachey's more serious work he was a debunker, puncturing reputations, and was thought by his contemporaries to be opening a window on the corridors of power and allowing the draught to blow away the dust. But who reads his biographical studies now? They remind me of the clever weakling at school who blows raspberries at the bloods from a safe distance.

The art of writing is not necessarily 'delicate' in my opinion, and I would require a definition of 'humane' before I could agree with that epithet. Shakespeare was not merely 'delicate', nor was he 'humane' in any sense. He was a creative writer, the leader of the pack of the recreators of reality, the seminal poets, the novelists fashioning new worlds instead of picking old ones to pieces.

But alas, here in the land of Shakespeare and co., Strachey's claim that he was doing the right thing and the imaginative writers were wrong has been influential. There have been too many literary critics who dared not review fiction in case they were mistook, failed to spot a winner, tipped also-rans, made fools of themselves and ruined their reputations as know-alls. The consequence is that high literary art has languished in my lifetime. Readers are not guided towards better books, they stick to biographies which neither strain nor endanger. Commercial interests as usual follow rather than lead public opinion, and therefore shun the best of everything; publishing houses have started to shut out fiction, which is our national literary glory;

gifted writers can seldom afford to write the books that virtually no publisher will look at; and in the twilit field of literature the Philistines stand with their flat feet on the necks of the beautiful beasts they have slaughtered.

26 January

Philistia is another world, and its denizens speak only a limited pidgin version of our language. If you talk to them of creative writers, they think you mean productive ones. If you refer to imaginative writing, they point at inventive books by Jules Verne or Ian Fleming. Their idea of the recreation of reality is Coronation Street, and the only difference they see between Coronation Street and *War and Peace* is that the latter is foreign and takes a long time to read. For them the written word spells trouble compared with films and TV; and the only good read is the book of the film. The adjectives 'distinguished, sensitive, moving, intricate, subtle, unique' put them right off the reading matter they are applied to.

In Philistia, as in every other expression of life on earth, vegetable, animal, human, political and social, a class system exists, and it defines reactions to the arts. In the lower depths, 'art' and 'arty' are terms of abuse. As soon as status enters into the picture, 'artistic' is synonymous with a claim to superiority. Then there are families with children doing 'art' at school who live in houses with bookshelves and pictures that are not calendars hanging high on lounge walls. Middle-class wives go in for interior decor and trips to London to shop and if possible take in a fashionable exhibition of paintings. Next come the Philistine intelligentsia with their addiction to the novelties that they call 'art'; and the rich, who are proud to pay for the favour and flattery of the clever people, and begin to buy pictures because they are expensive.

On another subject, I cannot for the life of me imagine why many women have now fallen for the theory that they are better off not married to the men they live with and whose children they bear. I can see that dishonest and dishonourable partners and fathers may think they will more easily escape women to whom they are not married; but why do decent sensible men put up with being permanently on approval, and decent women ditto? The perks of being an unmarried or married mother, or a wife or mistress, are nowadays more equivalent – a baby begat out of wedlock is no longer socially disadvantageous, and palimony has become good business. But the propaganda about freedom, that marriage is human bondage whereas love is meant to be a free for all, is drivel and dangerous.

27 January

In my lifetime Adolf Hitler rose from nowhere, conquered an empire, committed suicide, and his empire disappeared. The Soviet Union disintegrated, communist tyrants eventually died, Marxism became un-fashionable, and all the fellow travellers of the most oppressive political regime in history have been made to look nasty and stupid. The unexpected has shown over and over again that it is bound to happen. Change is inevitable, to coin a phrase. The ultimate value of democracy is that it speeds up the process of change. People, the electorate, people lucky enough to vote in free and fair elections, may not be particularly wise or well-informed, but they are fickle, they change their minds and sack their rulers as soon as possible and for any old reason. Eden began his televised addresses to the nation, 'My friends'; Lord Home had a toothy smile; Macmillan dared to warn the electors that they 'had never had it so good'; Wilson told a half-truth about the 'pound in your pocket'; Heath had a comical laugh; Kinnock was shown on TV falling over in the wavelets of Brighton beach; Margaret Thatcher was a woman; William Hague wore a baseball cap; John Major had connections with circuses; and Tony Blair went to a function in India in a Nehru jacket – it only remains to be seen if Blair is not forgiven for doing so, just as the others were for their offences in the eyes of voters.

29 January

Maybe I should apologise for trying to bear witness to the decline of culture in poor old England. After all, more books are published year on year, more music played, more museums opened, more prizes for 'art' awarded; and every English citizen of every age seems to be either writing a novel, painting a picture, singing in a choir, turning a pot or doing something sculptural. But I stick to my opinion that cultural standards have already gone west or are going south, partly in hopes that the young will contend that I am wrong and prove it.

29 June 2002

I have again hearkened to the call of the wild, that is of fiction, and written *The Stepmother*, a novel inclusive of my idea of another book called *Duress*, instead of attending to my diary. I hope that my final entries will ring down the curtain, switch on the houselights, and send the punters home satisfied and unharrowed.

The best ending of any play or book that I have come across is Armado's little speech at the end of *Love's Labours Lost*: 'The words of Mercury are harsh after the songs of Apollo. You, that way; we, this way.'

The edition of *Roget's Thesaurus* revised and modernised by Robert A. Dutch is the oldest-fashioned and most pedantic of books although it was reissued in 1975. It is a mine of superseded synonyms and a defunct English vocabulary, and I love it. Here are some surprising words listed under the heading 'Darling': favourite, dowsabel, sweetling, chou, mavourneen, pippin, laddie, sonny, fondling, cosset, top seed, top liner, honeypot.

2 July

Misuse of the English language: alarmed car, leather described as 'piggy calf', and a dog as a 'pedigree mongrel'. These are two examples of politically correct fibs: 'vegetarian dragon', and 'Baa Baa, rainbow sheep'.

I cannot help wondering if butterflies were meant to be called flutterbys – flutterbys is more descriptive, and butter is nothing to do with the insect. Mistakes are often made, believe it or not. The first Duke of Devonshire is supposed to have wished to be called the Duke of Derbyshire, but wrote so illegibly that he was awarded a county where he had no interests.

The following quotation from *Adolphe* by Benjamin Constant is more useful than comment on politics: 'What surprises me is not that man needs a religion, but rather that he should ever think himself strong enough or sufficiently secure from trouble to dare to reject any one of them. I think he ought, in his weakness, to call upon them all.'

4 July

A man on the London to Brighton train was overheard speaking on a mobile phone probably to his wife thus: 'It's me, dear ... Okay, thanks – yourself? ... That's good ... A bit long and boring, but we're in the outskirts of Liverpool now ... Just for the night, dear – I'll be back tomorrow ... Oh, I'll find somewhere to stay – my business contacts will have arranged accommodation, I daresay ... No, sweetie, sorry, I won't have time to ring today, not with all the meetings that are planned ... Well, I'll ring you tomorrow morning to let you know when I'll be home ... Same here, my dear ... Bye-bye, sleep well!'

We have recently had an old lavatory replaced by a new one. The latter bears as trademark on its pan the word Bloomsbury. To use it is a form of literary criticism.

5 July

On the white wall of a humble out-of-the-way church in France there is a small marble plaque bearing this touching legend: *Merci* 1915–1918.

Another wall in France was defaced with the sprayed rallying cry '*A mort les ar..*.' If the graffiti merchant had not been interrupted, would he or she have completed the last word thus, '*armes*' or '*armées*' or even, nostalgically, '*aristos*'? As it was, a wit had added two unexpected letters in oil paint, 'ts' – 'Death to the arts!'

6 July

The first rule of craftsmanship, literary composition included, is to carry on as if time were unlimited. You aim to get the thing right however long it takes – deadlines are of secondary importance, ideally even money should not be allowed to exert its baneful influence. Perfection is unattainable, they say, but rightness can and must at least be targeted.

   In my seventy-sixth year, after fifty-five years of literary composition, I continue to struggle to curb my impatience, convince myself that I must revise my diary until it is as right as I can make it, and will still have time to write a few more stories, for instance the one already begun, *The Sodbury Crucifix*.

I also promise to remember that no one, no outsider, can help with creative work – yes with polishing it, no with the act of creation or, in a deep sense, with what has been created.

7 July

Dreams wake me almost every morning. They are fraught with anxiety, never carefree. I mourn lost loved ones. I recount my sins of omission and commission. Against my will I remember the twentieth century that I was lucky to survive, and that it could all happen again. I used to try to describe these dreams to the dedicatee of *The Time Diaries*, but they are as senseless and tedious as surrealist art, and now when I begin to recount one she is apt to say: 'Cut it short!'

She is quite right. Here – again – yet again – I shall follow her advice, bow to my readers and wish them well, and take her out to lunch.

TIME SCALE

22 November 2004

Marking Time was written between 11 June 1999 and 31 January 2000. *Extra Time* was written between 1 January 2001 and 7 July 2002.

My three short novels, *The Third Time*, *The First Nail* and *The Last Straw*, were written during the writing of *The Time Diaries*, and published as *Tales of Love and War* by The Book Guild of Lewes.

The Book Guild has also published *Byron's Diary* and *The Stepmother* in the year 2003, and *The Sodbury Crucifix* and *Damnation* in 2004.

Games of Chance, finished in November 2003, is ready for publication in February 2005, and *The Time Diaries* in the autumn of 2005. And I dare to hope that *According to Robin* and *Odd Woman Out* will be published in 2006.

Further books beckon me, 'in my dreams', as today's jargon would put it: *The Poor Rich*, a novel, *Harlequinade*, a selection of the books in the Harlequin Edition, and *The Best of Three*, a reissue of my selection of items from my three books of short stories.

The Time Diaries began by being my answer to retirement. Having publicly stated that I would write no more fiction, I had either to write something else, for instance a diary, or give up the ghost. So I became a diarist, but temporarily. Fate begged to differ, as proved by the paragraphs above. They, those paragraphs, not only advertise my wares, but also, since I have been prolific against my expectations and despite my age, re-emphasise the explicit and implicit message of all my books, which is: you never know.

INDEX

ODD WOMAN OUT

CONTENTS

PROLOGUE

THE TWENTIETH century – peace after two world wars – London in summer in the 1950s – the small hours of morning.

Moonlight in Pimlico Road, and an open-top two seater with the hood down. A man in the driving seat, his passenger female, a girl with short blonde hair. He wears a white shirt, black bow-tie, dinner jacket with lapels of satin that reflect light, she a white party dress. They take no notice of the occasional passing car or a late or early pedestrian.

They are talking. They may be arguing. He puts an arm round her shoulders, she opens the passenger door. He restrains her from getting out of the car, reaches across with his other arm and turns her head so that she faces him. He tries to kiss her, but only connects with her pale cheek. She pulls away but he is saying something in her ear, and she is listening. He succeeds in kissing her lips although she does not make it easy, her head remains upright and she looks along Pimlico Road. Now she sinks down in the passenger seat and inclines her head backwards, as if to offer him her lips. He kisses her, leans over, is dominant, shifts in his seat in order to be more on top of her, and the kisses seem to become passionate. She objects to something he has done, pushes him aside, rises up, possibly scolds him, opens her door again and struggles out. He is laughing at her and perhaps calling her back. She crosses the pavement, trips across in her long white dress, unlocks the door of a house, enters and closes it. He lights a cigarette, starts the car and drives off fast with loud exhaust noise.

PART ONE

S HE WAS Celia Farr, twenty-one years of age, a Christian, a virgin, and a trained nurse. The door she had unlocked was at the side of the antiques shop called Wellingham. She was staying the night with her friend Dot, Dorothy Wellingham, the daughter of Geoffrey Wellingham, proprietor of the shop, and his wife Sandy, who all lived over it. The name of the man in the sports car was Owen Pennant.

Celia was born and bred in Broadstairs, Kent. Her father was Bernard Farr, schoolmaster. Her mother, Christobel, known as Chrissy, worked in the little local Museum of the Sea, and as receptionist in a solicitors' office. Celia Farr's paternal grandfather lived at Westgate-on-Sea – Bill Farr had also been a schoolmaster. Her mother's mother was a widow ekeing out her existence in sheltered accommodation in Ramsgate. The Farrs were Isle of Thanet people. Celia's home was 42 Thanet Steps, a semi-detached Edwardian three-bedroomed seaside house in a back street.

She was an only child. She was the type of child who stares – her eyes were big and dark blue, her gaze unwavering and possibly critical. She was good, polite, bright and quite affectionate; also independent and strong-willed. She was at once fairy-like and tough.

Her father adored her, her mother was jealous, she was fonder of her father – they were a predictable family in some respects. Bernard Farr taught English at The Welcome School, and was Deputy to the Headmaster, William Hauntly, known as The Ghost. He had been employed by Welcome pre-war; had served in the army while the School was closed; and been able to buy ten per cent of the relaunched establishment after peace broke out. He was a cheery, sporty, un-sentimental good chap, and treated Celia like a son. When his wife Chrissy moaned that she was unfulfilled and underestimated, he would take Celia to the park to kick a football about or play cricket. He was a slow left-arm bowler and would put up a stump and tell her to keep wicket. In the evenings, when she was in bed, he would give her a hug and a squeeze, which made her laugh: as a result her mother would say, 'That's enough,' and switch the light off and on resentfully.

Celia was taught her ABC by her father, then attended the Lower Class at Welcome. She did not flourish there. Co-education startled her, she was shy of boys, and embarrassed to be the daughter of the Deputy Headmaster. But when she was eight she moved into the Middle Class and met and made two friends, Constance Shelby and Dorothy Wellingham. Con was plump and giggly, Dot was a bean-pole. Con was bad at her books, Dot was clever. Con's father worked in a bank in the City of London, Dot's had recently moved his antique business up to town: the former was of special interest to the girls because he left Broadstairs at five on weekday mornings and only got home at eight in the evening, the latter was remarkable because he lived in London during the working week. Dot's mother was interesting for two different reasons: she had a boy's name, Sandy, and was inclined to call herself 'a grass widow'.

The three girls fell into friendship almost at first sight. They were close without ever being distant. They sat near one another in lessons, held pow-wows during breaks, walked round the playing field together if they were not involved in games, talked and laughed non-stop, and never fell out. Their conversational topics in order of importance were: their pets; hair styles; how babies are born; what was wrong with boys; their crushes on boys; school and holidays; their parents; and their physical developments and natural functions.

Celia and Dot ascended into Upper Class six months before Con: they had to relate to Con the full story told in Biology. They were all pretty disgusted by childbirth, but it had its exciting sides. Puberty likewise – they were proud of their new selves, and humiliated to discover they had a lot in common with chickens.

Forms of romanticism now preoccupied them. They read books about love and, with luck, sex. They bought and repetitively played records of light tenors singing soupy ballads. They discussed courtship, marriage, maternity, and their wedding dresses. They studied boys from a different angle, and wondered how on earth their mothers and father could have conceived them.

At the same time they all experienced difficulties at home. Celia turned against her guinea pigs, and was rebuked by her father for giving her mother – who claimed that she could not let them starve – an additional cause for complaint. She had outgrown her teddy bear, and, she protested constantly, her clothes. She was unwilling to play football and cricket with her daddy, and when she did deign to be wicket-keeper she would drop the ball and let the bowler run after it. She was funny about paternal embraces, and turned the back of her head for her mother to kiss. She was a 'changed girl', an 'ungrateful girl', and 'unfeeling' according to Chrissy Farr, and she brought tears into the eyes of Bernard on several occasions.

Dot was creating similar problems. Sandy Wellingham tried to enlist Celia's help in dealing with her daughter's moodiness and uncertain temper: Celia shrugged her shoulders and said Dot was a sweet person.

Mrs Shelby also approached Celia. Con's mother had four children, three sons, then the daughter. She said Con had become so lackadaisical and lazy that her brothers called her 'the pudding', which reduced the girl to tears. Con never had been a cryer, Mrs Shelby said, she had been a laugher, but now she could not see a joke. Her father, Mrs Shelby said, was threatening to catch a later train home in order to see less of Con, and if he carried out his threat he would only reach Broadstairs at nine and scarcely have time to eat his dinner before he was rushing back to London.

The three girls were inclined to blame their parents, who were 'stuffy ... out of date ... intolerable'. A symptom of their indispositions was an inability to reason why. They were disturbed secretively by their hormones, and, consciously, by the wall of difficulties that seemed to loom up between themselves and the future. They talked of jobs, of remunerative work: which was bad enough. But they were not fools or exclusively frivolous: the responsibilities of finding the men who would love them truly, of giving away their virginities, surviving weddings and honeymoons, and making babies and caring for them and being cared for by them, these tests and tasks that nature set were frighteningly oppressive.

They finished with schooling in their eighteenth years. None of them even thought of further education at a university: they were not academic, and in those days girls who were not brainy were not encouraged to waste their parents' money. Celia returned to Welcome as extra teacher to the children in the Lower Class, and helped to organise games. Dot assisted her father, serving on some days in the shop in Broadstairs and on other days travelling up to London to the other shop in Pimlico Road. Con landed a job at Chicque, the

Broadstairs boutique, but soon lost it because she was too sleepy and overweight, and then had to settle for Boots.

Being grown up was a big change, and brought about bigger changes.

Celia realised that family and home shielded her from the pressures of the wider world, and almost forgave her mother. She was less impatient, and more willing to lend Chrissy a hand. She not only gave Chrissy advice in often hectoring terms, she sometimes asked for it.

In return, out of relief, and with gratitude, Chrissy Farr somehow resigned in favour of her daughter, and yielded to her youth and strength. In practice, she thanked her for favours instead of asking for them, and praised instead of criticising. One day she said: 'You're much prettier than I was, you've become very pretty, you know.' Celia had not known it. Celia was startled. She was stunned. Of course she had wondered if she would ever be pretty, but had hated her buckteeth, despaired of her freckles, prayed in vain to be taller, wished her two best friends would not study and metaphorically pull her face to pieces. As for her mother, her mother had previously been the sworn enemy of Celia's attractions. Praise from Chrissy had the extraordinary force of mercy. It was touching, exciting. It excited much more than her father's hackneyed compliments.

Celia thanked her mother and laughed as if in denial. Then she was persuaded that her mother was not far wrong. She again looked in the mirror and realised why she was whistled at by men and on the receiving end of pleasant and unpleasant attentions. Her reflection told her that her thick blonde hair moved nicely, her eyes were far apart, her nose was straight and small, and her teeth had reformed and were capable of a wide white smile. And she knew she was lithe and her body was slender and neat.

Her excitement was soon fraught with other emotions. She might be pretty, she was pretty, which was nice, but the consequences were leading to difficulties with the opposite sex. She was not a flirt; she was shyer than ever, more self-conscious, and felt hunted.

She was fearful for another reason. She was prettier than Dot and Con. If a man or men saw the three of them together, he or they looked at her. Dot was a handsome girl, but her nose was too long and she was gawky. Con was a sweet bundle, but not an obvious object of romance. The trio had always been a mutual admiration society: how long would that, could that, last?

She foresaw disruption of their triangular friendship. When they went to a movie in Broadstairs, and then ate chips from Frankie's barrow, she suffered from the idea that they were all under threat. She had to sit between them in cinemas in order to foil roving male hands. She linked arms with Dot or Con or both in the streets, so that she would not be pestered more than they were. When Con's father wanted to show her the workings of a great banking house, involving a day trip to London and lunch at a restaurant, Con did not like it and Dot was a bit put out although Celia had declined immediately.

She arrived at a possible solution of the problem, or at least a postponement of what seemed to her inevitable, and in her forthright way broached the subject.

'I've been thinking,' she said.

The others expressed surprise, and there was laughter. They were in the attic playroom in Dot's home in Marine Drive, half-listening to her records. Celia sat on the floor, Con on the broken-down sofa, and Dot on the rocking horse, her long legs dangling.

'I've got to break new ground,' Celia said.

What did she mean?

She was going to be twenty, she had hardly spent a single night away from Thanet Steps in her whole life, she was tired of being a mini-school-marm, the teachers at Welcome were either female, married men or her father, and she wanted to take a risk for a change.

'Oh dear,' Con said, and Dot asked: 'Is it sex you're after?'

They all giggled.

Celia said: 'Not only – not that – I want something different – and not stupefying.'

'Like what?'

'I don't know. I don't know yet.'

Con wailed: 'You'll go away!'

'Maybe.'

'And Dot may have to go to London!'

She was referring to Mr Wellingham's plan to shut up shop in Broadstairs and unify his two businesses in Pimlico Road and move his family along with his antiques.

'May or may not,' Dot said in her sharp way. 'Don't cry before you're hit, Con! You could keep me company in London, if the worst comes to the worst. Anyway, you've got three big brothers – you've got men to spare – and we can't marry one another, for heaven's sake.'

'I wish we could,' Con said, provoking more laughter, which was roughly the end of the conversation.

It was more like a beginning for Celia. The motives that had spurred her to mention her own wish were superseded by a rush of restlessness, she would clamber out of her rut as best she could and as soon as possible. She considered her options seriously. She had no particular talent; was not cut out to be a career girl; and was definitely not an adventuress. On the other hand she was supposed to be kind and believed she would be a loving mother. She remembered her deep relationship with her guinea pigs, Walter and Rose – Rose who turned out to be a boy – a relationship that only proved shallow when she forgot to feed them. She would like to make up for that lethal omission. She would like to compensate for the brief period of her maltreatment of her parents. What she wanted was to do something better than she had done.

In the Lower Class at Welcome she was addressed as 'Nurse' by a toddler called Theobald. It was Theobald's mistake. But she answered to the name. Impulsively she thought that Theobald had hit the nail on the head.

She broke the news to her father while they walked home after a day's teaching.

'It's a hard life,' he said.

'I'd like that,' she replied.

'Have you any idea of the range of a nurse's duties, hours of work, pay and so on?'

'I'll find out.'

'How long ago did you take your decision?'

'Yesterday, but I won't change my mind.'

'You never do.'

'Is that a fault?'

'No, no. Oh well, I was bound to lose you in one way or another.'

'You won't lose me ever.'

'Thank you, dear. I've been lucky to have had such fun with you. And you'll make a lovely nurse.'

Chrissy Farr was not averse to the prospect of having her husband to herself again, and responded to Celia's prospects merely by saying: 'Rather you than me.'

The grandfather in Westgate-on-Sea, Bill Farr, known as GranFarr to Celia, called her 'Sister', and Edith, a great-aunt, also confined her reaction to a single word: 'Fancy!'

The grandmother in Ramsgate, a self-pitier like her daughter Chrissy, said Celia would be able to make her comfortable on her death bed.

Dot said, 'Congratulations,' and Celia sensed that Dot too thought the time was ripe for the friends to search for their separate destinies.

Con listed the inescapable horrors of a nurse's work: bed-pans, catheters, enemas, injections, operations, amputations, and so on.

Celia applied to St Mildred's Hospital in Canterbury for information and guidance. She read pamphlets, got through interviews, swotted and passed exams and tests, was accepted for training, worked long hours, slept in a dormitory with other would-be nurses in a lodging from which men were strictly excluded, and did not complain. She was branded a crackpot for enjoying herself.

Her weekends off and holidays were spent at Broadstairs. The Wellinghams had removed to London, but Dot sometimes stayed for a night or two with the Farrs in Thanet Steps. She would sleep on cushions on the floor of Celia's bedroom, and occasionally Con would bring round an inflatable mattress and doss down too.

The friends' main topic of conversation was now boys, men, suitors or the lack of suitors. They were all twenty-one – slow off their marks even by the current sexual conventions. Dot was considering two proposals, one from a limp youth who painted furniture to make it look good enough for her father to sell, the other a customer, who actually bought the furniture painted by his rival – the latter was getting on for forty, divorced, father of two, but also rich and amorous. Dot was afraid the first might be impotent as well as poor – he only seemed to want to hold her hand – and that the second would be all too virile – she had so far fought tooth and nail to permit no more than manual liberties. Con, unexpectedly, had a follower who appeared to be faultless – twenty-six, well-to-do local family, handsome, gentlemanly and keen – whom she dared to call 'Serf' and teased with the yes-and-no routine. Celia confessed that she loved nobody 'in that way' – she had fended off all the medical students, doctors and importunate patients – and said she must be frigid.

They discussed the question of whether they could be or would be 'aroused'. They agreed they would like to have children, and were prepared to pay the price. They talked of almost nothing else. Celia regretted the fact that she had no time to read books. Dot said she was not sure she liked the thrills and spills of London. Con said she was being driven mad by her mother. They missed one another, they agreed.

They planned a reunion at Broadstairs on one of Celia's free weekends in the month of July. But Dot developed appendicitis and rang to ask Celia a favour: her father had taken tickets for a charity ball, she had been roped in but was now out of action, would the friend of her family come to the rescue? Mr Wellingham's party so far included himself and Sandy, his best customer and wife, and a single businessman. Celia demurred. Dot said she could spend the night in the Wellingham home, in her bedroom there, and wear the dress that Celia knew, had once tried on, and loved, the white one with spangles.

Celia obliged. She arrived at the Pimlico Road premises at seven o'clock by arrangement. She was overwrought and frightened – Dot was still in hospital. But Mr Wellingham greeted her gratefully, and Sandy was kind, led her up to Dot's room, which had a bathroom adjoining, and left her to change.

She wallowed in a bath, then tested the perfumes and used some of the make-up on the dressing-table. She had never known such luxury. The dress fitted. It had an upstanding collar, a snugly shaped bodice, a long skirt glittering with the spangles, and seemed to weigh nothing. Her last look in the full-length mirror was satisfactory. Downstairs the Wellinghams were complimentary, and Mr Wellingham ushered her out and into a chauffeur-driven car. They arrived at a hotel in Park Lane, queued to enter a ballroom where a band played, were directed to one of the tables laid for dinner, and introductions ensued. Celia shook the warm large hand of a man of thirty or so – the businessman, Mr Pennant.

She was seated next to him. On her other side was a deaf old gentleman, no doubt the 'best customer'. She had scarcely taken her seat when she was asked or rather commanded to dance. Mr Pennant immediately danced so close that it flustered her – it was another first, she had never had such detailed practical experience of male physiology. He did not talk, and she was too breathless to try. He returned her to the table, interrogated her, told her not to bother with her deaf neighbour – 'Concentrate on me,' he said, smiling at last. He had a gap between his front teeth and brown curly hair on his forehead, like a bull.

'You're Celia,' he said, either stating a fact or asking a question. 'Celia what?'

'My surname's Farr,' she replied – but she did not know how to talk to him, he was difficult to talk to. He had a sun-tan and dark-brown eyes.

'Celia Farr, that's not bad,' he commented, as if she had been a wine and he was tasting it. 'Do you know my name?'

'No.'

'I'm Owen Pennant. I'm Welsh. Where do you come from? From under a mushroom, judging by your appearance.'

'I was brought up in Broadstairs – that's in Kent.'

'I know where Broadstairs is.'

Champagne was served. She had sampled it once before and hated it; but now she took a gulp and spluttered and sneezed. When he laughed at her, she found the strength to ask him to explain his reference to a mushroom.

'Because you're a fairy or an elf, that's what you look like to me,' he said. 'What are you in real life?'

'I'm training to be a nurse.'

'A nurse! You're wasted on your patients.'

He paid her other compliments: they bewildered, dazzled her – or was it the champagne? He went too far too soon, calling her beautiful, appetising, untilled, using other suspect adjectives, and saying she was at least an improvement on Dorothy Wellingham. She did not like it but could not stop herself listening, blushing, grinning foolishly, and hoping she was not behaving badly by the Wellinghams' standards.

Food arrived. She ate it without knowing if it was animal or vegetable. She drank white wine, and danced with him again, and willingly, either to stop him talking and cross-questioning, or because he did dance well, or for another strange reason. Her father had never held her as she was held by Owen. Although she had slapped men at St Mildred's who tried to get as close, she could not do so in this ballroom, in front of all these smart people, and was not even inclined to.

He insisted on her calling him Owen. He called her 'Twinkle'. He pretended to dread midnight, when he expected her to hurry back to sit by the ashes of her home-fire and be abused by ugly sisters. He made her laugh. He pressurised her to encourage him. Dot and Con would have thought him 'cocky'. He was sure of himself, arrogant, spoilt, certainly rich, and not a good sort and quite possibly a bad lot – she knew it all, but her anatomy overrode her critical faculty and her common sense.

She ate meat and drank red wine, she ate a pudding and drank more champagne. She drank sips, she was not drunk, but something had gone to her head. She was trying to maintain her dignity, to preserve her individuality, to have reservations and remember rules, but their dances betrayed her secrets, she felt. Discretion was somehow beyond her when he was so indiscreet, so intrusive and seductive.

Sandy Wellingham told her that they were going home, likewise the other couple. Owen Pennant said he would drop Celia back at Pimlico Road shortly.

Sandy asked: 'Do you want to stay? Don't do as Owen tells you. What would you like to do, Celia?'

She hesitated. There was laughter, and she missed her opportunity to say, 'Save me, take me with you!' She was being kissed good night by Sandy, given a key to the front door of their house, and getting instructions about burglar alarms from Mr Wellingham. The 'best customer' and his wife said goodbye. Celia overheard Sandy's aside to Owen, 'Take good care of her,' meaning herself; and then he and she were by themselves in the crowd.

She was torn in two by excitement and terror. They danced again – it was better than struggling to talk and worse in that it seemed to rob her of the vestiges of self-control. When they returned to their table he looked at his wristwatch and accused her of keeping him up too late.

'I'm a working man, I'm at my desk at seven-thirty,' he said. 'Come on, let's pack it in.'

She was quite furious with him. She was sure she worked harder than he did, and for less money. Yet when he took her hand and pulled her towards the exit she hung on and squeezed his.

At last they were in his car, in the dark, in the rush of fresh air. He did not speak, she could not – anyway, because the car was open and noisy, speech was impossible. Her heart thumped – would he hear it, she wondered. What was going to happen, she wondered. He pulled up outside the Wellingham shop.

'Thank you very much. Good night,' she said, fumbling with the door handle.

'Where are your manners?' he retorted.

'What?'

'Highwaymen used to say "Your money or your life!"'

'What do you mean?'

'A kiss or yours.'

'I don't … I can't …'

'Don't be stupid, darling.'

He put his arm round her shoulders. She succeeded in opening the door of the car. He reached across with his other arm and turned her face. He managed only to kiss her cheek. She pulled away, but did not get out of the car. He was speaking, whispering into her ear, saying amazing things.

'Relax – let go – you'll learn a lot from me – we may be dead tomorrow – I can give you thrills you've never dreamed of.'

He was kissing her tightly closed lips. She was aware of tears in her eyes. She could not move or escape. She sank down in her seat and turned her face in his direction. She shut her eyes and realised she was crying or panting.

★   ★   ★

Celia spent the rest of that night or early morning alone, but did not sleep. For breakfast she had a cup of coffee with Sandy – Mr Wellingham was already moving furniture in his shop.

'I didn't hear you return,' Sandy remarked.

Celia understood the question, and replied: 'I tiptoed – we didn't stay much longer at the ball – I must have been back here soon after you were.' And she thanked her for everything.

'Did you enjoy yourself?'

'Oh yes.'

'You had a success with Owen.'

When Celia blushed, Sandy added: 'I can see he had a success with you.'

She continued: 'What did you think of him?'

'I didn't have much time to think.'

'No – he's quick on the draw.'

They laughed, and Celia began: 'Sandy' – she and Con had been told to call Mrs Wellingham by her first name, but still addressed Mr Wellingham formally – 'he's not married, is he?'

'Never – not quite, he's been hooked by a good few women, but not landed.'

'What's he like – really?'

'Very clever at making money, and thinks he can buy anything. No, that's not fair. Sorry, my dear. He's a charming Don Juan, but he isn't nasty to women and might be domesticated. Did he mention another meeting?'

'No.'

'Hard lines! They seldom do. May I state the obvious?'

'Please.'

'Don't give him everything he wants for nothing in return.'

'Oh but he couldn't be interested in me.'

'Why not? Don't underestimate the worth of your wares. You see, I'm not my mercantile Geoffrey's wife for nothing. You'd better hope Owen values you as highly as you deserve. If he doesn't, more fool he!'

'Thank you, Sandy.'

Celia returned to Broadstairs and spent the second and last night of her free weekend in Thanet Steps.

Her parents noticed a difference in her. Her mother thought she looked well, perhaps suspiciously so, her father thought she looked tired.

Bernard Farr said: 'You'll find us awfully bread-and-butter, dear, after the jam of that swish house of the Wellinghams and waltzing the night away in Park Lane.'

'Oh Daddy!' she scolded him. 'Of course I won't. And I wasn't waltzing, we don't do waltzing any more.'

'Is that so?'

Chrissy Farr asked: 'Did you get off with someone, Celia?'

'No, Mummy.'

'Did Geoffrey Wellingham dance with you?'

'No, he didn't, but he and Sandy were tremendously nice.'

'Who did you dance with?'

'I can't remember – it was a big party – I never knew anybody's name.'

'But you had lots of dances?'

'Not lots – some – we had dinner to eat – and we weren't very late – we were back in Pimlico Road at about one o'clock.'

'I see.'

During the weekend Celia went for a walk with Con, who was thankfully more interested in her own love-life than anyone else's. Con satisfied her curiosity about the charity ball with a brief question and answer routine, and was in a hurry to report that she had actually slept with the 'serf'. He was a land agent, which was apparently much better than being an estate agent. He was called Ian, Ian Thornton – 'a pretty dull name, but it suits him,' Con said. She and Ian had been together at local dos – he was an amateur actor and played 'older' parts – 'the gravedigger in *Hamlet*, for instance,' she giggled. 'Poor old Ian,' she remarked apologetically, 'I mustn't make fun of him.' Anyway, while Mr and Mrs Shelby were on holiday, Con had their home in Kentish Road to herself. She invited Ian to supper, there had been a spot of canoodling afterwards, and then his car would not start, a development that would have been promising if Ian had not called in the AA, who towed the car away. She said to him, 'Stay the night,' and he said to her, 'Thank you' – not exactly romantic. They adjourned to her bedroom – she had not dared to let him sleep between clean sheets. They undressed in the dark, but she kept her underwear on and stipulated that he was to wear his boxer shorts. Her bed was so narrow that they were a sandwich almost from the word go. The rest was all anti-climax. He shook with nerves, she had had a heavy day stocktaking at Boots, and after false starts and commiserations she fell asleep. In fact they both slept like logs. At least they agreed in the morning to have another bash at it, and no damage was done.

Celia laughed at the story, then asked: 'When is the next bash taking place?'

'I haven't a clue. Poor Ian – he moves more mysteriously than God.'

'But do you love him?'

'I do. Of course I do. There's no other man around.'

'Are you planning to marry him?'

'Well – seeing's believing, isn't it? I'm waiting to see.'

Celia wished Con luck, and in the afternoon of the same day fitted in a visit to Dot in a nursing home in the Harley Street area.

Dot also had a story to tell without delay. Her surgeon, Mr Pinner, was dark and dreamily handsome and had wonderful warm hands. Shaking hands with him was almost too much for her, and when he palpated her naked stomach she thought she would disgrace herself somehow. She was now counting the minutes until he came to take her stitches out.

Celia laughed with Dot, and they both laughed at Con's damp squib, then Dot asked about the ball.

'Who was meant to have been my partner?'

'Owen Pennant.'

'Was he one of Daddy's frightful old customers?'

'No.'

'Did you have a ghastly time? Those charity balls are such a sweat.'

'It wasn't like that, he wasn't like that.'

'Mum said you looked a dream in my dress.'

'Thank you for letting me wear it. Your room was lovely and your people were lovely to me.'

'No, don't mench – it was angelic of you to give up half your weekend, when you might have been with your parents.'

'I enjoyed myself. Honestly! I'd never been to such a grand party.'

'Oh well – I'm glad.'

They reverted to the subject of Mr Pinner, then Celia said goodbye.

Travelling back to Canterbury and St Mildred's, she mentally measured the chasm that had opened between herself and her parents and friends. Perhaps the chasm was an abyss, into which she had fallen and suffered damage to body and soul. She was no longer the person they had known. She herself no longer knew the person she had become, who told lies and sanctioned misunderstandings. Nobody else's love stories bore the slightest resemblance to the tongues of flame leaping inside her.

She tried to dowse them down. She poured cold water on them. But they were inextinguishable. They flared again and again. They were acquiring more intensity. But it was all as ridiculous as Dot's and Con's games with men. A few hours in Owen's company could not make so much difference. He could not have changed her from one girl into another overnight. Where was her strong character? What about her nurse's training, and her adoption of scientific approaches to life and death?

Romance should bear no resemblance to what had happened at the charity ball and in that rightly named sports car. She had expected romance to be like friendship that slowly expanded into love, marriage, sex and motherhood. She had thought it would be beautiful, not brutal, not bestial. She had been waiting to give her consent, not to be bullied.

She tried to despise or to pity Owen Pennant. He was a playboy. He wished to kiss or be kissed good night. The scene in his car, under the stars, could be regarded as a variation of 'Night night, sleep tight'. But she had not slept. She could not sleep in her babyish bedroom in Thanet Steps. She had seemed to cease to need sleep. She pined for the taste of his mouth. She was homesick for his embrace. She balanced on the tightrope of joy, with no net below, and misery underneath.

She was back at work at St Mildred's. A matron called her absent-minded: 'What's wrong with you, Celia?' She was shamed into pulling herself together – she had been proud of her reputation for dependability.

Nothing worthwhile would happen. Nothing much had happened, she told herself. In the past, long ago, she had tried dancing close to boys, and boys had tried it – but those were clumsy experiments, minus the x-factor. She had been kissed by boys – meaningless kisses that involved her in nothing. One of the doctors had cornered her in the laundry, but the consequences were only a wrestling match and accusations that she was a lesbian. She suspected Owen would categorise their dances and kisses as trials similar to hers, amusements, and a way of making the best of a bad job at the charity ball. 'Twinkle' was not her real name. He would have difficulty in finding her, and more in contacting her at the hospital. He had not bothered to ask any of the important questions. She must not waste her whole life in hoping to hear from and see him again.

Yet she had attracted him. She was aware that the attraction was mutual on the dance floor. On the other hand somebody had said – or she had read – that men were not like women inasmuch as they were not choosy. Owen's physical compliments might have been routine, a mechanical reaction to the proximity of female flesh. But the last of his kisses must have meant something to him since it meant everything to her.

The empty days passed. She fell from the tightrope and clung by her fingertips to the net. Misery was her next stop – if there was to be any stopping. She had chances to read when she did night duty; 'events' – hospital jargon for mortal crises – were minimal. She chose the saddest stories and shed tears over *Tess of the d'Urbervilles*. She envisaged spinsterhood – she would be the sort of spinster faithfully grieving for the man who was loved and lost. She belaboured herself additionally for having missed opportunities. Why had she not begged to be taught, when he had said she had a lot to learn? Why had she not asked him to make love to her there and then, in public, and in spite of the gear lever?

Eventually she was almost accustomed to her sore places. In this period of new experiences, she had been faced with a test never bargained for, and had summoned the energy to scrape through it. She was blooded, initiated up to a point, and certainly bloody, but unbowed. Taking matters into her own hands, tracing and tracking Owen, was not done; and if it had been, if she had been living when it was done, she would have been too diffident to do it. She was not so arrogant to wish she could or should reverse the natural roles of the sexes. If Owen did not want her, so be it – he was probably right – and he might be protecting her in a roundabout way. She would not criticise him adversely. She was lucky to have spent one evening in his arms, roughly speaking. The refrain of the song of love was that there were as good fish in the sea as ever came out of it; which was supportive, even if she was convinced that it was inapplicable to her case.

She smiled by day, and reserved her tears for the night, for the privacy of beneath the covers of her bed in the dormitory of trainee nurses. She had taken happiness for granted. No – she had been childishly blithe, blinkered and blithe, self-centredly blithe – and then ecstatic – and then wretched. She had yet to know happiness. She could not imagine what happiness was like. But she did not sink under the waves of her unhappiness, and derived some satisfaction from being able to keep afloat.

A month or so after the charity ball she received a letter. She did not recognise the writing, the postmark was London. She tore it open; but it was from Sandy Wellingham.

She read: 'Dear Celia, Owen Pennant would like to see you again. If you're interested, drop me a line to say where he could reach you. Oh yes, telephone number, too. Hope you're saving lives. Love, Sandy.'

She replied without delay. She listed the days on which she was doing night duty: she was free from four until eight on those days. She thanked Sandy with underlinings for writing.

Amazement mingled with doubt was her response to fortune's favour. That he should take trouble to try to see her was amazing. The rush of blood to her face, head, body and extremities while she read Sandy's letter was more so. That the long-drawn-out storm of her emotions subsided in a minute or two was almost miraculous. She could scarcely remember how wretched she had been. She looked forward to the future impatiently.

Of course she was dubious, too. How could they see each other – he was in London and she in Canterbury? How could a busy man find time to ring her, why would he, why should he?

He rang at five o'clock on the first of the days she had listed in her letter to Sandy. She was standing by the pay telephone in the corridor outside her dorm.

'Celia?' he queried.

'Yes.'

'This is Owen Pennant. Do you remember me?'

'Yes.'

'We were with the Wellinghams the other day.'

'Yes.'

'Where are you speaking from? Your voice echoes.'

'It's a public telephone.'

'Can you hear me?'

'Very well.'

'If I was ever near Canterbury, could we have a drink together?'

'I'd love to.'

'They seem to work you hard. What are these afternoons off?'

'I'm free before night duty.'

'Night duty? I wouldn't object to some of that. Is tomorrow any good to you?'

'What?'

'You're free at four, aren't you? What about four tomorrow?'

'Yes.'

'Do you mean you'll meet me at four o'clock outside the main entrance to the hospital tomorrow?'

'Yes – thank you very much.'

'I'll take you out to tea.'

He was laughing, laughing at her, laughing at himself, because tea in the country was not his line. She saw the joke and joined in. He rang off.

Her mood of semi-suspended animation carried her through the intervening hours. In the afternoon of the next day the sun shone – it was August and a heat wave. She wore her usual civilian summer clothes, shirt, skirt and sandals – she had nothing smart in her locker.

He was standing by his car at a little distance. The car was sky-blue – she had not noticed its colour in the night. He wore an open-necked white shirt and red slacks. He did not see her at once, and his appearance, his pose, his clothes and car were like an advertisement or a scene in a film. He looked remarkable, powerful, out of the common run.

She approached him. He welcomed her – a smile, a move in her direction, no kiss – and opened the passenger door of his car. She slipped in, he got in the other side, and they were again sitting where they had sat. It had all been slightly awkward, but she did not mind that – instinct told her it was as it should be.

'What shall we do?' he asked. 'Do you really want to be taken out to tea like a schoolgirl?'

They again laughed in unison, she said no, she would be eating hospital food at seven, and he suggested Whitstable – 'Shall we have a look at Whitstable?'

They did not talk much during the noisy breezy drive. Then they found a spot of dry sand on the Whitstable beach and sat with their backs against a breakwater. The calm sea lapped in and out, and hurdy-gurdy music reached them faintly.

'Is it comfortable enough?' he asked.

'Yes. I'm used to sand and shingle.'

'I come from wild Wales,' he said, and picked up a pebble and tossed it aimlessly away.

'Have you been busy today?' she inquired in order to break a silence although she knew it was a boring question.

'I've driven to see you.'

'But I thought...'

'I don't do business in Canterbury. You're my business in Canterbury.'

She would have giggled if she had not been so tense.

She said: 'It's a long way from London.'

'I didn't think so, and I was right.'

He threw another pebble.

'Tell me what you do,' he said.

'I've been nursing for a year and a half.'

'Do you nurse men and women?'

'And children.'

'Are the men shy with you?'

'Not when they're ill.'

'Are you shy with them?'

'It's the same – you can't be shy when they're ill.'

'Are you shy with me?'

'You're not ill.'

He laughed.

'You'll get used to me,' he said. 'You will if you're patient – or have you other fish to fry?'

'What do you mean?'

'Have you got a boyfriend?'

'No – not a special one.'

'I'm not a boy – I'm thirty-one. How old are you?'

'Twenty-one.'

'I'm ten years older than you are, and I've been around. That's one of the differences between us. I'm here partly because of the differences. Don't let me be a bother to you.'

'You're not. You couldn't be.'

'You're the stuff to freshen up a jaded palate.'

'What?'

'Nothing. You know nothing compared with all I know. I'm not being rude. Your ignorance is your point for me, my experience could be hell for you.'

'I'm not as ignorant as all that.'

'All what? Don't answer. I'll try again. You're not like the women I'm used to, which is more okay for me than for you. I'm not like the boys from Broadstairs or your invalids.'

'Who are your women?'

'Ghosts. I used to know young girls, but they didn't go in for useful work. I never was a monk, and I've been called fickle along with other names. Freedom has disadvantages. That's another reason to be in Whitstable.'

'I'm sorry, I'm not sure I understand.'

'Forget it – my method of clarifying issues with the opposite sex can lead to more misunderstandings. Have you any idea of my business?'

'No.'

'I'm a chartered accountant.'

'I know what that is – there's one at St Mildred's, and my father had a friend who's an accountant.'

'They wouldn't be anything like me. I'm Croesus. My work is to earn parts of businesses by improving their business. I look at the books of firms, tell the owners how to do better, and in return they give me a share of the equity. Are you with me?'

'Sort of.'

'I make money as a result.'

'I see.'

'Women usually can't read the bottom line.'

'Mr Simms only helps my father with his tax.'

'Mr Simms wouldn't be a rich man.'

'No, he isn't.'

'I follow in my pa's footsteps. He made money in haulage when he was young, and then bought and sold land in Wales. He gentrified our family. I was reared like a princeling. Are you with me?'

'Yes, but ... I wonder – are you an only child?'

'Why ask?'

'Because I'm one.'

'The answer's no, not to speak of, I've a sister but I might as well not have one – Ruth, older than me and married to a Scotsman. We don't see each other, and the same applies to my pa. I've got beyond them, I've left them behind. Who cares? I don't! What's your family?'

Owen threw another pebble, which discouraged Celia.

'My father's a schoolmaster,' she said. 'He teaches at The Welcome School in Broadstairs.'

'News to me.'

'It's quite famous actually. I was a pupil there, and I taught there, too.'

'That's a claim to fame.'

She giggled and said: 'My father owns a bit of Welcome, but we're not rich or anything.'

'What's your mother like?'

'Not like me.'

'What are you like?'

'What?'

'You're ripe, you're ready for picking, you're a pupil now, not a teacher, I know that, but what goes on in your head?'

She blushed and hesitated. She was excited and outraged. She had been looking at the sea and straight ahead at nothing in particular throughout this conversation. Now she turned, was provoked to turn her head and look hard at Owen Pennant. He was smiling at her, as relaxed as a panther in a tree, so beautiful and luscious that her eyes filled with incomprehensible tears, tears of mingled love and hate, of desire and frustration and revulsion, and she burst out: 'You shouldn't ask me impossible questions, you shouldn't...' She failed to finish the sentence, she dared not scold him.

He laughed then and replied: 'You're right, I shouldn't. I shouldn't be here and shouldn't be standing you on that pretty head of yours. Take my advice, darling, give me a miss. I'm not a good boy, and you won't teach me different. There, I've said it. Let's have a drink before the credits roll!'

Abruptly he stood up, extended a hand, pulled her to her feet, and walked ahead of her in the direction of his car. She was horrified. Was he chucking her? Was he objecting to her half-hearted rebuke?

They walked to a pub. He had a gin and tonic, smoked a cigarette, passed the time of day with the barman. She had a small sherry, could think of nothing to say to him, and began to wish she was dead. They did converse, but even more disjointedly, and by platitudes.

Soon he was saying it was time to drive her back to the hospital. She protested that she would be early. She could not believe that she had lost him and was lost.

They returned to his car. He drove off almost savagely. She was afraid she was going to cry. But he stopped in a side street with a screech of brakes.

'What's wrong?' she asked. 'What's the matter?' she besought him.

'This,' he said, switching off the engine and embracing her.

So the kissing began, and ended when he took hold of her left breast.

She pushed his hand away. It was involuntary, she was not ready, she might be acting against her interests, but she was unprepared and unwilling to submit to rough treatment.

He laughed at her and then drove on.

He said: 'That's something new – back to the class for beginners. Oh well, so it's got to be like riding a bike with no hands! You amuse me, you little primrose! You're a breath of fresh air. I'm guessing you're a virgin. You'd be fun for me, but I'd not be right for you – those are my last wise words, and could be my first, if it comes to that.'

She had to join in his laughter, even if it was at her own expense. She could not explain herself, she would not be able to find the words, or be tactful enough to convey her mixture of feelings. She let him mock her because mocking was preferable to goodbye. His kisses had been a great relief. They were expert kisses, thrilling kisses, but the best thing about them was that she was on the receiving end.

He dropped her at St Mildred's. He made one of his jokes by way of a goodbye: 'Steer clear of those big bad gynaecologists!' He did not mention another meeting.

Momentarily she was stricken by the omission. He was not planning to carry on with their affair – if it could be called an affair after her rejection and repudiation of his caress. At the same time, almost in the same moment, she remembered all the compliments he had paid her, verbally and orally, and was able to view the future in a not altogether gloomy light. Her intuition suggested that he might be back for more. She had plumbed at least the competitiveness of his nature.

Of course she had regrets, the curse laid upon lovers. She should have been quicker on the uptake, and not stumbled along in his wake. She had failed to entertain him, after he had driven so far. And how stupid she had been to resist him, considering she had rather loved his fondling, and, when all was said, wanted him wantonly.

But there was also opposition to such reasoning. On duty in the night, as she waited for a bell to ring or for her next tour through the wards, she recollected the difficulty of Owen, his uncosiness, and that he was ten years older than she was and seemed to inhabit an alien planet.

She could not draw back. She could not politely even if she had wanted to. But her sweet captivity had connections with quailing. She drank cups of tea not only because night nurses did so in order not to fall asleep, and certainly not because she was sleepy: to the contrary, she drank them to steady her nerves and still an internal tremble.

Two questions nagged at her in the next few days. What would she say if he should either proposition or propose to her: secondly, what would she do if he did not?

She had her optimistic moments. She had proof that for him she was an object of desire. And she was unfinished business after all, which he would probably want to wrap up in bed or elsewhere. Her farthest flight of fancy was to imagine that she was his destiny, as she was his.

But pessimism ruled. She was nobody, she was nothing. He could not stoop to care tuppence for her. There were millions of girls prettier than she was eagerly waiting to devote their lives to the service of a man like Owen Pennant. He was above her station, above her in all respects, and she was presumptuous to dream that he could ever be hers.

Despair drove her to seek consolation from Dot and Con. She still guarded her privacy, she could not bear to drag Owen's name into the dust of gossip. She rang Dot from the public telephone and announced that Mr Right was treating her wrong, and she was feeling mis. Dot replied, 'Join the club,' and went on to say that her surgeon had rebuked her for declaring that she was falling in love with him as he undid her stitches. Celia fared even worse with Con, who responded to her confession with the news that she was bitterly regretting having 'gone the whole hog' with Ian Thornton, who had turned out to be an absolute sex-fiend.

Again, as before, she tried to fill the vacuum with work, volunteered for extra duties, exhausted herself, and was more attentive to her parents.

He rang when she had ceased to expect to hear from him. He rang when she happened to be within earshot of the telephone. It was four o'clock on a weekday afternoon. She lifted the receiver in passing and stated the telephone number.

He said: 'It's Owen.'

'You...' she gasped, she repeated, and then, unstoppably: 'How wonderful!'

'I've been abroad,' he said, perhaps to apologise for not having rung sooner. 'I forgot to find out when you're reachable. Can you speak now?'

'Yes.'

'Are you okay?'

'Yes. Are you?'

'I want to see you.'

'Do you really?'

'When is your next free weekend? Come and stay with me in London.'

'Oh ... oh, heavens!'

'Are you putting off the evil hour?'

'I'm not − no − I'm free next weekend − it's Wednesday − I'll be free on Friday evening − but I've promised my parents...'

She lost her voice or her thread, and he laughed and suggested: 'You promised them not to stay with strange men in London?'

'No, no...' she joined in the laughter. 'I've promised to spend the weekend with them.' She was unaccustomed to fibbing and brought it out in a rush.

He saw through her.

'You're a good girl but a bad liar.' He was mocking her again. 'You'll be at Broadstairs, true or false?'

'Yes...'

'Will you allow me to be at Broadstairs?'

'What?'

'I'll come to Broadstairs.'

'Oh, Owen!'

'It's 42 Thanet Steps, isn't it? I'll call for you at eleven o'clock on Saturday morning – okay? What's that noise?'

'There are other people waiting for the telephone.'

'Did you hear what I said about Saturday?'

'Yes.'

'Does it suit?'

'Yes ... thank you! Thank you so much, Owen.'

She was thrilled for obvious reasons, and appalled by the prospect of having to introduce her parents to Owen and show him her home. They were dim and dowdy, and his car with the foreign name put her father's battered old Austin to shame. What would her mother say? What would her mother not say?

Eventually, at last, she arrived home in time for supper on the Friday evening. Her parents said she looked well, which was odd considering she had scarcely eaten for days and was worried stiff. Halfway through the meal, before the cheese and fruit, she spoke her piece.

'I'm going out with somebody tomorrow. He's calling for me in the morning.'

Her father said regretfully, 'Oh well, that's nice for you, dear,' and her mother asked, 'Is he your boyfriend?'

'He's my friend, he isn't a boy. I met him with the Wellinghams, when I stood in for Dot at that party in London. He's called Owen Pennant.'

She bit her lip, she was annoyed with herself for not keeping the tenderness out of her pronunciation of Owen's name.

Bernard Farr began to ask, 'What's his line of work?' when Chrissy barged in: 'Are you serious about him, Celia?'

'Oh, Mother – I don't know – and wouldn't answer if I could.'

'How old is he?'

'Thirty-two.'

'Good gracious! Is he rich?'

'Yes ... I don't know, I don't care.'

'It's not clever not to care, Celia.'

She called out, 'Father!' – as if to save her from her mother's inquisition.

'It's all right, dear,' he assured her. 'Any friend of yours will be our friend. He'll get a warm welcome here.'

She shone a grateful smile at him, but felt she had to say to her mother: 'You will be polite to Owen, won't you?'

Her mother replied: 'I don't need to be told how to behave.'

The evening drew to an end, the night finally yielded to morning, and Celia's mix of emotions almost amounted to illness.

His car's powerful engine noise, an exception to the rules of Thanet Steps, announced his arrival. She opened the front door and stood in the doorway, waving both her hands at him defiantly. The weather was grey and damp, the soft top of the car was in place, and Owen emerged in checked golfing trousers, a red cardigan and open-necked pale blue shirt. He was extracting a great bouquet of flowers from the boot of the car.

Her embarrassment became reproachful. What would the neighbours make of his flashy clothes? Had the neighbours seen the flowers? He was compromising her, which was different from her compromising herself.

He carried the flowers in his right hand, and reached out his left by way of greeting her. He was smiling and saying, 'They're for your mother.' She took his hand and led him indoors, bewildered by events but impressed by his left-handed handshake. In the sitting-room, where her parents stood in front of the fireplace, he took charge of the introductions and presented the flowers. Chrissy Farr's frown was replaced by a skittish smile and an offer of refreshment. Bernard Farr was asking for details of the drive down from London, and soon they were all sitting and drinking coffee together. Celia was silent. She was ashamed of her mother and even critical of her father's slow pronouncements. She silently loved Owen for being vivid and vibrant and a social star.

At half past eleven they left Thanet Steps. There had been badinage between Owen and Chrissy – 'I'm stealing your daughter away' – 'Bring her back in one piece' – and then they were in his car, they were pulled into the verge on a country road, in each other's arms and kissing.

That day was full of kisses. Their talk sometimes seemed like background music. But everything he said was also like treasure to be gloated over at a later date. They walked in Deal, had lunch in a restaurant in Dover, bought return tickets for a cross-channel trip to Calais on Sunday, spent time in the fun-fair at Margate, drank local apple cider and ate fish and chips in a cosy pub in Sandwich, and parted at Broadstairs at ten-thirty, as arranged with her parents.

She had assured him that she had never been so happy. He had assured her in various ways that she pleased him, although love was not mentioned. He said: 'I was bored when you twinkled at me... You're what my doctor would have prescribed.' He said she was almost as much fun as making money. He compared her with amber amongst the pebbles on the beach of Broadstairs, and the best apple in the orchard of Kent. He said it amused him to play at being boys and girls again.

He spoke autobiographically.

'I was born by Caesarian section – spoilt at birth because it didn't hurt... Ma was great, but I scarcely knew her, she died in a car crash when I was five – I inherited her soft spot for fast cars, she was killed in her Bugatti, she drove it into a tree... I did my first deal when I was nine or ten. I sold chickens that had been raised on one of my pa's farms – investment was zilch for many happy returns.' He referred to his 'flat' in London that sounded more like a house, it had an office with secretaries, and a staff of two, a married couple, cook-housekeeper and butler-odd-job-man, as well as his own accommodation. He revealed that he also had a house in Hertfordshire, called Pennygate. Moreover, even as he patronised and mocked her, he acknowledged her superiority in some areas. He asked for guidance in roundabout ways. For example he challenged her: 'How can you believe in God? ... What's so special about God? ... What's this faith that people bang on about?' He said: 'You think you do a better job than mine, you save poor people, I'm out to prove I'm rich – no contest, probably.' He asked: 'Money means independence – you and your family aren't really independent – why don't you worry?' He asked intimate questions, too. 'Why do you contradict your kisses? They give me one message, you give me another – what's your game? Why not carry on from where your kisses stop?'

Towards the end of their day in the Isle of Thanet, his more personal questions were backed up by the urges of her own constitution. Chastity seemed hypocritical. She longed to say: 'Go ahead, now, now!' But she could not make the first move in that direction – it would have gone against her ladylike grain, against nature, against the form of their relationship. He was staying the night in a hotel near the golf courses in Sandwich: she wished she had shown interest in his room there.

He was boastful yet dissatisfied with himself and his life. 'I've got the lot, but it ain't enough... What's next on the agenda?' He was restless and knew it – 'I never got high marks for concentration. I should stop running around, but I get itchy when I'm not running.'

Of all the perturbing things he said to Celia, at least perturbingly self-centred, the worst was: 'Gambling and girls are my scene – not a rosy prospect for a wife and mother.'

His personality was strong to the point of oppressiveness. He was beyond her, maybe above her, and distant when he was not close. He was comparable to a tiger in the zoo – he had to be approached with care. Metaphorically, he did to her those things described in cheap tales of romance, swept her off her feet, bowled her over. If he had not been glamorous, and not had a 'different' side, she would have fled and given him a general thumbs-down. But he kissed so well, and they were on nearly equal terms while lips and their lives were in contact. She realised then, if briefly, temporarily, that she was invested by his desire with a kind of transcendent power. It was all new to her – all news. They kissed some more before she got out of his car at Thanet Steps, and she could not help agreeing inwardly with his parting shot: 'What about giving love a chance? Think it over! We could make beautiful music.'

On the Sunday, in Calais, there was no mistaking their happiness.

During the return journey, on the ship, she fell asleep with her head on his shoulder. She woke, looked at him, smiled, and he asked, smiling back: 'Do you love me?'

Her expression was affirmative as she asked: 'Could you? Do you?'

He embraced her, they embraced.

Then in his car, driving her from Dover to St Mildred's Hospital in Canterbury, he said: 'You wicked witch, I must see you again soon.'

She laughed, she was very flattered, and offered him her Wednesday afternoon off.

'Hopeless girl, it's not what I wanted, but it'll have to do,' he replied, and continued: 'Don't you yet know I'm impulsive? Wake up, sweetheart! You can't dangle a man like me on a string, and I won't be twisted round your little finger. So you can't accuse me of bullying, I'd just like you to pencil me in as a possible spouse. No comment – no commitment on either side – no publicity – there you are, a card on the table!'

He drew up at St Mildred's, would not let her speak, almost pushed her out of the car, and called out as he drove away: 'See you on Wednesday!'

She was in a dream for the next thirty-six hours, until the Tuesday morning, when she was rung by her mother early.

Chrissy Farr said: 'Owen Pennant came to see us yesterday evening.'
Celia was startled.

'He wanted our blessing. Can you hear me, dear?'

'Yes.'

'He's a fine man. We think you couldn't do better. Your father
agrees with me. Owen's invited us to stay at his place in the country.'

'I must go, Mother.'

'Don't be obstinate, Celia.'

'We'll talk another time.'

Celia was not pleased. At first she blamed her mother more than
she blamed Owen. She realised that her mother had been brainwashed
by materialism, Owen's flowers, signs of wealth, sweet talk and invitation;
and that now her secret would be common knowledge in Broadstairs,
and that she was going to be under pressure from all and sundry.
Her romance was soiled by market forces. But her second thoughts
were that Owen had broken his word about publicity. She was too
honest to conceal the fact from herself that he had gone behind her
back to force the issue of his peculiar proposal and rush her to the
altar. Her doubts recrudesced, her spirits drooped. She was unsure of
him, had never understood him, had been attracted to him for wrong
reasons, because he was strange, a stranger, out of her league, a law
unto himself, and unpredictable if not untrustworthy. What was she
to do? He might not let her escape, he would not allow her to get
the better of him. Her happiness vanished like the mists of morning.
She saw a present fraught with indecision and controversy, and a
future overshadowed by filthy lucre and not to her taste.

She dreaded Wednesday; it arrived nonetheless, and again he was
standing by his car in the sunshine, in his summer slacks and a suede
jacket, exuding manliness and confidence.

He drove her away from St Mildred's, from the humdrum world
of difficulties and threats, into his almost imaginary kingdom of
excitement, pleasure, novelty and hope.

'I called on your parents last Monday,' he said.

'I know,' she replied.

'They gave me the green light.'

'Yes.'

'I didn't want to be accused of baby-snatching.'

'I'm not a baby,' she said.

'And I'm waiting for you to prove it.'

They both laughed. Owen was funny. Everything was fun, after all. Their Wednesday hours together seemed to clarify their 'understanding'.

However, late in the evening, after dinner, human nature asserted itself, not only in physical communion but also in relation to seeing more of each other, and claiming more than they already had. He begged her to be a little more available, and she revealed that she could apply to take the week's holiday that was owing to her. He urged her to do so without delay. Amorous reasons apart, he wanted her to see Pennygate, and his flat in Belgravia.

Celia duly applied to the St Mildred's authorities, and was surprised to be granted leave of absence from that coming weekend until the next. She communicated the news to Owen, who said she must bring her parents to stay the weekend at Pennygate – he would send a car to Broadstairs, it would be at Thanet Steps at eleven o'clock on the Saturday morning. Celia was taken aback: she had thought he wanted to see her; she had not expected her parents to be included in this visit to Pennygate; she felt he was paying more attention to her parents than to herself; and who would be driving this car that was going to pick them up like parcels?

'I'm looking forward to seeing you,' he said.

'Oh yes – so am I – and thanks,' she replied.

Later in that day Celia happened to hear the public telephone ringing and ran to answer it. She was hoping that Owen might have decided to change the plan. But it was Con on the line.

'When's the wedding?' she began. 'Can I be your bridesmaid?'

Celia asked how she had heard such gossip.

'Your ma. Hasn't he been to ask your pa for your hand in marriage?'

'Oh Con! You know my mother too well to believe a word she says.'

'The rumour is he's a millionaire and drives a Mercedes-Benz.'

'I don't know what sort of car he drives. Who told you that?'

'My Ian saw you in an open Mercedes with a sun-tanned man. What's the true story?'

'I'm friends with someone called Owen Pennant. Okay, yes, I'm walking out with him. But I'm not marrying him yet.'

'What's he like? Is he really rolling in it?'

'He's nice. I'm not interested in how rich he is or isn't.'

'Golly, you're a heroine, Celia, not to mind about money. My Ian thinks of almost nothing but. It's money or sex with him, and I suppose it's beginning to be ditto with me.'

[185]

'Is he still pressing his suit?'

'Is he not!'

'Successfully?'

'Up to a point – no pun intended.'

'Are you going to marry Ian?'

'Maybe – he'd be better than Boots, provided he could afford me. I wish we could have a double wedding. If you were with me I could face it.'

'I couldn't be with you on the honeymoon.'

'Poor old Ian, he is a bit of a nagger. He's on and on about marriage. He's nagged me for saying the other day that if I let him have enough of me now, we might have got through the seamy side before the honeymoon.'

Yet another telephone call figured in this period of Celia's relations with Owen. She rang Dot Wellingham to ask if she could stay at Pimlico Road for a night or two of her free week.

Of course, Dot said. She had been longing to see and talk to Celia. She knew about Owen Pennant, who had just invited herself, her parents and Celia to dine with him in his flat on the Friday evening of her holiday. Con had also dropped a hint or two. What was the state of play?

Celia confessed guardedly, and asked questions instead of answering them as soon as she could. Was the surgeon any good?

'Good at sending in a colossal bill, good for nothing else.'

'Oh well! London's full of men, Dot.'

'My new beau's one of Daddy's customers. He's a collector, he collects corkscrews and fire-irons and Chinese pots, and wants me to belong in his collection.'

'Are you willing?'

'No – able but unwilling – he's fifty and fat. Hope springs eternal. Look at what's happened to you!'

'Don't! Nothing's signed or sealed. I'm dithering intactly. You'll have to hold my hand.'

They laughed together, as Celia had laughed with Con. But life had become less light-hearted for her than it was before Owen introduced other people into the act.

The car that arrived on Saturday morning was a large black saloon. The driver was a middle-aged man in a blue suit, who called himself

Ernest and Mr Pennant's 'factotum'. In the course of the drive Celia asked Ernest what sort of car it was and was informed: 'Mercedes-Benz, Miss.'

It embarrassed her that Owen should have a factotum, whatever a factotum was. She was embarrassed by Owen having two Mercedes-Benz, each of which must have cost many times more than the Farrs' Austin. That her father seemed to be bemused by Owen's lordliness embarrassed her, as did her mother's relentless matchmaking. Celia had not known she was swapping kisses with a millionaire. She had loved Owen for being well-dressed, for having the wherewithal, but had not done any sums. Now she thought of Pennygate as Poundgate, and felt like Cinderella with a difference, half-wishing she was not bound for his palace.

It was a house, and apparently not too big. She was pleased to see Owen again, and grateful to him for making a fuss of her parents. He showed them up to their bedrooms, Ernest following with the luggage. The Farrs had been allotted a large bedroom with a double bed and dressing-room adjoining, another single bedroom and a bathroom: all in a line, opening into a passage which was a cul-de-sac with a door at the other end.

Owen managed to murmur in asides to Celia: 'You see I'm playing your game,' and again, 'Note how difficult I've made it for myself,' references to her chastity. She was not responsive, she was afraid he would be overheard.

Lunch was three courses. Owen discoursed on the subject of Pennygate and its late owner, his Aunt Susan, his mother's sister, who had bequeathed it to him. In the afternoon he conducted a tour of the garden, and Celia noticed a wing stretching out at the back of the house, making it more roomy than its front suggested. He then drove them in the Mercedes saloon to look at his model farm.

Tea was served in the drawing-room, where lengths of a tree-trunk smouldered on a pile of ash in the grandiose fireplace. When Owen offered to show Bernard Farr his study-cum-office, Chrissy dragged Celia upstairs ostensibly to rest and change for dinner, in fact to listen to a lecture on the advantages of Owen as gentleman, husband, son-in-law, father, breadwinner and all-round attraction.

Dinner was too much of everything, and the period between dinner and bed-time was a strain. Chrissy was encouraged by Owen's wines to try to flirt with him. Bernard Farr cleared his throat continually, Celia's toes curled, the small talk ran out and Owen smoked cigarettes, looking pained. They retired to bed early thanks to Celia's announcement that she was dead-tired.

Sunday was again testing. Owen wanted Celia to meet some of his neighbours: that was how he put it. He had asked people in to drinks before lunch, more people to lunch, and still more to dinner. They were all older than Celia, and often older than Owen himself. They were mostly businessmen. There was a great deal of noise and chatter, which was better than awkward silences. Chrissy enjoyed it evidently, but Bernard was not used to social extravaganzas and cast despairing glances at his daughter, who was doing her best not to look as wet a blanket as she felt.

That evening, as the house party was on the stairs going up to bed, Owen told Celia that he had to go to Paris in the morning – something had turned up – he would be leaving early – and would she convey explanation and apologies to her parents?

'Has the weekend been all right?' he asked. 'I'll be back from Paris mid-week, and I've invited the three Wellinghams to have dinner with us on Friday night – they're good friends of yours, aren't they?'

She answered yes to both questions – she was dumbfounded, and seemed to have no chance to say more – she kissed him good night and he kissed her – and they went to their separate bedrooms.

In hers, as soon as she was alone, she was critical, rebellious and sad. He should have warned her about Paris before. He should have explained to her parents rather than ordering her to do so. He should have remembered that at his urging she had taken her week's holiday so as to be free. She suffered from a sense of loss: where was the Owen she had fallen for? She did not know what to do. She did not know what was going to happen.

On the Monday morning the Farrs were driven back to Broadstairs by Ernest in the Mercedes. On the Tuesday and Wednesday they recuperated as if after shocks to their systems. On Thursday Celia was due to go to London; she was to report at Pimlico Road where the Wellinghams' shop closed at five o'clock and Dot would be free. After lunch on Thursday father and daughter walked along the Broadstairs beach, where they had played cricket once upon a time.

They harked back to days gone by, then Bernard said: 'You must have noticed that I haven't bothered you with words of wisdom and sage advice.'

'I have,' she replied, 'and I'm grateful.'

'Don't worry, I won't start now.'

'Thank you.'

'But...'

'Oh dear!'

'But, after much cogitation, I've decided I can't keep a secret from you. Owen spoke to me when he came to Thanet Steps on his own.'

'I know. Did you bless him?'

'No. But I didn't curse him either. Everything was hypothetical. Anyway, he spoke to me again at Pennygate. He gave me details of matters that might influence you, although I don't believe they will. He talked about a marriage settlement.'

'What's that?'

'Money that he would settle on you, give to you, if you were to marry him."

'How much?'

'Two hundred and fifty thousand pounds.'

'Well I never!'

'It doesn't stop there. He'd allow you a thousand pounds a month, twelve thousand a year, pin money, for you to spend as you wish. You'd also have the interest on the quarter of a million.'

'Are you proud to have a daughter worth such a lot of lucre, Dad?'

'I felt faint when I realised how much you were or could be worth.'

'Good Daddy! I'm not bribable.'

'Good Celia!'

'Money makes a difference to me. It really does! It puts me off. It's causing me problems, Dad. I didn't have a nice time at Pennygate.'

'No – well – your mother and I were in the way, which didn't help. Owen hasn't done wrong to be rich. He's multiplied the money he inherited, and in the Bible a man like him was called a faithful servant. You'd find excellent uses for the money you'd have if you were Owen's wife, and it wouldn't necessarily be bad for your character. You wouldn't forget how difficult it is to make money, or how lucky you were not to have to worry about it.'

'Are you urging me to marry him, Dad?'

'No.'

'Are you telling me not to?'

'No.'

'What are you telling me?'

'You can choose either to be a nurse and wait for Mr Right, or you can choose to marry Owen.'

'Mother could make the choice without hesitation.'

'True.'

'A pity I've not got more of Mother in me.'

Later in the afternoon she hugged her father very tight on the up platform at Broadstairs Station.

His parting words were: 'I think you're a bargain at the price' – and they made her laugh.

Dot was the only Wellingham at home when Celia arrived – Mr Wellingham and Sandy were involved in some antiques fair. The two young women talked non-stop throughout the evening. Celia mentioned Owen intermittently, she could not stop herself speaking his name, but in response to Dot's initial questions she said she could not answer them, and would cry if she tried to. At other times she revealed that she was missing him, did not know him well enough, was bewildered in spite of their 'understanding', doubtful about his intentions, uncertain of her own, and was doing her level best not to go mad. For light relief they talked of Con and Ian Thornton, and Dot discussed her 'collector', Hubert Maclaghan, who was apparently refusing to take no for an answer.

On the Friday morning Mr Wellingham had business elsewhere and Dot was minding the shop. Sandy, sitting at the breakfast table with Celia, referred to Owen's dinner party.

'I can't imagine why he's asked us,' she said. 'We'll be playing gooseberry.'

She then noticed tears in Celia's eyes and asked: 'How's the romance going?'

Celia said she did not know, a phrase that was becoming her refrain, and added: 'He invited me and my parents to spend last Saturday and Sunday at Pennygate, and asked lots of his friends in on the Sunday.'

'Did you enjoy that?'

'We didn't see much of each other.'

'Where is he now?'

'He went to Paris.'

'Wasn't this week your holiday, when you and he could make up for lost time?'

'He's invited you for this evening to please me, I think – and I am glad you're coming. He said he asked the people in at Pennygate for me to meet them, but they were his business cronies and wanted to meet him.'

'Dear me! Bachelors lead wild lives, they're wild animals, and we have to tame them.'

'Would he want me to do that?'

'It's the price he'll have to pay for you.'

'He's terribly rich. He's offered my father pots of money for me. I couldn't cope with the money side – we're not a financial family.'

'My dear Celia, believe me, you'd be surprised by how easy it is to cope with having more money than you've ever had before – what's difficult is vice versa, having less. Remember the witticism – money, not manners, maketh the man.'

'I wish – I don't even know what I wish – but perhaps I wish most of all that I was worthier.'

'Heavens alive! Owen's an outstanding man, but I'd never call him worthy. We've all been hoping that you were so good that he wouldn't dare to be unworthy.'

Later in the day Mr Wellingham returned and took over in the shop. Dot was released to endeavour to calm Celia's nerves before the dinner party.

Owen's flat was in Eaton Square. The house was imposing, they were admitted by an entryphone, travelled up in a lift, were welcomed by a man in a white jacket, who ushered them into a sizeable hall and then into a large sitting room. It was brightly lit and seemed to glitter. Celia unexpectedly felt weak at the knees when she set eyes on her host.

She survived the sensation. She was a nurse and had watched operations in the hospital. She summoned her courage, and gradually the occasion caused her more pleasure than pain. Owen had not invited strangers to dinner. He sat her on his right at the dinner table and Sandy on his left – a breach of etiquette and a sort of honour. He kept on looking at her in such a way as to raise her temperature, and once, between courses, covertly held her hand. He included her in every conversation and sought her opinions. She was the centre of his attention, and recovered the confidence he had stolen in the earlier part of the week.

After dinner, when the ladies left Owen and Bill in the dining-room, Sandy said to Celia: 'He's yours, like it or not.'

It was the first of a trio of turning points.

The second was Owen's offer to fetch her from Pimlico Road on the next day, Saturday, and drive her back to Broadstairs.

The third occurred when she had gone to bed in the spare bedroom of the Wellinghams' home. There, in the night, contrarily, it dawned on her that she was his at least as much as he was hers, and, by accident or design, by means of his expert male machinations or her innate subliminal female ones, she was trapped. Her alternatives actually were to marry him or to break her heart. She had gone too far while she thought she was going nowhere. She could not willingly retrace her steps, she therefore had to go farther, to the end of the matrimonial road. The best reasons were the simplest: she could not bear to lose him again.

She had one residual doubt and anxiety: would her unilateral decision telepathically inspire Owen to pop the question she was ready to answer in the affirmative?

Saturday was sunny, the hood of Owen's car was down, and they drove out of town and into the full summer leafiness of the country. In side roads they stopped for kisses, on main roads they shouted apologies, pardons and terms of endearment at each other. The rush of air as they sped along ruffled their hair, and Celia reached out her hand to smooth his down.

He knew a pub in the middle of nowhere. They parked nearby, at a wayside clearing in a wood, and got out of the car to embrace more comfortably, and he asked without preamble: 'What's the verdict?'

They were married in the church in Broadstairs where Celia had been christened and confirmed. The wedding ring was engraved on its inner surface with the two words 'For Ever' – the engagement ring was a solitaire. The reception was held in the Shelbys' house – Con Thornton, née Shelby, had been one of the bridesmaids, and Dot Wellingham the other. The honeymoon was in Biarritz on the Atlantic coast of Southern France. The marriage was consummated within minutes of the couple finally finding themselves alone in their hotel bedroom.

They spent a fortnight in Biarritz. For Celia, it was a crash course in the realities of marital rites. Owen was virile, surely virile to an extraordinary degree, and she immediately derived satisfaction from their sexual exchanges. He congratulated her and himself on her responsiveness – she was a rare bird, he said; he also called her one of the quiet demure types who turn out to be sex-boxes in bed. His complete confidence as performer was infectious, and his expertise and ingenuity were aphrodisiacal. For both of them, but probably more so in her case, the novelty of commitment spurred them towards repetition.

Celia was happy. She had always been a cheerful girl, but now she was a happy woman. She was in love with Owen – he was the monarch of her heart and mind, body and soul, he was her pride, her destiny, and he reassured her over and over again that he reciprocated. His past was past, he was hers in the present. The faults she had found in him seemed to have been amended by his vows in church and the blessing of their union.

The sun shone on them in Biarritz. The weather was kind, and at night stars in a deep-blue sky shone through the windows opening on to their balcony, and the breeze drifting in from the Atlantic Ocean was exceptionally balmy.

On the third or fourth day of their honeymoon she was aware of a change in Owen. He was again a little more like he had been and a little less like he had begun to be since marrying her. His attention wandered: it was no longer fixed on her good points, external and internal. His thoughts were elsewhere – their roads had diverged – there was distance between them – and she was disappointed, but not downcast. It was inevitable, she reflected. He was a professional man. He had his work at the money mill, just as her father had had his at The Welcome School. She forgave him for buying more newspapers and for being absent while he was with her. The knock-on change made itself felt in their sex life. Whether or not he noticed it, she had recourse to sex to reclaim him. The love that they made acquired another meaning, it was an axe to grind. She comforted herself by thinking her discovery was also womanly, and she was enlisting in the ranks of wives and mistresses through the ages, who had fought as she prepared to fight the battle of the sexes.

They travelled home. And the busy round of their life began. She had thought she might not have enough to do, she would become as lazy as she had been energetic before, especially at St Mildred's. She had made Dot and Con laugh by saying she would be surrounded by servants, hairdressers, manicurists and masseurs, while she lay on satin cushions. Not so: the opposite occurred. She was working overtime to win the friendship of Aunt Susan's old retainers at Pennygate and the staff in London and to remember their names; to house-keep two residences; to arrange, double-check, supervise, inspect everything, and not to be browbeaten by her staff; to dress well in order to be a credit to Owen; and to please or at least not to displease him.

At Pennygate there were Stanley the butler and Mrs Stanley the cook, Jean the housekeeper whose husband Bill was the head-gardener, two tweenies, who helped Mrs Stanley in the kitchen and Jean in the house – they were called Madge Bright and Dulcie Boon; and out of doors Ernest presided over the garage and cars, Bobby, a lad, was the under-gardener, and an old man, Mr Richard, did odd jobs. The Stanleys occupied one cottage, Jean and Bill another, and Madge and Dulcie occupied attic rooms in the house. Over at the farm, the manager was Arthur Otway, and he and his wife lived in the farmhouse. In London, in Eaton Square, the couple in charge were David the butler and Molly the cook – Mr and Mrs Arkwright. Celia formed friendships or alliances with all these people in a hurry. She could not have coped with Owen's way of life without their assistance, and she had to convince them that she posed no danger to their jobs.

The Pennants entertained in town and in the country, and consequently were entertained. They had to go out in the evenings, stay for weekends, and agree to be included in shooting, fishing, golf and sailing parties. They were often weary, even exhausted; but Owen explained that he could not afford to be stand-offish and they had to repay hospitality. They were young, they recovered, and they had a good time, an interesting varied amusing time.

Celia was not going to complain of her lot and her luck, as some of the young women in her position whom she now met were inclined to. She was grateful to find she was somebody rather than nobody. She was glad to be pretty and popular, and to move in a circle where the arts and devices of womanhood were appreciated. She learned the lesson of how the world worked, ignorance of which is the commonest failing of women; and by means of discrimination she sought to improve the quality of Owen's guests and would-be hosts.

She had days off: a similarity with her previous experience. Owen would have to be somewhere else, she would be free to spend time with Dot, or to motor in her new car, a Mini, to Broadstairs to see her father and mother or Con. But Chrissy's triumphalist attitude to her daughter's marriage, Bernard's mournful queries, then her friends' efforts to be noticeably generous and her own not to be smug – all strengthened the magnetic charms of her life with Owen, its glitter and fun.

The months hurried by. A whole year passed without Celia noticing that their intimacy had been partially eclipsed by their social engagements. One or the other or both were sleepy at night, and Owen had breakfast meetings in hotels. Weekends largely belonged to their guests or their hosts. It was natural, she reflected. The fires of desire had been bound to simmer down. Owen's work, or rather his ambition, was important and perhaps merited priority, she allowed. Her reflections, in so far as she had time to reflect on anything, brought home to her the fact that loving couples are designed by nature to replace the missing element with a baby.

Then it struck her that she had never started the suspicion of a pregnancy. Why not, for heaven's sake? It could not be for want of the necessary. She was a maternal woman, she now discovered she was pining to be a mother. She also wondered if she was failing Owen, she feared she might be, although he had not mentioned children. She felt healthy, had confidence in her constitution, had used no contraceptive devices – surely her prayers would be heard, she must be patient.

A postcard from her mother was cathartic. Chrissy had written on it, 'Where's my grandson?' She contacted a doctor she knew at St Mildred's, Dr Richard Leaf, a gynaecologist, and kept an appointment with him on one of her free afternoons. His diagnosis was that her Fallopian tubes were constricted, but could be cleared in a surgical operation that would enable her to conceive a child.

Celia returned to the flat in Eaton Square. She was longing to tell Owen that they could soon have a family. He returned late from a business meeting and wanted a quick bath – they were going out to dinner with friends of his. She waited for him in his dressing room. He emerged, drying himself with one of their huge towels.

'I've something exciting to tell,' she began.

'Go ahead,' he replied, casting the towel aside and opening drawers and cupboards.

'I've been to see a doctor.'

'Why? You're not ill.'

'It isn't that. I've found out why I haven't given you a baby.'

His head was in his clean white shirt.

'Sorry – what?'

'I need a little operation – on my Fallopian tubes – there are two of them and they're clogged up.'

'Spare me the details,' he said. 'I'm feeling sick already.'

'Aren't you pleased about a baby, Owen?'

'Female babies are better when they reach the age of consent.'

'But I was so happy for you,' she said.

He was tying his tie.

'I'm happy too, of course I am, but I'll have to leave the gynaecology to you. Are you dressed and ready?'

'Yes.'

'Well done! I'll be with you in a minute, and we can hit the road. Talk to the tall bald man tonight – he's called Thompson and I'm trying to get my hands on his crock of gold. Good news about the little one!'

As a result of this conversation Celia decided not to go ahead with the operation.

Their life was more of the same. The weeks and months continued to whirl by. Celia made umpteen acquaintances, but no friends. Men flirted with her, women were given no cause to be jealous, she was polite to everyone, and ready to hide her light so that Owen would shine the brighter. Their wealth was like a gauze in the theatre: they were on one side of it and the rest of the world was on the other, where outlines were softened and faces not quite recognisable. Celia had adjusted to a fate that bore resemblances to Cinderella's, but privately, following her decision to postpone the op, she was shocked to realise that her reaction to her prince had become objective.

She was not willing to have his child just yet. He was not ready. He was not a bad husband. He was not cross, violent, stingy, dull. He was still amorous sometimes, and never failed her if or when she was. But he was selfish. He liked to win, and was not interested in whom or what he had won. She was harmed by that characteristic, for he had begun to take her for granted, along with his money and houses and servants and social success.

Celia judged him as never before, but loved him still. She believed that one day, when she was more used to him and he was more appreciative of her, she would be able to have children and that they would fill the small area of vacuum in her marriage. Meanwhile she would 'soldier on' – one of her father's pet phrases.

She had been married for nearly two years, and a regular weekend party gathered at Pennygate.

It consisted of six guests: a married couple called Longden, stockbroker Mark and Tanya, a company director called Oliver with Lucy, his sleeping partner in every sense since she owned a large percentage of shares in his business, and another couple, Jim Town, a banker, with his American wife, Mary-Ann. Celia had feelings for two of the six: affection for Tanya Longden, and dislike of Mary-Ann Town. Mary-Ann was a career girl, raucous, provocative, striking rather than pretty, and too friendly with Owen.

Lunch on the Sunday in question was prolonged and noisy, and after it Tanya Longden agreed with Celia's suggestion of a siesta, Mary-Ann said she was ready to lie on her back, and they all drifted upstairs.

Celia had a snooze and prepared to return to the fray. On the landing at the top of the stairs she noticed that the door into the bachelor wing was ajar: which was strange as none of the bachelor rooms were occupied. A housemaid must have forgotten to close it. She went to do so, and heard a noise. She thought of summoning Owen, but instead tiptoed along the passage. The door of the room from which the noise issued was half-open. She pushed it and beheld Owen in a chair and Mary-Ann on her knees between his legs.

Mary-Ann raised her head, looked round at Celia, and said: 'Whoops!'

Owen was gazing at Celia in a recognisable way. He was also fumbling with his trousers.

Mary-Ann stood up and said to Celia, 'Sorry – but at least I've still got my knickers on,' and walked out of the room.

Owen now said, 'Celia,' in fairly plaintive accents.

She turned and ran to their bedroom and locked herself into the adjoining bathroom.

Owen followed her and said in a hushed voice through the door: 'Celia – Celia, let me in – please talk to me – we must talk – please!'

She stood, leaning back against the locked door, heard him out, then spoke in an equally quiet voice: 'Can you hear me?'

'Yes –'

'Listen! There's nothing to talk about. We've nothing more to talk about. Leave me alone, Owen.'

'No, I won't – please open this door.'

'Leave me, Owen. If you break down the door I'll jump out of the window.'

'Oh my God – be sensible – it was damn all – I drank too much – forgive me!'

'Goodbye.'

'What?'

'Goodbye.'

'Don't be silly! Celia! Celia, are you listening? You can't do this to me – I'm sorry – I'm grovelling – don't punish me too much for nothing. Where's your Christianity?'

He broke off, and a moment later said: 'The Towns are leaving, so's Oliver – I'll have to put in an appearance. My darling, think again! I can be tough – don't try to be tough on me – it won't work. I'll come and talk to you properly as soon as I can. I love you.'

He absented himself. She could hear the voices of the departing guests in the house and then out on the gravel sweep. She unlocked the bathroom door, seized a small travelling suitcase, stuffed underwear, shirts and a pair of jeans into it, snatched her bag which was luckily in the bedroom, retraced her steps along the passage of the bachelor wing, descended the staff staircase, and stole out of the house by a side-door close to where her Mini was parked. She drove to Berkhamstead railway station, left the locked car in the station car park, bought a single ticket to London, and caught the next London train which drew in a quarter of an hour later. At Paddington she found a telephone and rang her home in Thanet Steps.

Her mother answered and then spoke.

'How are you, Celia?'

'Fine!'

'And your gorgeous husband?'

'Fine!'

'Are we going to see the two of you soon?'

'Yes, Mother.'

'I know you're busy, but you should remember us, Celia. We were always good to you, and now it's your turn. Your father does miss you.'

'Is he about, Mother?'

'I thought you'd be wanting him. All right – here he is.'

Her father came on the line.

'Lovely to hear from you,' he said.

'Dad, I need to talk to you urgently and privately. Could you go to the phone box on the corner and ring me as quick as you can. I'm in another phone box and other people might try to get in.'

'What's your number?'

She gave it to him, blessing him for being so quick on the uptake, and waited for what seemed a century for the telephone to ring – no one had bothered her.

'Tell me,' he said.

'I've left Owen.'

'Are you safe?'

'Yes.'

'Where are you?'

'In London, near Paddington – I'm going to find a room with b and b.'

'Why, Celia?'

'He betrayed me. We're done for, it's all over.'

'Was it so bad?'

'Yes – for me, yes – I'll never go back.'

'Never say never.'

'I mean it.'

'Are you very sad?'

'Yes. But I swear that I won't kill myself. I'll be better one day. Dad, Owen will be looking for me. He'll ring you. Can you just tell him I'm okay, but have to be left alone?'

'If that's what you want.'

'I do.'

'Can I reach you, Celia?'

'I'll ring in a few days, when I'm organised.'

'I could come to London.'

'Thank you, Dad. Thanks for everything. You'd better go back to Mother – what did you say you were doing?'

'Seeing a man about a dog. You've got enough to worry about.'

Celia had one hundred and seventy pounds in cash in her bag: she had resolved not to use her cheque book on a joint account, and credit and debit cards were not yet available. She walked along Praed Street, into the Edgware Road, passed small hotels that charged too much for a single room, and in some poorer area farther north found a terrace of modest dwellings with advertisements for bed and breakfast in parlour windows. She rang a doorbell, but did not like the look of the man who opened the door, mumbled an excuse and hurried away. At the other end of the terrace she tried again. A respectable middle-aged woman opened the door. She had only one room to let, it cost three pounds a night in advance, was on the first floor back, and Celia paid her twelve pounds for four nights. She had the use of the bathroom at specified hours, and of the lavatory when vacant on the landing. She gave the name of Farr to the landlady, Mrs Harris.

'Will you be going out for a meal?' Mrs Harris asked her.

'No – I can't.'

'I don't do supper,' Mrs Harris explained.

'No – don't trouble yourself – I'm very tired.'

'I could give you a cup of tea.'

'That's kind. Thank you. I'll pay you, of course.'

'Are you all right, dear?'

'Yes – I will be – I promise not to be a nuisance.'

'I'll get you the tea.'

Celia lay on the lumpy bed in the cramped little room. Tea with two digestive biscuits arrived: she drank the tea and nibbled one of the biscuits. The light faded, night fell, the noise of traffic subsided, at last the milkmen rattled their bottles, dawn came to her rescue and morning began again.

She agreed to eat a boiled egg for her breakfast in Mrs Harris' neat kitchen. Afterwards she went out – the weather was grey but dry. She bought an envelope and a stamp, put the key of her Mini in the envelope, also a scrap of paper on which she wrote, 'Owen, My/your car is in the car park at Berkhamstead station. Thank you for marrying me.' She sealed the envelope, addressed it to Pennygate, stamped and posted it in Oxford Street.

She was trying to cover her tracks. She became aware that she was more likely to be recognised by Owen's friends and acquaintances in the West End than elsewhere, and headed north once more. She sat in Regent's Park, watching the grey squirrels. She bought a cheese and pickle sandwich from a stall – how different from the food she had eaten for lunch only yesterday! She had nothing to do.

At one o'clock she took the tube to Highgate. She had been doing her sums. A hundred and fifty pounds would have looked like a fortune to the Celia Farr of yore, but for Celia Pennant it had been the pettiest of petty cash. Now, for different reasons, it was scarcely adequate. She might have to buy something warm to wear and something rainproof. She might have to buy more strengthening food. She could last about a fortnight, counting contingencies. In Highgate, she walked to St Hugh's Hospital and asked if she could complete her training as a nurse there. St Hugh's and St Mildred's were connected somehow; she had once been posted from St Mildred's to work at St Hugh's for ten days of an epidemic. The office staff checked up on who she was and so on, and, no doubt because of staff shortages, granted her wish. She signed forms and was told to report at six o'clock on the next Sunday evening to Appleton House, accommodation for St Hugh's nurses.

That evening she rang her parents from another phone box and got through to her father.

She said: 'I've got a job, and I'll manage now. You needn't worry, Dad. I'm sorry if people are harassing you about me.' She added, because she could hear Chrissy screaming in the background: 'And I'm sorry to have upset Mother.'

He said: 'I'm so glad you've rung, my dear. Thank you for thinking of us. The people you mention wonder if you'd meet Sandy Wellingham. Sandy's offered, she's very fond of you, and, if you wished, you could give her answers to the sort of questions I'm being asked.'

'Yes,' Celia agreed.

'Would you meet her?'

'When and where, Dad?'

'Wait a minute – yes, here it is – the bar of a small hotel called The Lytton in Wigmore Street behind Selfridges at eleven o'clock on Wednesday morning.'

'No tricks?'

'Sandy's promised me that no one else in the world has or will have the information I've just passed on.'

'Okay – I'll be there.'

Shortly afterwards, the money that Celia had paid for the call ran out.

In due course, after long intervening hours had dragged by, Celia kept the appointment.

The wan young woman and the smart brisk older lady embraced. Sandy ordered cups of coffee, and led the way to a table at the far end of the room.

'Do you want to tell a tale?' she asked.

'Not particularly, no.'

'Do you mind if I ask for guidance? Stop me if I'm too inquisitive or boring.'

'I will.'

'Have you any intention of going back to Owen?'

'No.'

'Ever?'

'Never.'

'I gather he was unfaithful?'

'With Mary-Ann Town.'

'That baggage!'

'Exactly.'

'He regrets it. He's miserable.'

'I can't be sorry for him. He broke his vows to me. I believed him and was wrong. I have nothing more to give him. I couldn't let him touch me again.'

'Some women can cope with the awfulness of their men.'

'I speak for myself.'

'No tears for Owen?'

'I do my crying at night.'

'You justify my faith in you, dear Celia. Forgive me for introducing you to a rotter. Poor girl! I sympathise with you exclusively. Brass tacks now – are you going to divorce Owen?'

'Yes – some time.'

'And blame him?'

'No.'

'You're entitled to take him to the cleaners.'

'I'm not keeping or taking any of his money. Here's our joint cheque book – will you return it to him?'

'You have a marriage settlement which belongs to you.'

'Not any more – it's his – he can have it – I won't be beholden – cancellation's the object of the exercise for me.'

'Is that a bit hasty?'

'No.'

'Owen can afford to discharge his debt to you.'

'There's no debt.'

'He should pay – he's always been allowed to get away with treating women badly. Don't ruin yourself financially, too.'

'I'm not going to be ruined. I can't let him ruin me. I didn't deserve to be treated as I have been. He must have told me a thousand times that I satisfied him physically. Tell him that I'd be grateful if he'd organise our divorce. He can settle the bill for that.'

'You won't change your mind? I don't want to carry a message you'll regret.'

'I won't regret it, Sandy.'

'Well – I was always fond of you – but I didn't know quite how exceptional you are – I can't say whether or not you're being wise, but I respect you, dear Celia, and I'll do your bidding. Concerning money – one word more – do you need any?'

'No, thanks.'

'I could lend you some.'

'No, honestly.'

'Ask me if you're ever short – I'd be flattered if you did.'

'Thanks again.'

'My Dot – your Dot – she's pining to see you, and Con ditto. Any chance of a get together?'

'Not yet. I'll have to settle into my job first.'

'You've got one already?'

'I have.'

'Good for you!'

'I'll have to leave you now.'

'I was hoping you might lunch with me?'

'I'm sorry, no – I've nothing much to do – but I don't want to talk any more about my situation – and I'm afraid I can't talk about anything else. Please understand! Sandy, one other favour – would you kindly give Owen my wedding ring and my engagement ring? Here they are. I haven't run off with any of the jewellery he gave me.'

'Oh dear! I can't help feeling sad.'

'I know – but there it is!'

They stood up, embraced, and Sandy patted Celia on the back until the latter turned and walked out of the bar with her face averted.

Two days later, again in the evening, she rang her home, hoping to speak to her father. Unfortunately her mother answered the call, and began to cry and curse.

Celia waited. She had known Chrissy would side with Owen, and say that she was being hard, cruel, unforgiving and foolish, but nonetheless she felt sick at heart.

Eventually the incoherence boiled down to a question: would Celia at least meet Owen and listen to what he had to say for himself?

'I wanted to talk to Dad about that. Is he there, Mother? I'll tell Dad,' she replied.

Chrissy complained, but, when Celia was silent, gave up and handed over the instrument.

Celia and her father hurried through the preliminaries, knowing time was limited.

'Dad, I can't resume more or less normal life until I know that Owen won't track me down or seek me out and try to put pressure on me. I have nothing to say to him, and won't weaken or be persuaded. It's all over. Has he spoken to you?'

'Frequently. He wants to know where you are. As you haven't told me I can't tell him.'

'I need an undertaking or a guarantee that he's not going to persecute me. Could you try to explain to him?'

'Yes – but I don't know how dependable he'd be.'

'There are legal injunctions, aren't there, to stop one person persecuting another?'

'Oh, I don't think it would or should come to that.'

'No. Owen would agree with you. That's why I'd go for it if the worst came to the worst.'

'I'll make him see sense.'

'Thank you, Dad. I'm sending you my love, Dad.'

'Same here!'

Celia had paid Mrs Harris for three extra nights of her stay, Thursday, Friday and Saturday. They had become friendly by the Saturday evening. Mrs Harris had not only continued to give Celia evening cups of tea, but had often provided a jam or ham sandwich as well as the biscuit. She was more motherly than Chrissy had ever been, and was concerned that Celia looked 'peaky' and 'down'.

On the Sunday morning they reminded each other that Celia was having her final breakfast. Mrs Harris said that she would be missed, and Celia gave her twenty of her remaining forty pounds to cover the extras.

'Oh no, please – I was never one for charging for nothing.'

'Of course not – but I'd like to give you a present in my turn – I'll have other money after today.'

Mrs Harris was duly grateful, then asked: 'May I ask you a question, Miss? It's personal.'

'I'll answer if I can,' Celia replied.

'Is it a convent you're going to?'

Celia laughed.

'No, nothing like that, I'm not cut out to be a nun. I came to your house because of my marriage, because of the end of it.'

'Oh, I'm sorry.'

'So am I.'

'Did you love him, dear?'

'Yes, once. You lost your husband, you told me, but he died.'

'He was called John – Johnny, we called him.'

'Were you happy with Johnny, Mrs Harris?'

'We were married for thirty-four years, and we were happy as the day is long. I don't think we had words more than once or twice, and it was always kiss and make up with us.'

'Did you have children?'

'No, dear. I had a miscarriage early on, and that was that. It was a pity, and might have been a sadness to Johnny, but we were closer because two's company, and he never showed me he had regrets.'

'What did Johnny do?'

'He repaired antique furniture. He was a cabinet-maker by trade. He was a good carver. He was a good man.'

'Did you live with him in this house?'

'Oh yes. We saved to buy it. We were proud to own the house, we were. Johnny wouldn't leave it – for holidays, I mean. We did day-trips to Brighton sometimes, but we were both happier to be here quietly, laughing and making improvements. Thirty-four years wasn't a day too much. I've loved Johnny just the same every day since he died.'

Celia cried. She sobbed and the great tears ran down her cheeks and splashed on the breakfast table or her lap. She cried on and off for the rest of the morning and in the afternoon until it was time to kiss Mrs Harris goodbye.

PART TWO

FOUR YEARS have passed. Celia, who has reclaimed her maiden surname, is twenty-eight. Her paternal grandfather, her GranFarr who lived at Westgate-on-Sea, is no more. Bernard Farr, her father, has retired, and her mother Chrissy is no longer fit – she has a wonky hip and now complains mostly of pain. Bernard is a patient husband and the most undemanding of loving fathers: he attends functions at The Welcome School, reads books and studies his seabirds. Constance Thornton, formerly Shelby, has two children, Jessie and Jake – Celia and Dot Wellingham are Jessica's godmothers. Dot has a flatlet of her own in London, she has moved out of the Pimlico Road house, where Geoffrey Wellingham has his antique shop and he and Sandy occupy the upper floors. Dot is not married, but involved with a man who is – no, not the collector. She works full-time in her father's shop.

Celia is a State Registered Nurse employed by St Hugh's Hospital in Highgate – she finished her training there and stayed on. She is buying a flat within walking distance of her work. She has lost her girlish twinkle and the tensed slenderness of healthy young women. She is mature now, curvaceous, strong. Her nurse's uniform suits her, the headgear adds attractions to her neat blonde hair, and the buckled belt accentuates her small waist. Her complexion is fresh, her smile ready, her teeth nice to look at, her blue eyes wide and unflinching, and her regard steady and receptive, a trifle sceptical but not cynical.

She was very cut up by her divorce from Owen Pennant. She hated people thinking or hinting that he had broken her heart. She insisted inwardly and sometimes outwardly that he was a womaniser, not a heart-breaker. She was disillusioned and felt foolish when she overcame the sense of outrage. She was aware that the world would either think she should not have married Owen; or that she should have put up with the common lot of wives injured by their husbands' infidelity and sexual peccadilloes; or that she should have punished the adulterer financially. Chrissy, contrarily, reproached her daughter for not 'fleecing' her ex-son-in-law and former favourite.

For ages Owen refused to take no for an answer. In messages sent via Sandy Wellingham he demanded reconciliation and at least a meeting. He apologised and threatened. Then he begged her to pocket the money on offer, that was hers by rights. His final note on the subject ran: 'Okay – please yourself and my bank manager. I can't be sorry for ever.'

Celia had a spot of trouble with her best friends. Referring to the divorce laws and speaking as a trader born and bred, Dot could hardly bear to think of what was slipping through Celia's fingers. Con, who could see nothing wrong with money for jam, began by ranting at Owen and then ranted at Celia.

The three of them met in the fullness of time in Dot's flat in the cheaper end of Pimlico. The question and answer session regarding Celia's marriage began at the beginning.

The romance seemed to have been a whirlwind, why was that, considering Celia's cautious attitude to the opposite sex?

'He forced the pace,' she explained. 'It was kisses after the charity ball. I tried to apply brakes, but he was in the driving seat. He wanted it all, he wanted to sleep with me, and you can't ask a man like Owen to wait. I didn't want to lose him. I wanted to sleep with him, too.'

'Couldn't you have had him on approval?' Dot asked.

'I was set on being a virgin bride. I know it sounds Victorian but there it is – or was. And I knew in my bones and everywhere else that once I'd tried him out or tried him on I wouldn't be returning him to sender.'

'What was the honeymoon like? You looked so happy after it.'

'I was happy. We seemed to me to be made for each other. It was all lessons in love. It was an all-action movie. Our talk was baby-talk really. I can't remember any conversation or even much exchange of information. I think he's a Protestant, anyway we were married in a Church of England church.'

'Don't you wish you'd known him better?'

'My wishes had come true.'

'What happened when the kissing stopped?'

'It never stopped completely. But he was either churning out money or socialising, and I had Pennygate and Eaton Square to run. Our life was like a film that's winding on ahead of itself.'

'Why no baby?'

'I've got something wrong with my Fallopian tubes.'

Con had experience of Fallopian tubes. She said hers had been tested: the doctor had compared them to Welcome Hall.

Then she asked Celia: 'Were yours blocked?'

'Apparently, according to my doctor, and evidently also.'

'Didn't you have them seen to?'

'No. I did nothing, which was odd, because we weren't getting on badly, and I knew the operation was straightforward. I was longing to be a mother, and I had no idea that we might split up. Subconsciously, I must have been prepared for something to go wrong.'

Dot and Con wondered about the last chapter of Celia's story: 'Don't tell us if you don't want to.'

'I don't mind. We've always shared our secrets. We had people to stay the weekend at Pennygate, including Mary-Ann Town. On the Sunday afternoon I heard a noise in a room that wasn't occupied and investigated. Owen sat in a chair facing me and Mary-Ann was on her knees. She scrambled to her feet and said something unattractive as she left the room. Owen sat there looking at me – he was doing up his trousers, but still in the grip, if you catch my meaning. He looked at me without seeing me while he enjoyed himself – and that described Owen as a husband to a t. There was nothing left to hang about for, and never would be.'

Celia continued: 'I suppose I'm puritanical. I thought my marriage meant as much to Owen as it did to me. He proved he didn't think so, and it didn't, so our marriage was a lost cause by my standards.'

Dot said: 'Well, I understand you, I admire you, I've realised how serious your serious side is, but I'm afraid I wouldn't have done as you've done – I'd have eaten crow and humble pie and all those disgusting things.'

Con said: 'You're so brave, Celia.'

Some months later the friends met again, and Con asked Celia if she was feeling better and if by chance there was anybody else.

'Yes and no,' Celia replied. 'I am better, and I'm not looking at men. I shan't for years, if ever. But I must say that men in London, and at St Hugh's hospital in particular, look at women far more than they did at St Mildred's in Canterbury, or in Kent for that matter.'

She gave satirical accounts of recent propositions put to her by the medical profession. One of the surgeons at St Hugh's had asked if she would be excited by him wearing his rubber gloves. Another had suggested making love to her while she was strapped into the gynaecological chair. A large nurse of military bearing had put forward a plan for them to spend an afternoon together. And patients were worse. A man with his broken leg suspended from a sling had asked her to do something gymnastic for him. Lots of men asked more or less misleadingly to be kissed good night. Bed baths were never given by one nurse to invalids of the opposite sex – two nurses were meant to be safe, and the same applied to male nurses bathing women. As for 'mixed' wards for patients of both sexes, only a politician could have dreamed up such an unpleasant and impractical proposal.

The three girls' reunions were not devoted exclusively to the study of Celia's love-life. Con spoke of Ian Thornton in unflattering terms that were contradicted by her contented appearance. She had formed a habit of calling Ian old – her 'old' Ian, her 'poor old fool of a hubby', her 'old boy' and so on – although he was actually thirty-six: the word 'old' was clearly an endearment in her terminology. She said that the best thing about her marriage was not having to take a hot water bottle to bed in the winter. She said Ian was 'frightfully' law-abiding, and 'lost his rag' if she drove faster than the speed limit or tasted a grape in a shop to discover if the bunch was worth buying.

Con was a doting mother, and produced photographs of her offspring. Jessie, Celia and Dot's god-daughter, was unphotogenic or else lumpy and plain, and Jake looked a hundred years old in his cot. Con retailed their sayings and harped on their winning ways, but said, 'No more, they're the last of the Shelby-Thorntons.' She confessed she was sick of sex, and had chosen to take complicated precautions in hopes of putting Ian off. But after all, as she would wind up her reports to her friends, she was a lucky devil, since her 'funny old dear was on his feet and just about compos', and her little ones had a full complement of fingers and toes.

Dot's situation was more complex. After her virginity had been 'collected' by that collector, she fell for a married man with the typically difficult wife. She had made the mistake of allowing him to cry on her shoulder, sympathised with his tales of woe, offered him the treat of herself in an attempt to cheer him up, and discovered that she had become the pig in the middle of his marriage. 'I'm not his mistress, I'm hardly an adulteress, I'm nothing romantic or wicked,' she informed her friends ruefully. 'No – I'm a ragged old sticking plaster, and can't pull myself off for fear of more blood on the carpet.'

Celia and Con assured her that one day a wandering knight on a white horse would ride by and throw her across his saddle-bow: at which Dot laughingly reminded them of her height and weight.

Talking of wandering knights on a later occasion, in the second year of Celia's divorced status, she asked Dot and Con what they had really made of Owen.

Con said he had frightened her, he had reminded her of Johnny-head-in-air, he was haughty and impolite.

Dot said: 'He made my inferiority complex worse. When we shook hands he showed me I wasn't his type, and I knew he wasn't mine.'

Dot and Con together wished they had warned Celia to take it easy and not to be rushed off her feet.

Celia answered: 'It wouldn't have made a scrap of difference if you had.'

But two and a half years after her divorce, in the course of another session with her two friends she regaled them with the following story.

'I saw Owen from the top of a bus the other day. He was talking to another man on the pavement of the road running down from Hyde Park Corner to Victoria Station. I was sitting in the front seat of the upper deck of the bus. I thought he must be a male model or a film star before I recognised him. He wore a grey suit – Savile Row – long double-breasted jacket – light grey flannel – I remembered it, and I remember him talking about his expensive clothes, how they were made, how they had to look. He had an athlete's physique, clothes looked wonderful on him, and he knew it and carried a fortune on his back. He was the man I and others fell in love with. He had that beguiling sharp attentive expression on his face, reserved for women he didn't know well and wanted to know better, and for men who might help him to make more money. Don't pity me! I was immune. He inspired mild interest, nothing else. I was so glad I'd done what I did and was not his wife.'

To start with Celia had missed sex. But at St Hugh's she tended invalids and eased suffering, she was coping with other people's emotions as best she could, and before long she seemed to have no time for her own. Besides, she was resistant to any sort of involvement.

At some stage she noticed she was more restless than she had been. She found it difficult to concentrate on reading books or on radio or

TV when she was alone in her flat. At the same time she was touched by a tragic story unfolding in the hospital. A young woman who was chronically ill had also been pregnant, her baby had been delivered but had then died, the mother was a terminal case and the husband was desperate.

Celia had known worse situations. This one was different for all the nursing staff because the mother, May Sturridge, was so charming and sweet, and her husband Alan was such a dignified gentleman. Celia, on night duty, met and talked to Alan Sturridge.

He was tall and had a long face. He was in his forties and had a good head of dark hair going grey. May Sturridge was the only patient in a four-bedded room. Alan at night was allowed to sit with her far beyond visiting hours. When she slept with the aid of drugs, he would stretch his legs or drink a cup of tea or coffee in an empty annexe to the main ward. Celia, waiting to attend to May, would sometimes talk or listen to Alan there.

He was a solicitor and worked in the branch of a big firm in Stanmore. He said he was not a high-flyer, he did the conveyancing; he had been brought up in the country, and felt he was more a countryman than a guttersnipe. May was thirty years of age. They had been married for four years, postponed starting a family, then May fell ill yet managed to conceive their child. If the child had lived, Alan was sure May would not be dying. As it was, he blamed himself – the strain of pregnancy, the effort of labour, had exhausted her strength to fight against her disease.

Celia said: 'Who knows?'

He said she was comforting. He uttered paeans of praise of his wife, her beauty, her intelligence, her humour and humanity. They had lived the quietest of lives, for each other, and spent their holidays in England, by the sea, in Cornwall and Devon, in East Anglia. He dreaded widowerhood. What would he do with himself? He despaired of ever getting over the loss of May, his well-named better half, the spirit of springtime.

Celia mentioned her experience that slotted in towards the other end of the scale of matrimonial satisfaction, and he was unselfish enough to sympathise.

One night he cursed God, and she commented, 'If in doubt, kick the Almighty.' He asked her if she believed in God, and she answered, 'Yes – I was taught God, and He's a help when you're in trouble, whether or not He created the trouble in the first place. But I expect I've shaped my God to suit myself – everybody does.'

He sought further explanation.

'Oh well,' she laughed, 'my religion's about happiness. I think we have to pray to God to let us be happy – even happy again. I can't believe God's impressed by unhappiness, although some people are determined that He is, our Christian God is, aren't they?'

'What a difficult creed!'

'Sorry,' she said.

'Don't be! Thank you.'

May Sturridge died the day after the night in which Celia and Alan spoke of religion.

Some weeks later Celia buttonholed Mr Gibson, the gynaecologist, in a corridor at the hospital. They were acquaintances, and had a jokey relationship.

'Would you like to cut me up?' she asked.

'Don't tempt me,' he replied.

The consequence was an appointment in his consulting room. She was scolded for having done nothing about her Fallopian tubes for so long. An urgent x-ray examination followed, then an operation. It was successful. She recuperated for a few days at Broadstairs and returned to work.

Then Celia received a letter from Alan Sturridge. He had sent it to St Hugh's. She was relieved to see that the writing on the envelope was not Owen's – she did not recognise the writing. Seeing Alan's name was a shock.

The letter ran: 'Dear Celia, I wonder if you would or could have tea with me at the Queen's Head hotel next Friday? I have work in Highgate on that day, and would like to thank you again for your kindness when my wife was ill. Drop a line to my office, as above.'

The writing paper was headed Carter Johnssen, Solicitors, and the office was in Stanmore. Celia wrote back that she had a free hour between four and five o'clock on Friday, and looked forward to seeing Alan.

The Queen's Head in Highgate had once been a coaching inn. The two reception rooms where tea was served were small and dark, but quite cosy with wood fires smouldering on piles of ash in the blackened fireplaces. Alan sat at a table in the farther room – nobody else was present. He shook her hand and rang for tea and biscuits. He looked better, less drawn, than he had in the hospital.

Their talk was impersonal. They asked after each other's health. They touched on work, holidays, plans for the future if any, friends and family. His father was dead, he had an ailing mother in a residential home in Stanmore, and a sister married to a Swede, the mother of two, living in Stockholm but in poor health. She described Broadstairs, and she poured the tea.

In the last ten minutes of their hour he launched into a panegyric of May, and said how much he was missing her. Celia almost had to interrupt in order to say goodbye. He apologised for talking too much. She said he had not and thanked him. When they shook hands no second meeting was suggested.

She had not expected much more. She was hardly disappointed – she would not agree that he attracted her. She was just sorry for him, they were friendly acquaintances. And she suspected that, for all his talk of May, he was an unromantic chap, and inhibited. Nevertheless she had jumped to see his signature on the letter, and she had thought of him occasionally in the preceding months, ever since their nocturnal confabs in the hospital.

She had a more concrete worry. She had been shy with him in the Queen's Head. She was forced against her will to compare him with Owen, who knew too well how to excite a woman without making her feel uneasy. She had not been shy with Alan while May was alive. As a nurse she mixed with men. She had seen off members of the opposite sex who wanted to lay hands on her body, and made comrades of others. Now, aged twenty-eight and an ex-wife, she had not been able to meet Alan's simple and sincere blue eyes. She was annoyed by the effect he had on her, whatever it was, and resolved not to think of him any more.

But a month later another letter arrived. They drank more tea and ate more biscuits at the Queen's Head. This time he asked her to lunch – it had to be a month ahead – she had duties in Broadstairs, he was visiting his sister in Sweden. The lunch passed pleasantly, and they agreed to meet a third time: which was no use in any emotional sense.

Their fourth meeting was lunch on a Saturday. Alan fetched Celia from the hospital at noon, drove her to Stanmore in his car – not a Mercedes-Benz, a Morris Minor, he told her – and after lunch in a Chinese restaurant to meet his mother. Mrs Sturridge was a nice old lady; but Celia was not pleased to deduce that Alan had subjected her to inspection by his mother, who would tell him how far to venture along the primrose path. He should be capable of deciding if he wanted to make love and to whom, she thought. She also took exception to the possibility that he might be thinking of marriage before he had held her hand or kissed her even on the cheek – what was he – cold, restrained by snobbery of some description, lazy, homosexual? Yet May had died partly because of the baby he had given her.

They met another time or two. Her shyness was yielding to a challenging mood. She was too old for platonic friendship, and could not hang about for ever while he was in mourning. When he deposited her back at the hospital after another lunch at Stanmore, she kissed him. He had opened the door of the Minor to let her alight, he was strong on the gentlemanly gesture, and she reached up and kissed him in the region of his ear. He was startled – at least he looked round in a startled fashion – there was a small crowd of people arriving or leaving near the hospital entrance. He might have been embarrassed.

'Don't worry,' she laughed, 'I'll tell the gossips you're my brother.'

He laughed too, exclaimed 'No!' as if to deny something or other, he also mentioned the date of their next meeting, and she waved goodbye.

She wondered if that kiss would be a turning point. But nothing turned. The only change was that he kissed her on the cheek at the beginning and the end of their time together. She did not really care. She liked him – he was a decent kind sensible man, and rang much truer than Owen. She admired him, valued his friendship, thought she could see through him, and was sorry he was sad.

Their meetings continued. It crossed Celia's mind that her relationship with Alan was neutralising her attractions for the opposite sex in general. Time kept on passing, and her readiness for love merged with impatience. Out of the blue a third letter from Alan reached her.

'Dear Celia,' he wrote in his regular legible hand; 'A while ago you said you could pass me off as your brother. I know it was a joke, but I have never felt like your brother. Please forgive me if I have been slow to show that my feelings for you are of a different colour – you know the reason, I'm sure. At last my previous life seems to have set me free. Ever since I met you in St Hugh's Hospital I have admired you. At first you were my nurse as well as May's, and my comforter. I loved you in those roles, and then as an unattached man I grew to love you more and more. I would, if you permitted it, love you in the ultimate way, and devote the rest of my life to making you as happy as possible. I am presumptuous to be writing in this strain, for I am well aware that you are far above me in many respects, but I believe your modesty and kindness will let you read on. I am asking you to marry me. I know I don't deserve you. Tell me if I can hope. I shall not be a nuisance to you if your answer's no. Dearest Celia, all for now. Alan.'

She had Alan's office and home telephone numbers. She could have rung him immediately. Instead she wrote him the following note in the evening.

'Dearest Alan, Thank you thank you – I'm grateful for ever! My heart is touched and I'm prouder than peacocks. Give me a little time, please! It's Monday today, we've got a date on Saturday, could you wait till then? Loose ends to be tied up, nothing personal. With my love, C.'

She could have added crosses representing kisses, but did not. She posted her note with a sigh that expressed unaccountable contradictory emotions. She wanted a man, marriage, children, and that sort of security. She knew Alan filled the bill almost to perfection, and she was fond of him. But his letter had been a trifle dry, self-centred too. He put her on a pedestal and grovelled in the dust at her feet. Could she live up to the standards he was setting? Would he be fun to live with? And how good would he be at loving?

The telephone call she did make was to Dot. She called for an urgent consultation with both her friends with luck, with one or the other at least. Dot rang back to say that Con was 'tied by the leg' by her 'blasted kids', and that she herself would report to St Hugh's in Celia's lunch hour on the Tuesday.

'What's wrong?' she asked.

'Marriage.'

'What's wrong with that?'

'You'll have to tell me what's right.'

They met at twelve-thirty. They ate sandwiches and drank beakers of tea in Dot's mini – Celia had bought the food in the canteen.

She gave Dot a full account of Alan's courtship, and tried to describe his outward appearance and his character.

'He doesn't sound wrong to me,' Dot said.

'I don't know.'

'What don't you know?'

'I fell for such a different sort of man before, and might again.'

'You don't hanker after another cad?'

'No no no.'

'Why then!'

'I'm afraid of hurting Alan. I'm afraid of making another mistake. I'm afraid he may be too poor, just as Owen was too rich. I'm afraid of being contrary. And I don't know how to wriggle out.'

'My father says, "When in doubt do nowt".'

'I can't do nowt.'

'Your children could wait.'

'True!'

'Where would you live with Alan?'

'Not where he lived with May. We haven't got down to a single brass tack.'

'You're a good earner, Celia.'

'I wouldn't be if I was a mother.'

'Con's message to you was not to miss the bus.'

'Con's so adaptable. What about you, Dot? I've done all the talking – sorry!'

'I'm plugging along, and listening for the sound of horse's hoofs.'

'Are you still the sticking plaster?'

'I'm determined to get unstuck. I mean, it's not logical – I love a man who loves me, we wish we were married, but the love he receives from me weighs on his conscience and makes him more uxorious, he says he can't desert his frigid little wife, so I'm my own worst enemy and ruin my chances.'

Dot also said she was ashamed of committing adultery.

'I blush at the most inconvenient moments when I remember Owen and that Town woman, and your reaction,' she confessed.

Celia replied: 'You haven't made the solemn vows that Owen broke.'

They circled round their dilemmas, and discussed the various methods of tying the knot.

Dot said: 'I wouldn't care how it was tied as long as it was tied quickly. The last thing I want is my man wandering around without having promised to be mine. I'd lock him in if I could.'

'Alan wouldn't have to promise anything much because we'd be marrying in a Register Office,' Celia reflected. 'But he's not a wanderer. Oh dear!'

'What would I think of him?' Dot asked.

'You'd think he was charming, but a bit of a stick, a charming stick.'

'Have you slept with him?'

'Not yet.'

'That might settle it.'

'Yes.'

On the Wednesday Celia was torn almost in two by pros and cons, and on Thursday she rang her father. She told him her story so far as it went in hopes that he would tell her the inevitable ending. But her hesitancy influenced him to recommend caution.

'Time will decide, play for time, my dear.'

'But we're not playing, Dad – Alan's the opposite of a playboy.'

'I'm glad to hear it. Bring him down to see us. You've met his mother.'

'I haven't met his sister.'

'His sister's married with children and lives in Stockholm, she has more to worry about than her brother's second wife.'

Celia laughed.

Bernard wound up their conversation by saying: 'Remember your problem's a problem of success.'

Friday was again devoted to pros and cons, neither of which would yield to the other; and on Saturday she finished at the hospital at noon and returned to her flat by way of the shops.

She had decided to entertain Alan at home, rather than to be taken to dinner at the Chinese restaurant they frequented. She bought small fillet steaks, baking potatoes and salad, cheddar cheese, apples and peppermint creams, also a bottle of red wine that ought to be good considering the price, and a posy of flowers. There was no dining-room in her flat – it consisted of sitting-room, bedroom, bathroom and kitchen: the occasional guests she had cooked for had balanced their plates of food on their knees. Alan would be the first person she would entertain formally. She cleared space between the sofa and two armchairs, removed objects from the top of the table standing against the wall, pulled it into the open space, laid it with side plates, cutlery, wine glasses and tumblers, and placed the vase containing her posy of white roses and greenery between the settings. For chairs to sit on at dinner, she rescued one from the bedroom and the other from the hallway near the telephone.

She then had a bath, slightly made up her face for a change, did what she could to her hair, dressed in her best silky garment and waited.

The doorbell rang at seven-thirty precisely. For one more time Celia wondered how to greet Alan and what on earth to say to him. She opened the door and looked up into the eyes of the large man awkwardly carrying a bunch of flowers. His expression was nervous verging on hangdog. She had to cheer him up, and she threw her arms wide and embraced him.

'Come in,' she said, holding his hand and shutting the door. 'Come in, dear Alan – you've brought me flowers, thank you – let me take your coat and your cap – that's it – come and sit down!'

'What a very nice greeting,' he said.

She asked him to uncork the wine while she put his flowers in water. They sat side by side on the sofa, clinked glasses and drank, and he said the wine was excellent.

'Oh Alan,' she said, 'forgive me for keeping you on tenterhooks. But I will explain. We've so much to talk about I don't know where to start. I've arranged dinner here – you'll have to forgive my cooking, too. How are you? Are you well?'

'I think so, I hope so – all the better for seeing you.'

'You see me, but you haven't heard what I have to say.'

'Is it no?'

'No –'

'Oh Celia!'

'Not really no, but not quite yes.'

'I'll have to fortify myself with the wine.'

'We both have stories to tell each other.'

'I suppose we do, although I've had the feeling that you've always understood me.'

'Shall I see to things in the kitchen? The potatoes take about another half-hour to bake.'

'A capital idea!'

She left him on the sofa for a few minutes, during which she also marinated the steaks and put the cheese on a plate.

She returned and asked: 'How much do you know about my marriage and divorce?'

'Very little.'

'My husband was Owen Pennant. He's a millionaire. He's handsome and roughly ten years older than me. We married in haste – and marriage proved the point that he was not right for me. We had two homes and an army of servants – our life was a social roundabout, which made me giddy – too many people crowding in, too many lit candles, and he put business first. If I'm complaining of the life we led, I shouldn't – lots of girls long to live in a glamorous whirl. Have you met people such as I'm trying to describe?'

'I can't say I have, and I can't imagine that you would have enjoyed the whirling.'

'No – but it might have become more acceptable. The key to Owen's character is greed – but, again, I shouldn't run him down now, because once I thought he was okay. He taught me a lot of lessons.'

'I daresay, but...'

'There were two buts. He grew tired of me or tireder, and he liked the look of the grass in another garden. Are you with me, Alan?'

'Was he unfaithful?'

'I caught him out.'

'I'm sorry.'

'I lost faith in him.'

'No doubt.'

'I divorced him, but I have none of his money – no alimony, and his presents to me returned. I live on my nurse's salary.'

'I imagined so, but thank you for telling me.'

'What I specially wanted you to know is that divorce equals sin in my opinion, and even crime if children are involved. It always did, and still does. I'm not immoral or permissive or whatever they call it. Some people said I was hard on Owen to divorce him for a single act of adultery. My reasoning was that he had been unfaithful within mere months of marrying me, in my house, under my nose almost, and that I wouldn't be prepared to bear his children. I couldn't see the point of asking for trouble. Owen treated me wrong not only by his sexual behaviour, also by forcing me to sin by divorcing him. My heart isn't hard, it was awfully bruised by the whole business, and that's why I feel I can't rush into saying yes to you. Please...'

'Please don't apologise, Celia, my dear. I wouldn't rush you for the world. My opinion is that you behaved heroically to draw a line through your marriage and begin all over again.'

She kissed him. She leant across and kissed him – on the cheek – by way of thanks. He looked a little startled, as before. They both laughed, there was some small talk, and then she asked him a question.

'Would you like to talk about your marriage?'

'There's not much to tell that you don't already know. May was a sweet girl. Truthfully, she died before she had fully grown up. Our marriage had pain in it, owing to her illness.'

'Is it terribly painful to remember her?'

'Not so painful as it was. I've come to terms with it. I wouldn't have proposed to you if I hadn't felt free.'

She was grateful and sympathetic. They agreed that they were lucky to have found each other. She went into the kitchen to prepare dinner.

They ate at the table. They swapped memories of their childhoods and schooling. He had been called up into the army post-war and won a commission; but he served in office jobs because of injuring his back on an assault course – the back had cured itself. He aspired to become a barrister, but his father died young, the family was short of money, so he had to settle for the shorter and cheaper course of legal studies that qualified him to be a solicitor and breadwinner. He believed his job with Carter Johnssen was secure. He said he was forty-seven years old. Celia described Broadstairs, Thanet Steps, her parents, her two best friends, St Mildred's Hospital and St Hugh's. She said she was twenty-nine.

After dinner they returned to the sofa. They had chatted amicably; but the tension underneath was tightening. As he made no move in her direction, she put her arm round his neck, pulled his head towards her and kissed him on the lips. The kiss was disturbingly polite – nothing like those kisses to which Owen had accustomed her. When they drew apart, she smiled at him as if to challenge, and he said the kiss had been wonderful but that it was getting late and should he not be going?

'Stay here tonight,' she said.

'Would you like me to?'

'Yes. Wouldn't you?'

'I would indeed.'

They went in turn to the bathroom. He went first. She turned on no lights, and arranged the bed-covers invitingly. As he emerged from the bathroom, she kissed him again in passing.

He was not in bed when she re-entered the bedroom. He was sitting on the side of the bed, in his tweed jacket, collar, tie and trousers. She sat beside him and discovered he was trembling. She patted him on the back, said it would be all right, wondered momentarily if she ought to suggest postponement, yearned against her will for a touch of Owen's proficiency, and decided to forge ahead. Alan was mumbling apologies. She helped him out of his jacket and knelt to undo the laces of his shoes – she undressed him bit by bit.

'Come into bed,' she said. 'Don't worry!'

She almost bundled him in, then dropped her knickers and climbed in beside him. The bed was single and narrow. It was shaking for the wrong reason. They were clamped unavoidably close, but he offered her no caress. She felt it would be an affront to him to take charge and undignified for her. Besides, he was like an ill person: she could only kiss him gently on his forehead now and then.

He spoke in broken accents of his difficulties with May. She had hated the physical side, and not let him consummate their marriage for years. He could not be natural with her, he had lost his nerve, and, he feared, his capability. May's baby was conceived against the odds, and her attitude to pregnancy weakened her immune system. He had loved her for her youthfulness, and the worst thing had been her unpreparedness for death. Almost her last words were that she was setting him free, but, evidently, he was not free, not so free as he had hoped he was.

He loved Celia, he said repeatedly. He loved her too much. He rambled on, as Celia had heard tell that men do in such situations – there were jokes about it in the women's wards. She found him a tissue with which to wipe his eyes. She begged him to calm down, and offered him a cup of tea, which he refused. She said truthfully that he was tired, that they both were. She told him not to say sorry again. Finally she said she was going to have a nap, kissed him good night and turned over as best she could and snuggled down.

She had sounded cheerful for his sake, but now she surrendered to pessimism. She could not marry Alan. She was not a sex fiend; but the reasons why she could not be the wife of a sexless husband were innumerable. It was a shame: Alan was lovely in the other ways. She had almost made a second mistake, she was angry with herself, humiliated, and tonight's fiasco would be difficult to forget. Furthermore, while considering her own best interests she remembered Alan's: if she married him compassionately, she would end by venting her frustration and scorning him.

She was very unhappy. She was going to have to look elsewhere for a mate. Her tiredness was no exaggeration: she had had a busy day and stress galore. She tried not to feel hostile towards the great lump of a silent man occupying most of the space in her bed.

She must have fallen asleep. She was woken by Alan turning. He was breathing in a manner she recognised, and touching her with a warm hand. She was instantly excited. She moved a little in order to help him. When they cried out in unison, she could hear his sorrows, her regrets, and their embarrassment drifting away in the sound.

They thanked each other, laughing. He whispered something about marriage in her ear.

'Well, well...' she replied, and then: 'Alan, I took no precautions.'

Celia Farr was aware that one swallow does not make a summer. Alan Sturridge was aware of it, too. They were both encouraged by their first night together, encouraged to verify and gather proof. They tried again on Sunday; made dates to meet in the nearest future; as the weeks passed he gained confidence, not only appeared to be manly, and she was reassured.

But there was a new uncertainty in the back of Celia's mind. Her Fallopian tubes were not in perfect condition. She banned the topic of matrimony, hoped and prayed for a month. She longed for a baby, they both did; at the same time she was afraid of disappointing Alan, who had already lost the child May had conceived, also unwilling to subject him to a wife having to undergo gynaecological help and probable surgery. Even when she missed one menstrual period she hesitated, and did not inform Alan in case it should turn out to be another single swallow.

One weekend she dared to introduce him to her parents. They went to stay the night at 42 Thanet Steps. Alan drove Celia down on the Saturday afternoon. They all had tea together, then he had gone off to spend half an hour with an ancient cousin who lived in Folkestone.

Bernard Farr congratulated his daughter without reservations. Alan Sturridge was what – or who – he had always hoped for: straightforward, decent, and no fool. Of course he did not know Alan well, but he was a schoolmaster and had spent his whole life assessing boys, their characters, their destinies. He knew a good thing when he saw one. And Celia's particular gratification was that her father enthused about her new lover as he had never done about her old one, despite Owen's charm and wealth.

Her mother was doubly contrary: she vocally regretted Owen, whom she had loved, then hated. She approved of Alan with a sniff, but could not help saying that he was no Prince Charming. She wanted to know if Celia and Alan were living in sin. Supposing they married, would there be money to pay the bills, would Celia have to carry on nursing, and had she any idea of the expense of raising a family, even a family with an only child, as had been her mother's lot? Marriage to Alan would obviously not be the Easy Street that it had been with Owen, Celia was warned.

Alan's return was like the repudiation of Chrissy's diatribe. He was so large and strong. He was calm and convincing. The evening passed pleasantly, and ended in separate bedrooms for the visitors – Alan had the spare room, Celia was in her childhood bedroom in the attic. On Sunday Bernard took Celia and Alan to the Communion Service at St Mary's, and Alan for a walk after breakfast. Goodbyes followed Sunday lunch.

The weather was not good. Broadstairs would not have been Broadstairs without a breeze being wafted down from Russia via the North Sea, but today the breeze was not far removed from a gale. Celia loved it – in North London she had missed her hair being almost blown away. She asked Alan if he would mind parking the Minor for five minutes in a back street near the sea front – not too close, since the salt spume and spray from the breaking waves would strip his car of paint. He agreed. They got out of the car and struggled to reach and cling on to a railing along the esplanade. They laughed at the force of the wind, looked at each other laughing, and watched the white horses in the distance and the mountainous waves crashing on to the shore and rocks and the swirling clouds of foam. Her nose and cheeks were red, and his tie had blown over his shoulder.

'I love you,' he shouted at her.

'I love you,' she shouted back, but he pretended not to hear and made her repeat it for all she was worth.

'Won't you marry me?' he asked.

'What?' she said, laughing and lying.

'Marry me, Celia!'

'All right.'

'Did you say all right?'

'I did.'

'Is it yes?'

'Yes yes yes yes!'

They kissed. They sealed their bargain with a kiss, and they had to hold on to each other in order not to fall or be blown apart on the way back to the Minor.

That evening Celia was on night duty. She parted with Alan outside her block of flats – she had telephone calls to make as well as to get ready to report at St Hugh's, and he also wanted to tell people how happy he was.

She rang her father first, then Con, then Dot.

Her conversation with Dot went beyond congratulations.

'What cured your qualms?' Dot asked.

'Guess!'

'Was it my advice?'

'Yes.'

'Was all well in that area?'

'Fine – and fine ever since.'

'As good as Owen?'

'Oh no – Alan's not a pro – but he gives more, he gives himself.'

'Lucky you!'

'Yes.'

'Your luck the first time round turned out to be bad luck.'

'Yes.'

'Why the monosyllables? Is there something I don't know?'

'I might be luckier still, and it frightens me.'

'What do you mean?'

'I'll tell you next month.'

'Oh that! Does Alan know?'

'He will when I'm quite sure.'

'Listen, I don't want to sound like your Dutch aunt, but luck does seem to go bad quickly, so you'd better enjoy it while it's good.'

'Thanks, Dot – you're right. How are you? How's the sticking plaster?'

'Unstuck – and I'm fancy free – and Mum's taking me to Paris for shopping in a fortnight.'

'You might buy a French husband in a shop.'

'*Peut-être*!'

Celia again followed Dot's advice. She had lovely new things to think about. Happiness and her work excluded retrograde wishes and futuristic anxieties. She and Alan met whenever they could, and he bought her an engagement ring of a garnet nestling amongst pearls, and she bought him a pigskin wallet. They discussed their wedding. She was against marrying again where she had married before, that is in Broadstairs, and felt the same about Alan and May's Stanmore. They compromised on Hampstead. As for the reception, it would have to be in a hotel or restaurant – her flat was too far from Hampstead and too small, and his presented other difficulties, since it had been the home of May Sturridge, and Celia had an aversion to trespassing there.

They fixed the date, and settled on a restaurant that specialised in such functions – neither of the couple-to-be had ever eaten there. Celia invited Con, Jessie and Jake to stay with her for the night before the wedding – Dot lived within range of the relevant venues. Bernard and Chrissy Farr would stay with the Wellinghams in Pimlico Road – Geoffrey and Sandy were invited. Alan's sister Maureen, nephew Sven and niece Susan would stay with him – his brother-in-law Harald could not spare the time to leave Sweden, just as Ian Thornton chose to keep the home fires burning in Kent. Celia's friends and colleagues from St Hugh's were invited to the reception, also Alan's colleagues from Carter Johnssen and a friend from his school days called William.

The wedding occurred five weeks after it was announced. Celia wore a cream-coloured dress, Alan a blue suit, and the witnesses numbered six. The reception was a lunch party, and the newly-weds motored off in the Minor to spend the honeymoon of a week in a small hotel in St Ives.

They were living together, which was different. The news that she was bearing her husband's child was the cause of quiet rejoicing. Celia loved Alan no less for learning more about him, and he seemed to love her likewise. He was a tender-hearted man, amenable, and patient. He was an unquestioning Christian and a true blue conservative. He had not married May until he was nearly forty – he had been a bachelor for long enough to become set in his ways; yet he tried to fit in with a second wife's habits and indulge her whims. Her pregnancy was somewhat restrictive sexually, but she was still willing and he was unfailingly able.

They naturally discussed the bread and butter of family happiness. He was unambitious, would never be rich, but earned a good salary. Their joint earnings were more than the 'sufficiency' referred to by Victorians. However, if and when a child or children arrived, she would not work, would not be paid, and might need professional assistance. She deduced that they would keep their heads above water so long as he was fit enough to hold down his job; and the financial picture grew rosier in relation to the growth and independence of their children and her freedom to return to nursing. In a longer view of their finances, she would inherit Thanet Steps and he would no longer have to support his mother.

She did not worry Alan with quite such an onerous view of his responsibilities. He was dutiful and competent, yet he summoned from her a protective response. She noticed that, although he had become her guardian and shield, she did more of the guarding and shielding – they had started like that in St Hugh's, when she comforted him on account of May, and the pattern began to be repeated. She raised no objection: she had been dominated by Owen, and ended by divorcing him.

They were fully agreed on the marital home. They would sell his and her flats, and buy a house in a convenient position with a garden. And they would not buy a house in haste, after being so careful not to run the risk of regretting their marriage at leisure.

They met whenever they could, and he stayed in her flat if possible. Celia escaped the ills that pregnancy is heir to as a rule, a first pregnancy in particular, and especially so in the case of a woman of thirty. She felt better than usual, not worse. She had more energy and her spirits were higher. The Sturridges' times together were largely spent in walking round Highgate and its environs, house-hunting. They hunted by day at weekends and often at night midweek, stealing views of lit front rooms where families were eating a meal, peeping into bedrooms and imagining the scenes in progress behind net curtains. Their roaming was romantic: they invented the lives they might live, for example in a house with a front garden and a built-in barbecue, or again in a terrace house where they would cultivate wonderful window-boxes, or yet again in a flat with a south-facing balcony which would require an awning against the summer sun. They hoped for a back garden, a child-proof space, where their little offspring in the singular or plural could safely play. They linked the house they were looking for with their love – they would be destined to live in that house, just as they had been destined for each other, and sooner or later they would recognise it or it would recognise them, rather as their marriage seemed to them to have been written in the book of fate. She would explain her fitness for long walks through residential areas, and her inexhaustibility, by comparing herself with birds that tirelessly build complicated nests.

At last, after several false trails had led them nowhere, they found a little house and loved it at first sight. It was detached in a road of semi-detached houses built in an Edwardian seaside style. It must have been an afterthought, erected on a piece of ground not available until the rest of the housing development was complete. It had a porch with balcony above, a front door with stained glass inset, one ground floor window, two on the first floor, and a dormer. It had patches of garden back and front, a carport at one side, faced south-west and north-east at rear, was called The Homestead, and stood in Strawberry Road not far from Highgate's shops and transport facilities. Inside it had parlour, dining-room, two bedrooms, an attic, a bathroom and downstairs lavatory. It had belonged to two house-proud sisters, who had died and surely gained admission to heaven for leaving their Homestead so clean and smelling so sweet.

Celia and Alan sold their flats and bought it with the aid of a small mortgage. They were pleased to buy a double bed, and moved in with their furniture when Celia was seven months gone. Transplantation acted like a tonic. They were soon settled and comfortable. Problems were solved. Shopping was less of a strain than ever before for each of them, and buses and the tube took Celia within easy reach of St Hugh's if Alan was unavailable to drive her. She devoted her free time to preparing for the advent of the baby, while Alan hung pictures by Beatrix Potter in the second bedroom or so-called nursery, and created a garden suitable for a toddler.

Three weeks before Celia was due she said goodbye to St Hugh's, or, as her colleagues preferred to put it, 'See you later'. Coincidentally, Dot called for an urgent meeting of the threesome. She and Con came to stay for a couple of nights at The Homestead, Dot sleeping in the nursery, Con dossing down on a camp bed in the attic.

The urgency of this reunion was owing to Dot's love-life. She was half-engaged to marry Jason Tyler, a writer, an Adonis, adorable, two years younger than she was, an awkward customer and a hypochondriac.

When Celia's friends had admired The Homestead, questioned her about her pregnancy and commented on her figure, they tackled the subject uppermost in all three minds.

What did half-engaged mean, what about the other 'half', was he financially solvent, and should they have read his books?

'He hasn't published a book yet,' Dot confessed. 'And he's only written two so far.'

'Are they good?'

'I think they are, I'm sure they are and he'll be one of the best writers, but he's rather stuck at present, poor love. Our story's a bit like him, a bit of a muddle at present. That's partly why I'm here.'

Would she tell her story?

She did so with a mixture of excitement and bewilderment.

'I met Jason at a weird party thrown by two antique dealers I've known for years – we sometimes buy their stuff and vice versa. They're Bohemians with an extra big B. The party was for all sorts. I went in alone and came out with Jason. I was sliding away after ten minutes in the crush, almost in the dark, and he caught hold of me and asked where I was going. When I said, 'Out,' he said, 'I'll keep you company.' He took me to a pub and told me how miserable he was. He said he was a genius who wasn't recognised, a writer who couldn't write, a lover of women without a woman, and had no home to speak of – he actually had a room in the basement flat of a friend. Well – it's embarrassing – but there it is – I took him back to my place.'

Celia and Con were startled: they said they had always thought Dot was the sensible one.

There was laughter.

Dot resumed defensively: 'We had an amazing night. Jason's a genius in bed, I can vouch for that. And he's a sweet person, and clever, when he isn't dragging himself and everyone else down with his cares and complexes. He's stayed with me off and on since that first night. He disappears and then turns up – talk of wandering knights, at least he's a wanderer! The result is that he's more or less commandeered my private life, not that I mind much. But now he's determined to marry me.'

Celia and Con could not stifle exclamations of concern.

'To be or not to be is my question, too,' Dot said. 'Jason might become famous, and I'd feel a fool for having spurned him. He'd be an amusing husband, and I'd rather be the wife of a handful than a doormat. He presents enough problems to keep me busy. On the other hand, although he loves children, I wouldn't want mine to be subjected to his black moods. What do you two think?'

Con asked: 'Is he a gentleman?'

Dot laughed and replied: 'He speaks proper, but he doesn't abide by any rules except his own, even if his parents are pillars of society somewhere up north. I believe his heart's in the right place.'

Celia asked: 'Has Sandy met him, has your father?'

'They have, briefly,' Dot replied. 'Their reactions have been so discreet I could slap them. Mother won't say a word against Jason, and Father simply coughs when he hears Jason's name. They're leaving the decision to me.'

And what was it, the others queried.

'I could marry him. I'm in love with him, I suppose. I could afford him. There are two little problems. The first but is that I don't dare. The second is that I can't refuse to marry him, because I'm afraid he'd throw himself out of my window if I did.'

Which problem carried more weight?

'Probably the second one,' Dot answered, and began to cry.

Celia and Con lent their shoulders to cry on. They consoled and comforted. They discussed Dot's dilemma for hours. Nothing was decided, yet a conclusion was reached. It was Dot's, it was feminine, and involved Jason as little as possible. She would cease to use birth control.

Celia's uncontrolled pregnancy was also coming to a conclusion. The last three weeks went by. At the appointed time she felt a motherly pang and Alan drove her to St Hugh's. After a shortish labour she gave birth to a girl, a healthy baby, named Charlotte. Mother and child soon returned to The Homestead, and the three members of the family were happily reunited.

Celia had proved she was strong physically as well as morally; but her response to childbirth and to the success of her second marriage was humble thanksgiving. And gratitude to Alan meant that she wished to reward him. Consequently, three months after Charlotte was born she found she was again pregnant.

The same applied to Dot, who agreed to marry Jason Tyler round about now.

Celia's second child was a boy, a beautiful boy called Anthony, who perhaps inspired her to have yet another, Paul. In the course of her protracted labour to bring Paul into the world, something went wrong internally and put a stop to further procreation. She could not be sorry. She felt that her cup of good fortune was full, even to overflowing.

There was a church at the end of Strawberry Road, round the corner in Alyson Road. Celia passed it on the way to and from the shops. Sometimes the door of the church was open, and occasionally she would wheel her pram in and sit in a pew at the back for a few minutes. She was praising God, and resting her legs. She was exhausted, of course, but never short of the energy needed to tend her babies, and never disheartened.

Life in The Homestead was like an advertisement for marriage, or a definition of contentment, but Celia would not have gone in for such a fanciful description. Alan ventured to speak of their peaceful days in terms more glowing than he was accustomed to use. As parents, both survived the interrupted nights, the dramas and the fluctuating emotions of their children, and looked sleek even as they yawned and nodded off in the middle of a meal or did the non-stop dirty work.

Official breakfast time was seven-thirty. It was comical and tragical. Alan left to catch a bus to his office in Stanmore at eight: the second-hand Rover that now replaced the Minor remained in the carport in case Celia should need it to drive a child to hospital. She attended to one infant, then two, then three: who played in the playpen in the nursery, or slept in a cot or a pram, while she washed and ironed, hung more washing on clothes lines, cleaned the house and prepared food. After the midday meal, during the afternoon, her brood was buckled into an ever larger pram, an eventual pram for three, and wheeled out for a walk – her walk – and into the shops. Tea was exciting, as was Daddy's return between six and seven. Bath-time was always fun and games, and bed-time was a treat for the parents. Alan and Celia loved to see the children asleep, those carefree faces, those pictures of innocence. Repeatedly, in the evenings, one or other or both would tiptoe upstairs to check that all was as they had always hoped it would be.

Celia tried hard not to show Charlotte that she favoured her new baby, Anthony. But Charlotte, although she had been a late developer and charmless, was turning into a stout independent personage in her second year, whereas Anthony was quiet and wistful, moreover a boy: the fact that Celia was not altogether successful in caring equally for the two, she ascribed to his sex as well as to his strange charm. Anthony was an ideal specimen of male infancy. He was pale-skinned with curly brown hair. He had one fault, he was apt to snuffle when he breathed. Celia showed him to an ear, nose and throat specialist, Dr Robinson-Whitehead, who operated at St Hugh's. Dr RW, as he was known to staff at the hospital, diagnosed adenoids, which he could whip out in no time at all – and the anaesthetic would not be a cause for concern.

Celia was nonetheless concerned. Anthony was a year old, too young for the knife, too sensitive to be rendered unconscious. She agreed with Alan that Dr RW was medically right, but claimed that her woman's intuition could not rid itself of suspicions. She shrank

[233]

from the idea of an operation on Anthony of all little people. Yet she had to admit that he was not exactly flourishing, and might be held back by the congested breathing. She also knew that human physiology had a weakness for making mountains out of molehills, or, more realistically, for letting a snuffle develop into a proneness to pneumonia.

In the end she consented. She sat holding Anthony's hand throughout the operation in the theatre at St Hugh's, and sat by his bed in the hospital for twenty-four hours of recuperation. At home she gave him as much attention as she could spare, although he seemed well, breathing better than before. The improvement in his breathing continued, and Celia devoted more time to Charlotte – to Alan, too.

A few months later she was pregnant with Paul, and six months after that, when Charlotte was getting on for three and Anthony for two, it came to her notice that Anthony had not started to talk. He made moaning noises and pointed, but had not formed words, had not had to, since Charlotte was inclined to speak for him: 'Anthony wants cake ... Anthony's wet his trousers.' Celia rang Con, who said her 'old' Jake had been a slowcoach and could only ask for food when he was two. Con had heard of other children beginning at three, and advised Celia not to fret. But Celia asked other people. Dot, by now the mother of Adam Tyler and deep into motherhood, endorsed Con's opinion. Alan's sister recommended a canary in the nursery – its song would rouse Anthony to join in; and a liberal friend had a psychotherapist she swore by.

Nobody panicked. Celia bought the canary and called it Timmy: unfortunately Timmy was not much of a songster. Anthony was growing satisfactorily in size, and seemed to be none the worse for being wordless. He was a very active child, and surely had an intelligence to match.

Paul differed from the other two, he was jollier. He laughed at life and put Charlotte and Anthony in the shade socially. But what a darling trio they were! Alan and Celia could not disguise the fact that they were proud of their eldest, who had learnt to read with her father's help, of Anthony whose dreamy blue eyes had a poetic quality, and of Paul who was already popular with everybody and should go far in the wider world.

Double trouble, even treble trouble, was an unbargained-for blot on the landscape. It was a mystery in a house where all was open and above board. Paul was found to have a sort of bruise on the side of his neck. It looked like a bruise, but was not tender. Celia spotted it one morning, the morning after a disturbed night – Charlotte was suffering from earache and had woken everybody with her cries of pain. Celia had eventually taken Charlotte into the double bed she and Alan shared, and Alan had gone up to the attic room.

Charlotte needed to see the family's doctor, Dr Railton, and Alan took her to the surgery in Alyson Road before going to work. Dr Railton or one of the other doctors in the practice would at least prescribe a suitable painkiller. Celia waved the Rover out into Strawberry Road, and returned to attend to Anthony and Paul. Upstairs in the nursery she re-examined the purplish mark on Paul's neck and arrived at a conclusion that was hard to credit. It reminded her of a game she had played at school – there had been a craze for it – the girls had given one another 'French burns', which was their name for applying oral suction to flesh and thus bringing blood to the skin and causing the semblance of a bruise. The practice was not sexual, and was harmless.

But how could Paul aged eleven months have received a French burn?

Possibilities now occurred to Celia. She noticed, or noticed that she had noticed in the night, that a chair had been moved in the nursery. A hard chair, her nursing chair, had been shifted not far, but closer to the cot in which Paul slept; and Paul was a supreme sleeper, slept sounder than any log, and only occupied about a third of the mattress within the cot. Someone, some little person, could have climbed on to the chair, over the side of the cot, in beside Paul and given the baby's neck a kiss amounting to a suck that was sufficient to summon blood to the surface of his skin. If Celia was right, astonishingly right, although she began to believe that the astonishment would be equal if she was wrong, the culprit, the sucker, could only have been Anthony, for Charlotte in the relevant period of time was either being cosseted on her mother's knee or sharing her mother's bed.

As possibility merged with probability, astonishment took a serious turn. For Anthony to have done such a thing was worse than strange. Why should one boy steal into the cot of another to perform a physically damaging action? That the answer was love, brotherly love, was incredible: Anthony was the opposite of demonstrative, and had actually been rebuked for pushing and pulling Paul in a rough manner. That Anthony's motive was sinister was a Pandora's Box which Celia shied away from opening. Yet she could not duck a sudden flash of fear – she rushed to make sure the burn was on the left side of the neck, not the side of the jugular vein – if the skin over the jugular had been burned, the consequences were unthinkable.

She censored her horrible deductions. She was determined to assume that Anthony had meant no harm. The most pressing of her immediate problems was how to deal with him. She felt she must do so while Alan and Charlotte were out of the house – Alan might frighten the boy and Charlotte would be spiteful. The three of them, Anthony, Paul and herself, were together in the nursery: she called him by name.

Anthony's lack of response was another worry, although typical. He regarded her as if sightlessly and with no discernible expression on his perfect young face.

Celia carried Paul across to where Anthony knelt on the floor, knelt down beside him, and showed him the mark on Paul's neck.

'Look at this, Anthony! Poor Paul's been hurt. Do you see? Did you kiss him there?'

Anthony's reaction was almost nil. He did not look, let alone speak. He just slapped his thighs, a familiar gesture of his.

'Darling Anthony, won't you say something to me? I don't want you to kiss Paul so hard. I don't want Paul to be hurt. It was you, wasn't it? Can you hear me?'

He uttered a moan with a louder squeal at the end.

'I love you, Anthony, I love you and Paul and Charlotte. We must live happily and not hurt one another – no more kisses that make red marks.'

She kissed him: he was like a statue. She enfolded him in her arms and he at last raised his arms and put them round her neck, moaning and squealing louder still.

'It's all right, darling, all forgiven and forgotten. I'll have to get up and look after your brother. Let go, Anthony!'

He half released her, and she loosened his grip.

She shooed the cloud off, but it refused to disappear. She had become what she had always hoped never to be, a woman with secrets. She did not tell Alan what she suspected and what had happened between herself and Anthony: she told her husband and her first-born that Paul had somehow succeeded in bruising himself. Her new fears were unformulated, she could not contemplate them, and was far from ready to discuss them with any of the people who believed her golden bowl had no flaw, or to seek medical advice.

The situation returned to what had seemed to be normal. The Sturridges went to spend a weekend at Thanet Steps, where Celia again had trouble.

On the Saturday morning Alan took Charlotte to the seaside, Chrissy claimed a granny's right to stay with Paul, and Bernard drove Celia and Anthony to a local beauty spot, a stretch of ancient woodland. Father and daughter were walking and talking, they were happy to be together, especially in their beloved Wild Wood. Anthony disappeared. He had been toddling along behind Celia, and was nowhere to be seen. She turned round and called him. She spotted the red bobble of the tam-o'-shanter he was wearing, it protruded from behind a tree off the path. She called again, his face appeared, their eyes met, and instead of stepping forward, back on to the path, he vanished, moved deeper in amongst the trees.

She ran the fifteen or twenty metres to where she had last seen him. He was not there. She plunged into the wood, calling even louder. The branches of the trees scratched her face. Again she saw him, peeping at her from behind a tree, not laughing or joking, not far away but on the other side of a bramble bush.

'Anthony, please come here, don't run away!' she ordered and begged.

He disobeyed. He withdrew out of sight. She scrambled round the brambles, but again he was not where he had been.

'Anthony, Anthony,' she called.

He was in the open, had reappeared but not where she had expected, and close enough for her to snatch him up. He was calm, she was panting and nearly crying and had lost her bearings. She now had to call to her father, who answered back, and at last they were reunited on the path.

Her father said to the boy: 'You're a monkey, you've led your mum a merry dance.'

Celia did not dispute this interpretation of the episode. She merely remarked with a mixture of admiration and exasperation that Anthony was awfully good at hide-and-seek. She had not the heart to try to explain why the dance was the opposite of merry. She said it was time to take Anthony home.

All the children had to rest or at least not to get too tired, for Con and her two were coming to tea. The visitors arrived at four o'clock. Con was her normal smiling self, Jessie was a heavy-boned five-year-old in glasses, and Jake a sturdy little man of four. A large meal had been prepared and was slowly consumed by the five children. After tea it was musical chairs, with Chrissy playing the piano and Bernard, Celia and Con joining in. At nearly the end of the game, when only Bernard and Jessie were competing, a shriek from a corner of the room stopped everything dead. Jake was hurt, his nose was injured, he covered it with his hand, between the fingers of which blood oozed. Con rushed to pick him up, Celia and the others crowded round. Jake was blubbering: 'He hit me, he hit me.' Anthony had done it – she was half-expecting the third disaster of a set of three. She jumped to the conclusion that he had hit Jake before Jake pointed the finger at him. Nobody had actually witnessed the blow; but the story was that Jake had been watching the two final competitors for the one remaining chair, and Anthony had approached him and for no known reason taken a swing at his nose.

The party ended miserably for Celia. She was not only sorry for Jake, insufficiently apologetic to Con because she could not explain Anthony's action and in truth did not understand it, and similarly embarrassed with regard to her parents and even Alan; she was also deeply worried by a brief exchange with Con while they were kissing each other goodbye.

'Darling Celia,' Con had said in an undertone, 'Could we meet for a minute tomorrow morning? I long for a quiet word – it's pretty urgent.'

Celia had agreed. Con would drive to Thanet Steps at ten. That the 'word' would be about Anthony, Celia had had no doubt. What was she to say? How much should she say?

Yet another nasty experience occurred during Saturday night and early on Sunday morning. The sleeping arrangements for the Sturridges at 42 Thanet Steps were complex, since five of them had to fit into the spare room and the attic. Celia divided them up for safety's sake. Alan would share the attic with Charlotte on a lilo and Paul on a futon, and Anthony would have one of the twin beds in the spare room and Celia the other. The children were in bed and asleep before the grown-ups had supper. Celia did not stay downstairs for long, she pleaded a headache and retired. She had locked the door of the spare bedroom in case Anthony took it into his head to stray, and she did not want Alan or her parents to notice. When she unlocked the door she was relieved to see that Anthony had not moved and was still sleeping. But at about midnight he woke and started to moan. She hushed him, took him to the lavatory, rocked him in her arms, kissed and shook him, forced him to swallow a baby-painkiller, all in vain. She told Alan she was coping and sent him back to bed. When her father investigated, she put Anthony's distress signals down to toothache or tummyache and said he would stop soon. At last he did stop, he stopped and slept, he and his mother slept together in her bed.

At breakfast on Sunday she apologised to everyone. Chrissy as usual misunderstood: she said Anthony was trying to talk and should be seeing a speech therapist. She said it was cruel that he was not talking – a dig at Celia.

Con rang her doorbell at ten. Alan said he would see to the children and Celia joined Con in Con's car – the weather was not good enough for a walk.

Con's concern was unexpected.

'You're looking so peaky,' she said. 'You worried me at the party yesterday. Can I help?'

Celia laughed and said: 'I thought you'd be worried by Anthony.'

'For hitting Jake? Jake's okay – children are beasts – every mother's hoping they'll grow out of being beastly. Are you worried about Anthony?'

'A bit. Yes, I am. I'm very worried.'

'Is it the talking?'

'That's the least of it.'

'What's worse?'

'It's too long a story.'

'You mustn't make yourself ill. Are you eating properly?'

'Quite right, Con – I'll try to make myself healthy and capable.'

'Would you like to come and stay with me? You could bring Anthony – we'd look after him together.'

'Thank you, Con. You're a brick. But I can't – I can't do much except worry at present – and I'll have to go in now – Alan's with Anthony and Alan knows nothing yet. Listen, listen – I want to postpone our discussion, do you mind?'

'Be strong, darling Celia!'

'I will!'

The Sturridges were leaving Thanet Steps after lunch. Bernard and Celia managed to exchange only a few meaningful sentences before the goodbyes.

He said to her: 'You're worried, aren't you?'

'Yes,' she replied.

'Can you tell me?'

'In time.'

'If there's anything I can ever do, ask me, won't you?'

'Yes.'

'I could give you a little money, if it's needed.'

'Thanks, Dad. But nothing's certain yet.'

'No – it never is – that's the good news,' he remarked, smiling.

Peace reigned at The Homestead for a few days. But Anthony's symptoms had emerged so suddenly and in such quick succession that Celia lived fearfully, straining not to let Alan or the other children see anything was wrong. On the Saturday following the family's weekend at Broadstairs, in the afternoon, Alan took Charlotte and Paul out for a trundle in their chariot – Anthony had shown no interest and been left behind. Celia washed and ironed, she was either in the kitchen or the garden or the extension where the washing-machine stood, and Anthony was in the sitting-room. For the third or fourth time she interrupted her work to look in on him. She saw a dreadful sight.

The cage of Timmy the canary was on the floor. Its stand had fallen or been pulled over, seed was scattered everywhere. And Anthony was on the floor too, he was holding Timmy, and Timmy had lost feathers, Timmy was obviously dead. He looked at his mother innocently and without expression, and held out the corpse of Timmy – he had a spot or two of blood on his hands. She controlled a scream, swallowed the great lump in her throat, took the poor limp yellow bird, rushed with it into the lavatory and pulled the chain. She fetched a cloth and returned to the sitting-room and wiped Anthony's hands clean, then dragged him into the dining-room and shut him in. She carried the cage and its stand out of the room and into the extension, where she hid it under towels. She then lugged the hoover into the sitting-room and hoovered up all the seed, sand, pieces of cuttlefish. She had just finished removing evidence of the accident or whatever it was by the time Alan returned with the other children.

She met them at the door, smiling and asking if they had had a lovely expedition. When Charlotte had been unbuckled and Paul had been lifted out of the chariot, as Charlotte ran into the kitchen and while she held Paul in her arms, she said to Alan: 'Timmy's dead – I'm going to tell Charlotte he flew away – please back me up, Alan, I'll explain later.'

'Is it bad, my dear? You look as if something bad's happened.'

'Yes, it has, but it'll keep. I promise to tell you later.'

'Very well. Where's Anthony?'

'In the dining-room.'

'Has he been playing up again?'

'No, dearest, no – later!'

In due course, at tea, Charlotte took the news that Timmy had joined the other free-flying birds in her stride. She was not a sentimental child; and Paul was too young to notice Timmy's disappearace, and Anthony's feelings were unknown.

As it happened, between tea and dinner Alan had an appointment to meet a man who was trying to organise a North London cricket team. Celia, as soon as he had gone, seized her chance to ring Dot.

Dot answered the telephone, which was a stroke of unexpected luck. Dot's baby, Adam, preoccupied her, just as Celia had been pre-occupied by motherhood. The friends had not spoken or seen each other for months.

Celia began without preamble: 'I need moral support. Can we all meet soon? But I need your support now – so sorry – I've only got a minute or two…'

'Heavens! What's happened?'

'Advise me, Dot! I've got to tell Alan something awful – it's about my Anthony – question is – do I tell him the whole truth or lie and break it to him gently?'

'Is Anthony in trouble?'

'Yes – I'll explain everything when we meet – tell me in principle what I should do!'

'Is Alan strong enough to bear bad news?'

'He survived May's death – but this is different – I don't know – that's why I'm asking you.'

'Honesty's the best policy.'

'Thank you, Dot. I can't go on.'

'Are you surviving?'

'Just about.'

The Sturridge children were in bed by the time Alan returned. He went upstairs to say good night to them, reported to Celia in the kitchen that they were all asleep, agreed to sit down at the kitchen table and pour two glasses of red wine. She sat and was ready to talk.

'Anthony's ill,' she began.

'Is he? How ill? Are you sure?'

'Yes, I'm sure, but he may have extra illnesses that I've never heard of.'

'What is it, my dear?'

'Autism – he's autistic – it's a modern disease – he would have been called not right in the head or something worse not long ago.'

'But he's only slow to start speaking, isn't he?'

'No, Alan. Mysterious things have been happening. I didn't warn you because I hoped my suspicions were incorrect. He was probably born peculiar – I don't know – but there were no signs when he was a baby – at least none that I recognised. Since he's grown, recently, it's been one thing after another – and they're not mysteries any more. We'll have to take him to see doctors, I mean specialists.'

'Is the disease curable?'

'We'll find that out.'

'Do you mean it may not be curable?'

'I think, I'm afraid, not completely.'

'Oh no!'

'We'll take care of him.'

'How... Why...'

'We'll have the other two.'

'Wait, wait! Aren't you crossing bridges before we've come to them? What are these signs? I haven't seen them. What are the things you're talking about?'

'He has no words. His eyes are beautiful, but if you look in them you can see they're blank. He never laughs. His moans aren't attempts at communication, they're anguish. I saw a boy like Anthony at St Hugh's.'

'Is that all?'

'No. It's enough, but no. I believe he climbed into Paul's cot and gave him that blue bruise-mark on his neck – we used to do it to one another at school – you suck the blood into the skin – but Anthony might have injured Paul badly – he must have wanted to.'

'That's hypothetical.'

'He was very bad at Thanet Steps. He lost himself in Wild Wood to torture me.'

'He's not as bad as that!'

'He hit Jake to hurt him. His moaning in the night was somehow to punish us – punish me – for removing him from our Homestead.'

'You're imagining it, Celia.'

'I'm afraid he killed Timmy.'

'Timmy? Why, what happened?'

Celia described the scene of the crime in the sitting-room before she had cleaned up the evidence.

Alan said: 'But Timmy might have died when the stand fell over and his cage hit the floor.'

'No – the latch on the door of the cage is supposed to be child-proof – the latch was somehow opened – Anthony's fingers are bruised – he must have reached in to catch the bird because his arm's scratched – and Timmy was partly plucked.'

'What did you do with Timmy?'

'I flushed him down the lav.'

'Celia...'

'Yes, dearest – are you all right? What's wrong with you? Alan!'

Alan had turned green in colour and seemed on the point of fainting. She stood up and cradled his head in her arms. He hiccupped and yawned and seemed to be slightly better. He apologised and cleared his throat.

'It's very feeble of me,' he said, 'but for a moment I felt I simply couldn't go through another tragedy.'

'I do understand.'

'Of course we'll see it through together.'

'You must carry on with your life. We must keep cheerful. And I won't cross bridges prematurely. Now, let's have something to eat. I've got sausages and bubble and squeak in the oven.'

'I'm not very hungry.'

'No, nor am I – but you can drink more wine, and we'll try to nourish ourselves.'

'You're so brave,' he said.

'Appearances can be deceptive,' she replied.

They did drink a little more and did eat a bit. Then Celia spoke of bed-time. When Alan protested that it was early, she confessed that she was anxious in case Anthony woke and did damage. He made a gloomy grimace and wished that he instead of Anthony was to sleep with her in the double bed. She had to explain that she felt obliged to keep a close watch on Anthony.

'I can't let him be with the other children in the nursery – without supervision, that is. I'll devise a method soon of keeping Anthony under control. These awful discoveries – I've only looked at the opposite of the bright side today. I'm sorry to have distressed you, darling Alan. I'm sorry to have borne you an unhealthy son.'

'Not your fault, my dear, more likely mine – and as you say we must count our blessings.'

They agreed. They hugged and patted each other. She went upstairs – Anthony was still asleep – and in time she closed the bedroom door, drew aside the curtains and sat on the stool by her dressing table. Tears flooded into her eyes and cascaded on to her nightdress. She bent over from the waist, sobbing as quietly as she could and retching. The moonlight shone through the windows on her doubled-up figure shaking with surges of sorrow.

Three weeks elapsed before Celia, Dot and Con could meet again.

Meanwhile life at The Homestead continued naturally on the surface and far from naturally underneath. Alan still worked for Carter Johnssen in Stanmore. Celia kept house and looked after their children. Charlotte attended kindergarten, Paul learnt how to stand up. Anthony moaned and slapped his thighs. There was laughter, although Anthony did not join in. There were games for everyone except Anthony. The married couple did not share the marital bed – Anthony slept for parts of each night in Alan's place, and tired his mother by waking her with his moans and restlessness. He was averse to being comforted or cuddled. He was impervious to risk and apparently to pain: one day he jumped down about twenty stairs and fell like a sack of coal on the tiled floor of the hall, evidently spraining an ankle and hurting a shoulder, but he did not cry – and Celia did not dare to take him to a doctor for relatively minor injuries. Anthony was the ghost at the family feast. Anthony was the family's curse. Alan was depressed by him, but tried not to show it. Alan did not discuss Anthony with Celia. She was as steady as her unhappiness and bewilderment allowed her to be. She was obsessed – she and Anthony at least had obsessions in common. Hers was more straightforward than his: it boiled down to the question, what are we to do?

She read the entries about autism in medical dictionaries and encyclopaedias at the local library. The disease was only recognised in the 1940s. It was thought to be neurobiological – not a difficult diagnosis to arrive at. Treatment was experimental, which, in layman's language, meant practically non-existent.

She had friends at St Hugh's who might have had experience of her problem, but she was loath to spread the news of Anthony's illness, and was not ready to seek assistance from doctors.

Between the death of Timmy and her appointment to meet Dot and Con in Dot's new and larger flat in Pimlico, she could be glad that Anthony had done nothing positively bad.

They met at five in the afternoon. Alan was in charge at The Homestead, Ian Thornton was taking Jessie and Jake to tea with the Shelbys, Con's parents. Dot, first of all, had to introduce Adam to her friends – he was a handsome baby as babies go. Next she showed them round her flat. Jason Tyler was absent. He had rented a croft in the wilds of Scotland, where he hoped he would be able to create his masterpiece. He could not write at home – too distracting. Apparently he did better on a cruise ship or in the cafés of Paris. But his hypochondria brought him back to Dot. She was humorous on the subject of his hypochondria and produced a fake menu card – she would produce it and ask him to choose either TB, VD or MS.

None of these preliminaries took very long. Celia was urged to spill the beans, and she repeated the story she had told Alan.

After they had been amazed, incredulous, appalled, compassionate and sorry, they wanted to know how he had taken it.

'I thought he was flaking out, he looked like fainting, but he recovered, and he's been supportive ever since.'

'Is that faint praise?' Dot queried.

'Alan's a fine man, I respect and love him, I love him best, but he was put through the wringer by the death of his first wife, he's said to me that he isn't sure he can stand another tragedy, and terrible illnesses are beyond his limits. He's being heroic, as I knew he would be and know he will be. The fact remains that he's one of my worries. I don't want to wreck his life. I don't want it to be wrecked. That's why I didn't tell him everything. There's something he might find altogether unacceptable.'

What was that?

Celia hedged: 'Anthony's so perfect in other ways. I'm not boasting when I say he's beautiful – I'm not a boaster. He has a look that makes my heart ache. It's difficult to think he's not perfect through and through, believe me! Alan could be terribly upset by the last chapter of the story to date.'

What did she mean?

'Anthony's got a malicious streak.'

'Haven't we all?' Con queried.

'I'm afraid he wanted to hurt Paul and your Jake, and cause me suffering in Wild Wood. I think he murdered Timmy deliberately.'

'Are you exaggerating by any chance?' Dot inquired.

Celia shook her head.

'Would I?' she said. 'I'd do the opposite if I could. We three have no secrets – and I'm sick of secrets. My worst worry is that Anthony's homicidal.'

The others would not have it, but Celia carried on.

'We're privileged, we've been healthy. I've nursed ill people, but I've been well, which was my protective barrier. Lack of privilege isn't poverty – being poor is often just an option. Lack of privilege applies to my Anthony and all those people who are very ill through no fault of their own. I'm finding myself in an underworld of horrors and terror. Honestly, Dot, I'm not exaggerating. Anthony will probably grow up, even to manhood. I've reason to expect him to treat someone as he treated Timmy – sooner or later he'll do it maliciously but without appreciating the criminal or sinful issues, with heartless innocence, with nothing in his eyes. What then? Which of us is most at risk? I'm guarding Charlotte and Paul, but that's another complication. Oh dear, I'm sorry.'

She cried.

The other two sympathised.

Con asked: 'Could I help you to look after him?'

Celia laughed through her tears.

'Darling Con, thank you, but no, I'm not going to drag you and yours into my battle.'

Dot asked: 'I could help with money, and I know my parents would, too. You'll have to have extra help with your family, all of them, not only Anthony.'

'Thank you, you're both so kind. Forgive me for whining, but it's such a relief to tell the unvarnished truth, it's such a treat. My list of worries in the order of their priorities is: Anthony, Charlotte and Paul, Alan, nursing and coping, my own health, assistance, money, housing – because if we have to isolate Anthony and employ somebody we'll need a bigger house. I haven't dared to calculate costs as yet, and I'm sure the same applies to Alan, whose profession is money – he's clinging to the hope of better news also for financial reasons. Dot, I will remember your offer, and I'm grateful beyond words, but I want to try to mind my business. The picture will become clearer, it must, it couldn't be more muddled. What next, or what comes first, what shall I go home and get on with?'

Dot and Con unified their answers: take Anthony to a specialist in his disease, steer clear of your local medical practice, seek advice at St Hugh's, do not involve Alan yet.

Yes, she said, she would do as she was told.

Then she said: 'I'm not giving Alan and Charlotte and Paul their dues. Anthony steals the love that should be theirs by rights. I can't let him do it. I always hated the prodigal son. Forget my grizzling, please – Anthony isn't prodigal – and I shouldn't feel as I sometimes do.'

It was natural, the others assured her, and inevitable.

At this point Adam Tyler weighed in with a yell, Dot attended to him, Celia insisted on talking of things other than herself, and soon she had to leave to travel back to her no longer homely Homestead.

The next day she obtained an urgent appointment with Mr Gibson, her gynaecologist and friend. She saw him one evening at St Hugh's, after Alan had returned from work and could be responsible for the children, and Mr Gibson had finished operating.

With apologies, she explained the urgency of her case. He was sorry to hear about Anthony, and warned her that doctors who specialised in autism were thin on the ground since they knew little, had access to no scientific knowledge, and were not sure how to ameliorate the effects of the condition. However, Dr Edward Speed ran a clinic and a residential home for autistic patients in a house not far from Highgate. It was near Muswell Hill, called Orchard Grange. Mr Gibson was willing to bypass the Sturridges' general practitioner for the sake of privacy and refer Anthony to Dr Speed.

A week later a letter for Celia from Dr Speed's office arrived, suggesting a ten o'clock appointment for Anthony on a certain day, and that Mrs Sturridge might wish to plan to see work in progress at Orchard Grange afterwards – lunch would be available.

She brought Alan up to date with these developments.

'Could you manage the other children for most of that day?' she asked him. 'I don't know if I'll want to stay on, but I'd like to be able to if it was interesting.'

'Is this Orchard Grange reputable?' he replied.

'I imagine so – of course it is – Mr Gibson wouldn't have recommended a quack organisation – he said complimentary things about Dr Speed and that his clinic was a rarity.'

'I hope he won't put Anthony through a sequence of unpleasant tests.'

'So do I. There aren't any tests on offer, as I understand it. But

Dr Speed must know a bit more than we do, and might prescribe useful pills.'

'Does Anthony need pills?'

'Oh Alan! He needs something we haven't given and can't give him. Please don't be stuffy about Dr Speed.'

'I'm sorry, my dear. I realise how anxious you are, as I am. I've asked around in the office and been told that autism's a tragic disease. But I've also heard of gradual recoveries, if not cures. Anthony was a pest at Broadstairs, I grant, but since then he hasn't been bad. I feel that in a happy family atmosphere he might well improve, even grow into a fairly fit man – I'm sure the other children would teach him to talk in time. I merely beg you not to be hasty. I'm a great believer in letting sleeping dogs lie.'

'Alan, I'm so sorry to disillusion you, but I must, I love you too much to let you get a worse shock than the one I'm going to give you. Our home isn't happy any more, and we're under pressure to improve matters before we're all utterly miserable for years. I've no bright ideas, can't say how to bring about improvements, can only say I'm trying. Please support me! Now – what is certain is that Dr Speed's going to charge me money for Anthony's appointment – Mr Gibson didn't, but Dr Speed will and will live up to his name, I expect. Can I pay with our "household" cheque book?'

'Ah, yes – yes, my dear. I hope he'll earn his money.'

This conversation added to Celia's burden of anxiety. Alan had made a valid and disturbing point: Anthony had been good as well as silent for weeks. Had she exaggerated? Was she mistaken?

After breakfast on the morning of the appointment, Celia and Alan united to explain to Charlotte and Paul that Anthony had to see a doctor. They had agreed to make light of it. They announced the object of the exercise when Alan was carrying Anthony to the car. Charlotte was not particularly interested, and Paul showed no sign of comprehension.

Celia drove off with Anthony behind her. She talked to him cheerfully for part of the journey, although doubts gnawed at her. She resolved on no account to become too involved with Dr Speed. Anthony was loose in the back of the car – seat belts were not yet invented – but the rear doors and the front passenger door were secured by childproof locks. He clambered up and wedged a foot into the space between the front seats, apparently to see more through the windscreen. Then he reached forward and covered Celia's left eye with his hand. She told him not to, spoke sharply, and raised her hand from the steering wheel in order to remove his. She explained that he must not do a thing like that, and why. He did it again, the sequence was repeated, and yet again. She had to stop the car and give him a lecture.

They drove on. Anthony discovered a better way of driving them into the ditch. He stood on the edge of the back seat, leant on the back of the driver's seat, and, bridging across, put his arms round his mother's neck and covered one of her eyes with one of his hands. She shouted at him and released his hand. He clasped her neck with it and covered the other eye with his other hand. She was frightened, was driving all over the road and being honked at, and again stopped the car, this time in a dangerous position. She extracted Anthony from the back and plonked him on the front passenger seat, lectured him, and drove on, all in a rush.

His next act was to stand up on the seat, defying orders to sit still, and scramble on to her extended arms holding the steering wheel, and twist his body so that he was able to cover both her eyes with both his hands. She screamed at him and had to brake hard, swerved, expected to crash or be crashed into, but was lucky, was able to throw him off, pull into the side of the road, and turn off the engine.

Anthony sat beside her, showing no trace of emotion. He was so young, small, sweet − how could he be so dangerous? Celia's mind was changed. She leant across and hugged him.

'Oh my darling boy,' she crooned. 'I'm sorry for you and me and everything, sorry, sorry!' She pleaded with him to allow her to drive. She stifled an awful idea that he had taken steps to avoid being seen by Dr Speed. She started the car in a determined manner and drove very slowly forwards close to the verge.

They reached Orchard Grange late. She was exhausted and emotionally drained. She registered only that the house was large and welcoming. She held Anthony's hand firmly and led him in, and a pleasant person, middle-aged, not in uniform, one of several people bustling about in the hallway, said that her lateness was not a hanging matter and escorted her without delay along a passage and into a consulting room, where a youngish brisk dark-haired man stepped out from behind his desk, smiling, and extending his arms towards Anthony.

Dr Speed took Anthony into his arms, spoke his name − 'Hullo, Anthony, good morning, Anthony' − put him down and let him go.

[249]

He then shook hands with Celia, indicated a chair for her to sit on, and returned to the chair behind his desk.

He was friendly, encouraging, friendly enough for her to tell him why she was late and the awfulness of it. He listened, he did not take notes. There were toys on the floor – Anthony was fingering some wooden bricks. The room was empty otherwise – the desk was not a big daunting one.

Dr Speed prompted her. She talked as she had not meant to. A tray of coffee for two and orange juice for Anthony was brought in by another pleasant lady. The atmosphere was soothing. The doctor seemed to have time to burn. Celia ended by entrusting him with her whole story. Anthony was intermittently restless; but Dr Speed pointed out that there was nothing for him to damage, the window was discreetly barred and the door opened and closed by secret means. Celia shivered, but appreciated the common sense of the arrangements.

When she had finished talking, he spoke.

'About myself,' he said, 'I'm a qualified doctor and psychiatrist, married with two children, a boy and a girl, and we live down the road. I practised medicine, then psychiatry for several years, and began to specialise in autism. An aunt of mine died and left me Orchard Grange, a farm with a hundred acres of land. Instead of selling it, I set up a home for autistic boys suffering from the more extreme manifestations of autism – autistic girls are rare, and I couldn't cope with mixing the sexes. The aims of the Orchard, as we call it, are twofold: to study the condition of autism, and to provide the boys with a safe haven and protect their families. At present, as constituted, we look after our patients through the years they would have been educated at schools. We don't charge fees, we survive – to date – thanks to government grants and charity. We have room for twenty-five patients up to the age of puberty, and ten patients between puberty and the age of twenty: the two classes of patients are separated. We have four female professional nurses here, two male nurses, domestic staff, and many volunteers, mostly the parents of the boys. I hope you aren't in a hurry today – spend the day and see for yourself how the Orchard works! It exists, I regret to say, for children whose symptoms are not mild. There would be room for Anthony if you thought we could help him and your family. Do you feel up to investigating further?'

Celia said yes. She was escorted back to the hallway – Dr Speed carried Anthony, who did not protest, and introduced them to a middle-aged lady in civilian clothes, Maggie by name. Dr Speed took his leave, saying he would see Mrs Sturridge later. Maggie unlocked a door into a large room, like a drawing room, which had linoleum on the floor and only coloured pouffes scattered round. Anthony threw himself on to the pouffes. Spring sunlight and pained cries entered through fully open french windows, and Anthony ran out into a garden area that was part park and part playground. Celia followed, but he was already involved with the children and their attendants in the vicinity of a climbing frame.

Celia stayed at Orchard Grange until six o'clock that evening. She kept an eye on Anthony, who appeared to be more at home in these surroundings than he was at The Homestead. She received non-stop information that made her head spin, and struggled to believe her eyes and ears. She talked further with Dr Speed, who, eventually, assured her that Anthony would not be noticeably sad and might even be content to spend the night in one of his dormitories with nursing staff in attendance.

She drove back to Highgate alone. At least she felt safer than when she was driving in the opposite direction. She was in time to give Charlotte and Paul their supper and put them to bed. She hugged and kissed them good night fervently.

She had hugged Alan too. Now, when they were on their own, she tried to give a fuller description of Orchard Grange and explain why she had decided to let Anthony stay there. She told him that money had not been mentioned. She said the place was inspiring.

'It may do Anthony good,' Alan conceded.

'That's my hope,' she replied.

'He'll be all the more pleased to come home,' Alan said.

She did not answer.

'Won't he?' he asked.

'He may not come home,' she replied.

PART THREE

CELIA HAD regrets for saying what she had said, but no regrets for thinking it.

Alan was deeply shocked by her idea, and, it emerged, her plan to banish Anthony from The Homestead and consign him to Orchard Grange. The boy, the child had not been given a fair chance to recover from his illness – autistic children could sometimes recover, Alan had checked. That she, who was so maternal, and principled, was willing to chuck Anthony out, on to a sort of dungheap, because he was troublesome, passed his understanding. Moreover, she seemed to have arrived at this decision, which condemned her son to be a homeless outcast, in a matter of a few hours. What would become of him? What had become of her? He was afraid that something had affected her judgment. He felt he would never be able to agree to such a cruel solution of the problem of Anthony – and how were they to be sure that he would always be a problem?

Celia apologised for shocking him. She had only stated her opinion of what was in the best interests of Anthony, the other children, Alan himself, and her health, which would not be equal to the strain of caring for a chronically sick child as well as being a wife, housewife and responsible for Charlotte and Paul. The alternatives to boarding Anthony at Orchard Grange were horrid – perhaps Alan had not visualised the future with Anthony at home. She would need help. She would need at least a special sort of living-in-nanny who would help with the nights – Anthony could not be left to his own devices at night. They would need accommodation for Anthony separate from the other children and secure, and would therefore have to move into a bigger house. The more expenses were considered the more they mounted up, as Alan must realise.

The difficulties did not stop there, in fact they had scarcely begun. Alan did not know, had not as yet had to register, that their Anthony had a mischievous, spiteful, destructive and even malevolent streak – no, she was not saying so in order to justify Orchard Grange, she loved Anthony very much, she hated having to say his character was flawed, the whole business of reorganising his life and the family's life was breaking her heart. But facts were facts, and she had experience of them. Unhappily, she had had to accept that Anthony had intended to hurt his brother Paul, herself in Wild Wood, Jake Sturridge and Timmy the canary. She could agree that he had not been awkward for the weeks after Timmy's death, but today, in the car, driving him to Orchard Grange, he had done his damnedest to kill the two of them.

She described their battle in the car. When Alan suggested that Anthony was playing a game and had no conception of the dangers, Celia replied that such an assumption was too great a risk for her to run.

'You see, if he had administered the French burn to the other side of Paul's neck, he could have ended up like Dracula, sucking blood from Paul's jugular. I didn't oust you from our bed exclusively because I was worried about Anthony's health, it was because I was worried about the health of Charlotte and Paul if they were sleeping in a bedroom with Anthony. I thought Anthony – unsupervised – would injure or even somehow kill one of them.'

Alan protested. Celia allowed that she was taking an extreme hypothetical view, but said mothers had to expect and be ready for the worst even as they hoped for the best. She reverted to the episodes in the car: they had frightened her more than anything else, frightened and shattered her. On the way to Orchard Grange she had wondered if she was doing the right thing. After it she did not consider the possibility of turning back.

Time passed without their noticing as they talked. But Alan looked increasingly pale and tired, and Celia was overcome by the exhaustion of her alarming, topsy-turvy, and above all long day. They agreed that they were done in. He pulled her to her feet from the sofa where they had sat, and they held hands on the staircase up to the bedroom floor. They peeped in at their children, who slept safely, and retired to their double bed, where Alan fell asleep and Celia at length lost herself and all her tormenting pros and cons.

In the morning Celia was pleased that Charlotte did not mention Anthony – Paul was oblivious. After breakfast, while the children made mud pies in the garden, she again tackled the subject which, she sensed, Alan would have liked to postpone or avoid.

'I'm going to see Anthony this afternoon,' she began.

'Ah,' he commented.

'It's Saturday – I'll go this afternoon – will you take care of Charlotte and Paul?'

'Yes, my dear.'

'Can you bear more explanations?'

'Of course – please do explain.'

'Orchard Grange is extraordinary. It's a lovely house, and a lovely place, believe it or not. I wouldn't have left Anthony there if I hadn't thought so. Dr Edward Speed owns it and runs it, he's a philanthropist and a scientist. The patients are all boys, young ones and, in a separate stream, some older ones up to the age of eighteen or so. I only saw the young boys, about twenty-five of them. They were in a big garden enclosed by a wire fence – Anthony ran about with them. The Orchard – that's what they call it – is a registered charity. The parents of boys are expected to contribute to the expenses – we'd have to pay our bit, but parents also help out by volunteering to do a lot of the donkey work. The government gives grants, but the Orchard costs more than what's granted. There are professional nurses and other staff. Sorry if I'm sounding businesslike, but I don't want to be irresponsible.'

'Thank you for clarifying some of the issues. What might our monetary contribution amount to?'

'I'll find out. I understand that it wouldn't be beyond our means. I've taken another decision – don't flinch, darling – my decisions are taken partly to spare you – I'll return to work at St Hugh's. I could do two days of nursing and put Charlotte and Paul in the St Hugh's nursery. That would pay most of our contribution to the Orchard, and ... and I might be allowed to leave Charlotte and Paul in the nursery on the other two days I spend with Anthony. Alan, I can't lose touch with him, and my work with the other mothers would complete our contribution. I've already agreed to do four hours this afternoon. I'll be away from two until sixish. Will you manage?'

'Four hours!'

'Darling Alan, be realistic! Fathers take turns to at the Orchard. I know you'd be ready to do your whack, but I won't let you – one broken heart is quite enough in our family. I'm a nurse, you're a solicitor – I'm used to grisly sights, you only come up against them on paper. Am I asking too much of you?'

'No – no – but I wonder if your project will be successful.'

'I trust Dr Speed. You could meet him, I'm sure you'd give him the benefit of the doubt. The nurses in charge of Anthony are trained to deal with autism, they're therapists and teachers. If he shows any improvement, and might be able to live in a normal environment, we can bring him home. Until then, until that perfect day, because of Dr Speed, we could give Charlotte and Paul an upbringing without shadows and fears. We might learn to be happy again if we thought Anthony was not more unhappy than he was born to be for some unknown reason. Anyway, we've got to try to forgive God for moving in such a mysterious way.'

'Indeed! Will you promise me something?'

'In theory, yes.'

'Will you promise to bring Anthony back today if there's any sign that he's homesick?'

'I will, I do.'

They left it at that.

She duly returned to The Homestead at six-fifteen on the Saturday afternoon. She had to feed Charlotte and Paul and then put them to bed. At last she and Alan were alone together.

'How was he?' Alan asked.

'Not bad, okay, very good really.'

'What do you mean?'

'He took no notice of me. He was vaguely interested in the other children, and he stood and moaned. He didn't acknowledge my existence.'

She cried then, at last, again, and could not be comforted; but she had proved to her own satisfaction that she had not done wrong, and Alan was more inclined to agree.

The next day, Sunday, also in the morning, she continued her conversation with Alan. She was looking in at Orchard Grange in the afternoon, just to make sure that Anthony was no worse.

She said: 'Whatever happens, whether or not my plan can be worked out, it's going to be misunderstood and controversial. If people know, they'll criticise. I'll be called an unnatural mother, selfish, cruel, et cetera, and you'll be blamed for not having brought me to my senses or for colluding with me. Provided we mind our own business, they might mind theirs. Who needs to know, and what's our story?'

'Oh Celia,' he burst out, 'I can hardly bear to think of the untruthfulness, of you telling lies when you're such a truthful person

— I love you for your honesty — and for that matter I hate to think of myself spinning a web of deceit!'

'No — well — I'm sorry — but our children come first, Charlotte and Paul, also Anthony's good name supposing he were to get better. I'm taking action for all our sakes, because we're trying to salvage the family. We can't spoil everything by broadcasting our news from the rooftops. Our plight isn't gossip. Let's put our heads together, Alan — we must be prepared.'

She persuaded him, she compelled him. She would tell her father, not her mother; Dot and Con — the three of them always swapped secrets and secrets were safe with them; and their GP, Dr Railton. He would not tell his mother, whose heart was weak and health failing, nor his sister Maureen, who was stuck in Stockholm and seldom communicated, but he would tell the relevant partner at Carter Johnssen, Andrew Brook, and a younger partner, Michael Ayres. Andrew could draw up new wills. He and Michael could be the Sturridges' executors, have power of attorney if required, and, most importantly, could be named as guardians of the children, Anthony in particular.

Otherwise, in answer to inquisitive questions about Anthony, Celia thought she and Alan could reply that he suffered from an allergic syndrome and had to spend time in hospitals both in England and abroad. She was dead against publicising the word 'autism' — ignorant people would think it meant 'mad'. She was aware that some of the other mothers at Orchard Grange could have wagging tongues, but surnames were not used, the identity of patients was protected, and discretion amounting to secrecy seemed to be a rule observed by everyone concerned.

Alan went along with all her suggestions.

A month elapsed.

The plan was working smoothly enough for Celia to take Charlotte and Paul to stay the night with her parents at Thanet Steps, leaving Alan in The Homestead in case he should be needed by Anthony — he was willing to act in such an emergency, although he had never been to Orchard Grange.

They arrived at supper-time, after Celia had done her day's work at St Hugh's.

'Where's Anthony?' Chrissy Farr immediately asked. 'Where's my beautiful Anthony?'

Celia said she would explain later, and took her time to put Charlotte and Paul to bed.

Downstairs, Chrissy broached the subject without delay.

'Where is he? What's the mystery?'

'He's not well, Mother. I'm afraid you won't be seeing him for a time. He's allergic to everything and has to be in a completely sterile atmosphere.'

'Good gracious, when did this come to light?'

'In the last few months – he's in a sort of sanatorium – he's all right – I see him regularly – and we hope for better things.'

Bernard Farr spoke up.

'I'm so sorry, my dear. What an awful discovery for you and Alan as well as for the boy, although he's probably too young to be much affected.'

'True, Dad – and the situation's just about under control. To tell the truth,' Celia gulped and continued, 'it's a sore spot, and I'd be grateful if we could avoid it while I'm here. Besides, Charlotte and Paul don't know what's happened to their brother, and Alan and I are determined not to involve them in his trouble.'

'I understand that,' Bernard answered. 'And we'll respect your wishes, won't we, Chrissy?'

Chrissy had to have a last word: 'Can't I just send my grandson a get-well card?'

'Send it to me, Mother,' Celia replied with a touch of asperity.

They had dinner, and retired to bed early. The next day in the morning, Celia engineered a short walk alone with her father, leaving the two children in the care of their grandmother.

'Dad,' she began as soon as they were out of the house, 'I've told you fibs. Anthony's not what I said he was last night, he's autistic, and I've put him in an institution to give the other children a chance to be happy while they're young.'

He stopped walking, looked at her hard and sadly, kissed her and said: 'You're the bravest of the brave, my dear.'

She begged him not to praise her – 'I'll break down if you're kind' – told him a potted version of the whole story – and said: 'You're almost the only person who knows it, Dad. This afternoon I'm meeting Con and Dot, and I'll tell all because they'd tell me if they were in my kind of boat. That's how private I want to keep it, not on account of shame or embarrassment, but for the sake of Charlotte and Paul, also Alan, who has to be spared as much as possible.'

'I promise never to betray your trust, Celia, and not to drop the slightest of hints to your mother.'

They laughed. She hugged him gratefully, and he voiced a query by means of the two words: 'Brass tacks?'

She had them at her fingertips, the amount of money Alan could provide for Orchard Grange, her earnings at St Hugh's, the fact that Alan's mother was old and ill and costing a lot of money, and the outside chance that Anthony might become fit to rejoin his family.

How had Celia managed to get away to Thanet Steps, Bernard asked, and why on a weekday instead of at a weekend?

'The weekends are for us to be with Charlotte and Paul,' she replied, 'and play together and try to have a laugh. Today is actually one of Anthony's days, but I've asked another mother to keep an eye on him.'

'I'm sorry we've robbed Anthony of your company.'

'Oh Dad! I can't have explained very well. You know roughly what autism is — everyone who knows only seems to know roughly — but the reality is different from knowing like that. Anthony won't notice that I'm not at Orchard Grange as usual, at least he'll show no sign of noticing. I can't guarantee that he ever recognises me, although I'd love to be persuaded that he does. When I go to Orchard Grange to be with him, he spends most of our time running away from me.'

'I see now,' Bernard commented.

A little later, turning back to number 42, he asked: 'How is Alan reacting to your predicament?'

'Gallantly, stoically, as you'd expect, but it's really more than his temperament and constitution could or should have to bear. I left your telephone number with Orchard Grange in case I had to be contacted.'

'Poor Alan! Has he been to see Anthony?'

'Oh no.'

'Could I come one day?'

'I don't want to answer your question, darling Dad.'

In the afternoon of that day Celia escaped to the house in the country where Con Thornton lived. Bernard and Chrissy were to watch over Charlotte and Paul's siesta. Dot had been summoned to the friends' meeting and had motored down with Adam Tyler. The three of them were soon drinking tea at Con's kitchen table. They admired Adam, who had bawled himself to sleep. Con's two were visiting friends. Her husband Ian was looking at land and Dot's Jason had apparently found he could write best in an East End pub, and was relatively calm and contented.

'Where are your children?' Dot and Con asked Celia almost in unison.

At Thanet Steps, Celia replied; two were at Thanet Steps, she corrected herself; the third was not there – and that was why she had to talk to her friends.

She continued. Her answer was again Anthony's story, which she cut as short as she could. Dot and Con were saddened, and to some extent mystified.

Con had never heard of autism, and Dot had only a hazy idea of the illness.

Celia said it was new, its cause not fully understood, that it attacked children around the age of two and a half years, male children as a rule, and was incurable, although a small percentage of victims could throw it off.

Symptoms? Anthony was speechless, very withdrawn, introverted, had odd obsessive mannerisms, and could be unhappy. Celia then described the episodes that had driven her to take radical action, ending with his dangerous game in her car. She also mentioned his relentless moaning.

Celia said she had realised before she entered the Orchard that she could not cope with Anthony at home, that is at The Homestead as it was and as they had been living in it. The alternatives that were threatening her were either an impossible expenditure of money, or to let Anthony go into the sort of institution where people like him were controlled by sedation.

Dr Speed was an answer to her prayers. Orchard Grange was nothing like a tragic prison. Anthony in its garden, with the other ill boys, was neither worse nor better than he had been elsewhere. Truly, the main difference for him was that he had nurses and ten or twenty knowledgeable mothers looking after him all the time.

'I left him there overnight, and decided in the car driving home that the Orchard was the solution to our problems, his, Alan's, mine, and insured Charlotte and Paul's upbringing. It's not a life sentence for Anthony – we'll bring him home if or when we can. Sorry to talk so much, I had to tell you, I need support – God knows where we go from here!'

The support was forthcoming.

Then Dot asked: 'How old is Anthony now?'

'Getting on for four.'

'A toddler?'

'Yes, except that he never toddled clumsily – he was born quick on his feet.'

'He's very young.'

'How could I wait? I want the others not to remember him too clearly.'

'How old are the others? Remind me.'

'Charlotte's only eleven months older than Anthony, and she's young for her age. She's hardly mentioned him – I think he might have frightened her. Paul's one and a bit.'

Con had a question.

'What's Dr Speed like?'

'He's committed to his Orchards – there's another one opening in Scotland. His ideal is to relieve families of the strain of dealing with an autistic child, and at the same time to remove the child from a competitive environment, from comparisons with normal children, and provide professional care.'

'I meant, what's he like as a man?'

'He's in his forties, and extremely kind.'

'Is he attractive?'

All three of them laughed.

'He's admirable,' Celia replied, 'and I like him, but not in that way.'

They laughed again.

'Are you on Christian name terms?' Con persisted.

'Oh yes – he's Edward to everybody connected with the Orchard.'

Dot reverted to relevant matters.

'What happened when you took Anthony to meet Dr Speed? Was Anthony examined and tested?'

'Not at all – it was surprising – Anthony just meandered round the consulting room, and Edward talked to me for ten minutes. Of course he could diagnose Anthony's illness at a glance – anybody who knew anything could – and there are no worthwhile tests. Anthony and I spent that day at the Orchard, while Edward studied him. When I had to leave, he talked to me again. He said he could offer us a safe haven, no more. I asked if Anthony could stay overnight, and he said yes. The next day Anthony was okay, and I virtually accepted Edward's offer on a permanent basis.'

'Before Alan was in the picture?'

'Alan wouldn't have decided and I felt I had to.'

'You persuaded him?'

'Sort of.'

'Does he agree with you now?'

'With reservations – he's so kind-hearted, and he counts the cost.'

Con said: 'The money must be another problem.'

'We're managing. The Orchard office people make allowances if I'm late with my contribution.'

Dot and Con summed up by praising her realism, resourcefulness, maternal devotion, and heroic readiness to slave away to pay the bills.

Celia was reduced to tears.

They embraced her, and pressed her to have a fresh cup of tea.

'You don't understand,' she sobbed.

What did they not understand?

'My responsibility...'

She could not finish the sentence. But she dried her eyes, and was eventually able to resume.

'Everything bad that Anthony seemed to do could have been misinterpreted, and I'm haunted by imagining that Timmy died a natural death and Anthony only covered my eyes in the car for a joke. What have I done to him? He may just be retarded, and would have learned to speak if I had given him time. He might not have more than a touch of autism. By locking him in with all those really autistic children I'm afraid I've violated his soul and robbed him of his chance to cure himself. I've been fearfully bossy, yet I can't retract my bossiness. I feel more like a villain than a heroine, and there's no help for it or for me, and there it is.'

Alan Sturridge was badly hurt by the whole autism issue. He was a decent man, a law-abiding citizen, self-respecting and modestly proud of his record of filial duty, of having honoured his parents, done well at school, served in the army, qualified as a solicitor, held down a demanding job, paid his taxes and even gone to church occasionally. He could not adjust to having been singled out for two of the harsher sentences of fate. To have had to nurse his first wife into a premature grave seemed to have exhausted his powers of resistance to the visitation of cruel illness on his elder son. He did not grumble, he was stoical on the surface, but he felt he was being victimised, unfairly ill-used, and powerless.

Celia sensed it. She had married Alan knowing that he was less forceful than she was; but he was encouraged by her forcefulness and sexual warmth. He was man enough for her after the selfish masculinity of Owen Pennant. There had been trust in their marriage. They agreed to buy The Homestead, and he had not objected to her three pregnancies. Their happiness was not shadowy – they had both been unhappy and were grateful to have emerged into the sunlight. The misdeeds of Anthony, as she saw them and described them to Alan, were a fork in their road.

They travelled in gradually diverging directions. He could not quite go along with her dramatic interpretations of Anthony's behaviour. He resisted Celia's suspicions, he preferred to sweep them into a legally unproven void. He shied away from autism. He realised Anthony was not well, or normal, or like his other children, but took a wait-and-see line. And he countered her despair with his tranquillising truisms, which were apt to reduce her to grinding her teeth.

Sex is the tell-tale of matrimony. They were tired by parenthood, they were preoccupied by Anthony, and for a few months they exclusively slept in their double bed. But as soon as Celia faced the fact that Alan was not entirely of her mind, not convinced that Anthony was so ill as she believed he was, she sought reassurance in the feminine manner. He could not always provide it.

Orchard Grange exacerbated the marital problem. Alan did his bit with money, and more than his bit when his mother died and ceased to be a drain on his resources; but on one occasion he described the Orchard as a 'waste-bin for children', and on another he called Edward Speed a 'conman'. The new tension between the Sturridges had an inflammatory effect on her libido and the effect of cold water on his. She was frustrated, he was embarrassed; and both were annoyed that their personal relationship interfered with their feelings for their poor little boy.

Later, perhaps a year after Anthony's admission to the Orchard, Celia missed a monthly period and jumped to the conclusion that she was in for the change of life. It fanned the flames of desire, and he could not put them out. Their happiness was turning into sadness. They could operate separately and efficiently, but no longer as the team they once were.

Round about this time Alan's conscience-stricken regret for not having visited Anthony provoked Celia to call his bluff: she might not have done so if they had still been close.

'Come with me,' she said one morning, on a weekday on which he was working at home rather than in the office, as she was setting off for the Orchard.

It was a challenge – she had previously discouraged him from seeing Anthony.

He climbed into the car, he was not a coward. They dropped Charlotte and Paul at school and nursery, and drove on more or less in silence. Before they reached their destination she issued warnings.

They found Anthony in the garden with the other children. He took no notice of their summons, ignored his father, shrugged off physical contact and ran away, moaning. Alan looked ten years older than his fifty-two years – he had not believed it would be so bad as she had warned. She took him to the staff room, fetched him a mug of tea, urged him to go for a drive or have a long walk in the countryside, and left him in order to attend to her duties.

They met as arranged at one o'clock for a sandwich lunch and more tea, and at four she escorted Alan to Edward Speed's consulting room. She introduced the two men nervously – she had fixed the appointment, and knew Alan had questions to ask.

She was glad he did not want to probe into Anthony's lavatorial difficulties; but his first proper question was worse for her in that it related to her reasons for committing Anthony to an institution.

He wished to know if his son had recently shown any violent tendencies.

Edward Speed said no, nothing to worry about, and explained that children of his type were more inclined to hurt themselves than anyone else, since they were unrestrained by risk.

Alan's second and last question referred to Celia's bad experience in the car: had Anthony deliberately tried to blind her and cause an accident?

'I can't say, autistic motivation is still a closed book,' Edward replied.

'Could he have known it was dangerous to cover the eyes of a driver?'

'Possibly.'

'Could he have been playing?'

'Autistic children don't exactly play. Those in my care could be vicious if they were not watched over. They're so pent up within themselves that they need to use any safety-valve, vocal or physical. Whether or not they foresee consequences is another matter.'

Alan left it at that. He had made the point that Anthony might not be precociously homicidal: which consoled him, put Celia in the wrong and made her angry with herself for having allowed him anywhere near the Orchard. In the car going home he aired his opinion that Anthony was obviously deep in his disease for the time being.

He also said: 'I do see that in his present state he would exert an oppressive influence at home,' and she had to bite her lip in order not to retort, 'Stale buns!'

Alan did not return to the Orchard. He slightly compensated for not suggesting another visit by heaping praises on Celia's conscientiousness and energy – the slightness was the measure of his overlooking her love of Anthony.

In another year her father stayed at The Homestead. He drove over one evening and left about twelve hours later – it was like a secret assignation. He had not seen his grandchildren for ages – Celia had not dared to expose them to an inevitable interrogation by her mother. Now Chrissy was in hospital, she had had her gall-bladder removed and was doing well enough drowsily after the operation for Bernard to sneak away. He and Celia commiserated with each other over their lies; but he insisted that they were lying in a good cause, not to make mischief.

In the morning after his arrival he had breakfast with Charlotte and Paul and walked them along to school. Then, as promised, Celia and he drove in separate cars to the Orchard – he would drive on to Thanet Steps. He was upset by meeting, or rather seeing in the distance, Anthony. He was sorry for all the 'lost' boys, and especially for Anthony's mother, his daughter. Yet his afterthoughts were almost as distressing as Alan's had been. He said that if he should ever be a widower, alone, he would like to remove Anthony from the Orchard and care for him at Thanet Steps. The implications were that he thought he could do better for Anthony than Celia was doing. She could not let it pass. Although she knew her father meant well, she was roused to defend herself. When did he expect to become a widower, in five years or ten? At that age, in his late eighties or nineties, was he going to be capable of day and night nursing and restraint of an incontinent and escapist strong mentally handicapped young man? Would he be able to provide a large secure open space for Anthony to run about in, and physiotherapy, and a number of extra staff, and essential locks on doors and unbendable bars on windows? Bernard backtracked, Celia forgave him. It was nonetheless sad. They said goodbye sadly.

The idea that she had solved most of her problems at the Orchard was proving illusory. The Orchard was like a beneficial drug with damaging side effects. It was good for Anthony, but had driven wedges between herself and Alan, herself and her father, and was forcing her to lie and lie again to her two healthy children.

Unfortunately for her, the healthiest children catch infections. Charlotte caught mumps and measles, and gave them to Paul, who also caught chickenpox. Celia had to book an appointment with Dr Ward, a new GP who had taken over from Dr Railton. The consequential questions worried her more than the well-being of Charlotte and Paul: had Dr Railton told Dr Ward about Anthony, would Anthony figure in her other children's notes, would Dr Ward be discreet, could she ask him if she was likely to pass on the infection to her son at the Orchard? In the end she did not mention Anthony, nor did Dr Ward, and she stayed at home until she was out of quarantine.

One more regrettable setback for Celia was Con Thornton's tiff with her 'old fool', meaning Ian, her husband, who took the view that Anthony Sturridge should not be 'buried alive' with a 'whole lot of loonies'. Con intended to reassure Celia by revealing her fierce disagreement with Ian, but her good intention had the effect it is famous for, and Celia wished she had not been told, had not been the bone of contention between the Thorntons, and that her son and his fate could not be spoken of in such brutal terms.

An exception to the rule of disasters breeding disasters was a letter she received from Sandy Wellingham. Celia had allowed Dot to spill the beans to her mother – she trusted both of them. And Sandy showed her appreciation of the situation by enclosing her letter et cetera in an envelope in which Dot was sending Celia a frivolous women's magazine.

The letter ran: 'You are a hundred per cent right to have handed over Anthony to the professionals. Your other children owe you a huge debt, whether or not they ever repay it. Take no notice of the sentimentalists and do-gooders, who will want to do you down. You deserve a second medal for valour. Hope money will help. No thanks, please. Love from your fan.' Clipped to the writing paper were two hundred pounds in five pound notes. Celia rang Dot from the Orchard to say how grateful she was, to send a message to her mother, and to say the mag was a bright spot in a cloudy sky.

Time passed, the hands of the clock raced round while she was looking the other way. Now years added inches to the stature of all three children – or perhaps the inches were borrowed from their father, who had started to shrink and stoop. Celia forgot her looks, had no use for make-up, and asked one of the nurses at St Hugh's to chop off her overgrown hair. She cooked obsessively in order to keep those at home as well as possible, and to take titbits to the Orchard for Anthony. She forced herself to eat for her strength's sake. She was learning to laugh at nothing, since she had not much to laugh at anywhere.

In the fifth and sixth years of Anthony's exile she was aware of a strange transposition. She could not stop it happening, and, stranger still, was not sure that she wanted to. Charlotte was getting on for ten, Paul was eight, and they were extremely close. They went to school together, likewise did their homework, played together, had understandings and giggly jokes, and were or seemed to Celia to be a somewhat exclusive pair. Of course they had latchkeys – their mother was out four days a week and their father for five. She sometimes did night duty at St Hugh's, she was the tiredest of housewives, no wonder the two children had discovered how to amuse themselves. Celia could reflect that she was succeeding in her aim to give them the childhood they deserved. She nonetheless had to fight against feeling shut out by their closeness. She also hoped she was wrong in sometimes thinking Charlotte and Paul were short of friends, and that, because she was always afraid of being found out, the atmosphere at The Homestead was never carefree.

To drop the children at school on weekdays and drive on was not a chore, although varying degrees of exhaustion lay ahead. She had horrors to attend to at St Hugh's, but also patients who came in unwell and left much better. She had friends there, anyway colleagues, she knew what she was doing and was good at it. Moreover, her deeper emotions were not stirred.

Her days at the Orchard were horrific, too. But she was a trained nurse and prepared for what she saw and often had to do. And to be with Anthony, now, when she was used to him, satisfied her, whether or not it had any satisfactory meaning for him. Their days were peculiarly empty. He resisted affectionate gestures, his hand held, his back patted, let alone an embrace or a kiss. She spent hours following him round the garden or sitting with another mother or two on a pouffe in a bare assembly room, watching him slapping his thighs or standing motionless, frowning and moaning. Toys were scarce – toys could be put to perilous uses. Music played gently, high class music which helped to counter the patients' unrhythmical symptoms. Sometimes Anthony greeted her by means of an individualistic signal, possibly by averting his head or by leading her on a chase, and on rare occasions she had a more or less intuitive sense that he was sorry to see her go. Those signals of his, if they were signals, were payment in full by her standards for all the hours she devoted to his cause.

Above all, at the Orchard she was out of range of outsiders' opinions of her way with Anthony. There were no lies or secrets to contend with. It was a sad place, but the so-called normal personnel somehow made it happy – and Celia gradually had to admit that she was happier amongst all the sadness than she was at home – she admitted it with qualifications.

That admission was feminine: it was connected with an adult of the opposite sex as well as a boy. Her romantic interest in Edward Speed crept up on her. Perhaps it was traceable to Con Thornton's girlish interrogation when she told her friends about the Orchard; but she did not recognise it for many more years. He had been her hero from the start; but romance was the last of the thousand things on her mind. It was only when she had grown almost accustomed to Anthony, to anxiety about the other members of her family, money and the shortage thereof, and her daily, weekly, yearly expenditure of effort – only then did she spare a thought for Edward's head of greying hair, the charming set of his teeth when he smiled, his well-fleshed warm hands, and his tireless vigour.

He became the agency of her covert sighs. She looked forward to seeing him, even if from a distance, to exchanging a word or two; but was aware of the remnants of shyness and was apt to blush when they did speak to each other. Sometimes, against her will, for fear of disappointment, she avoided him. Her emotion was a Dead Sea fruit; how could it be otherwise since she had unbreakable ties, and he was married to Mary Speed and they had children. Besides, in reality, she was no Eve, not tempted by 'the fruit that was forbidden', and was sure that he with his idealism, also his fulfilled countenance, felt the same. It was all a dream for her, escapism, something to balance her unsparing practicality.

They discussed Anthony, but not often, and there was not much to be said. Edward ran the Orchard and studied autism: those were his business and his priorities. If his patients were ill, they were attended by the resident nurses or by the local practice of GPs: no opportunity for Celia in such situations. Ill patients were kept at the Orchard: an autistic boy or youth in a general hospital presented unacceptable difficulties and expense. Anyway, Edward rose above ordinary health problems in order to have time for paperwork and fund raising, and to be able to stroll through his premises, distributing smiles like blessings.

So far, Anthony's constitution had not failed. He had grown out of his infantile beauty, his teeth had come in crooked but nobody wanted to try to put them in a plate, and his expression was tortured and not easy on the eye; but his physique was slim and tense, and he had not lost his power of attraction. Occasionally, in those long spells of watching over him, Celia half-wished that he might need medical attention of a sort that would bring her and Edward together. She visualised them in a semi-dark room at the San, leaning over Anthony in the bed, whispering caring sentiments in close proximity. Another wish, an inevitable wish that had dogged her from the day she discovered Anthony was not like other boys, she now censored absolutely, for a reason supportive of maternal considerations, because if Anthony were to die she would be separated for ever from Edward Speed.

She was interested in his wife. The Speeds lived in a house about a mile from the Orchard. Celia once drove past it: there was a high hedge in front, also a pig-wire fence, and closed metal gates – she could just see an upstairs bay window under a gable – the bedroom Edward shared with Mary – and a couple of smaller windows. She knew that Mary never came near her husband's place of work, and had heard on the grapevine that she was scared of autistic boys: which must have accounted for the defences of her home. She imagined Mary would be quite pretty, and long-suffering on account of Edward's absenteeism from the family hearth, a limited person with little understanding of or sympathy with his work, probably a good cook because he looked well-fed, able to satisfy all his physical appetites, but not half good enough, judged by Celia's criteria.

She thought about her face as she had not done for ages. She even tried to look at herself in the bathroom. At a certain point she reverted to the application of a spot of lipstick. She was probably Edward's age, a few years older than Mary, but much more experienced. Her exertions had kept her figure trim, and miraculously her miseries had not transferred themselves to her complexion – her skin was tautened, not relaxed into creases and folds, and her eyes were lamplike.

She was not a flirt. She was not unfaithful to Alan. Her feelings for Edward resembled a secret garden, where she could roam without doing harm to anyone or anyone being harmed. For years they had behaved with perfect propriety, as two professionals engaged in making the life of a handicapped boy as tolerable as they could. Had he smiled at her with a mite more benevolence than he smiled at others, and had a spark of sexual electricity flashed between them? Those questions were not promises. They were simply a man and a woman, and propinquity told the rest of the story.

Anthony was now approaching puberty. At twelve years old his voice had begun to break. Celia knew that the step into manhood was fraught with dangers for autistic boys. In the winter he caught a cold. He had stayed out in the rain one evening, the Orchard people had been unable to persuade him to come in, and Celia was not there – it was a weekend. He was removed from his dormitory and kept in a room by himself in the San. He was clearly not happy, he was unaccustomed to and disliked the isolation. Celia kept him company when she could, but she too hated to be locked in, and disliked the aid-call or panic-button that she was required to hang round her neck.

Anthony got worse rather than better. His padding round his bedroom for the majority of every twenty-four hours, like an animal in the zoo, cannot have done him good. He developed a cough, a temperature, bronchitis, pneumonia – he now lay in bed, wheezing instead of moaning, staring at the ceiling, alternatively sweating and shivering. He had never been anywhere near so ill. Considering his autistic capabilities, he was quiet and co-operative.

Celia obtained permission from Alan and St Hugh's to spend extra time at the Orchard. She sat by Anthony's bed, speaking to him, wiping his hot forehead with a cool damp towel, spreading another blanket over him, trying to persuade him to drink water or soup, attending to his needs. The crisis lasted for the inside of a week. She stayed late for five evenings, when the nurses were busy getting the other boys to bed. Edward Speed joined her for ten minutes or so on each of them.

He arrived at about nine o'clock. They talked a little through the masks they both had to wear, and communicated more by their eyes. She thanked him, and he said he was always worried by pneumonia – Celia knew what he meant. She expressed concern for his wife and children, and he shook his head. He took Anthony's pulse, and when Celia asked if her son was going to die he shrugged his shoulders. She wished they could talk properly, at length, and not in the room in which Anthony might be giving up the ghost – she knew Edward through and through, but only metaphorically. He patted her on the shoulder, she touched and squeezed his warm hand. One night he said that Anthony would have been a splendid person but for the autism, and she loved Edward for that.

The disease burned itself out, perhaps literally with a sky-high temperature. Celia waited until Edward came in on the sixth evening, so that she could show him Anthony asleep, breathing more easily, not flushed, not restive. Edward led her out of the room by the hand and along the passages to his consulting room. Most of the ground floor of the building was empty at this hour. They had taken off their masks but were not yet speaking to each other. He shut the door of his room behind them, and opened his arms for Celia to almost fall into, saying how glad he was, how relieved she must be, what a splendid vigil she had maintained, and that she had to take some credit for the outcome.

Their embrace began as a hug, but extended into closer contact. Then she kissed his cheek, murmuring grateful words, and he kissed hers. And then it was lips, and a proper kiss, a kiss with passion thrown in by both parties, and hungry movements of heads and daring caresses of hands.

Celia broke away.

She said: 'No – I can't – sorry – it was lovely!'

He said: 'Nor can I – but thank you.'

They laughed into each other's faces.

She said she would have to go home, and he said so would he.

He said: 'I think the world of you – honestly – my kiss was a tribute.'

'I could say the same,' she replied.

'You're an amazing person, I've never known anyone like you, so pretty, and strong at the same time. I haven't seen you cry while Anthony's been ill, or before that, not once – most mothers of the boys shed tears constantly.'

'I haven't shed mine yet,' she replied, laughing. 'I've had better things to do. Look – this evening was exceptional – we mustn't muddle ourselves up.'

'I agree. It's a bargain. I'm sorry if I've muddled you.'

'You haven't. You've given me a great boost. I know there are clouds on my horizon, and I'll be needing your encouragement. But I promise not to be a nuisance.'

'You wouldn't ever be that. You're the odd woman out. Good night, sleep well.'

They kissed chastely, and he accompanied her to the exit.

The clouds Celia knew about referred to pneumonia for pubescent autistic males and its fatal implications.

She had learned the facts of life for boys like Anthony from books and the professional staff at the Orchard, and mainly from the women in her situation. Now she recognised their last common denominator, the probable early loss of their afflicted ones.

The sky was not altogether blacked out by the clouds. For Anthony, death could surely be described by the platitude, a merciful release. What had adult life to offer him? No freedom, no sex, no work, no hope − in short, no fun. It was hard to believe that he would be better off alive than dead, that was the truth; and she was too sensible not to acknowledge it.

As for the rest, his death would be a panacea. The money problem would be solved. Celia would not be exhausted. Alan would no longer be impaled on the horns of his dilemma. Charlotte and Paul would not be bombs timed to explode as soon as they began to meddle with the mystery of Anthony, the Sturridges could mingle with the Farrs at Broadstairs, the children's grandparents could ask questions till the cows came home, and sociability and hospitality would again be on the cards. Celia could probably afford to stop work altogether and become a proper mother and a good wife to her husband in his retirement. Hard-boiled analysis could claim in its post mortem that Anthony had been a cuckoo in the nest.

Yet the words on the relevant maternal lips that quivered were negative − no, not quite so soon, mercy, pax! The heart is not an analyst. Celia rebelled against her son's sentence that might be carried out on any day. Anthony did not deserve to die. Did she deserve to lose him? She appealed against the verdict of nature. She pleaded for an extension of his life. She would miss him unbearably. She was desperate to be with him as much as possible or more than was possible.

He had pulled through pneumonia. She had helped him, she was proud of him, and, on the way home after Edward Speed and she had kissed and come to terms, she was in a celebratory mood. Marvellous things had happened. But a few miles from the Orchard she had to pull into a lay-by on the road because she was blinded by tears. It was a storm of sorrow, and subsided quickly. She remembered that she had to smile and laugh for Anthony's sake, and Alan's, Charlotte's, Paul's, and the world's.

She felt incapable, but overcame the feeling. She was able to tell Alan that Anthony was well again – and Alan was glad. She slept then. That night and the next, and if she ever sat down in the daytime, she recouped the sleep she had missed. She drank coffee before she drove anywhere, and more coffee to keep herself awake at St Hugh's and back at the Orchard. Her sleep was not just the opposite of wakefulness; she knew in her bones it was also a kind of preparation. Her constitution was gathering its forces.

She and Alan agreed to play down her absenteeism from The Homestead so as not to worry Charlotte and Paul and arouse curiosity. There had been an epidemic, a lot of illness, and their mother had provided extra nursing, they said. They specified nothing, who was ill and where, and the children swallowed the story without demur. Charlotte was more than ever preoccupied by crushes on girls and teachers at school, and Paul was mad on cricket and moved from Point A to Point B only aided by the motions of a fast bowler.

Another agreement with Alan smoothed her path. He indicated that he was aware of Anthony's critical illness, and raised no objections to her stealing off to the Orchard even during weekends.

She was able to see Anthony in the San as she could not have seen him if he had been in a dormitory. She would arrive with the dawn, and leave him in the night. She could let herself into his room. She could talk to him – he was at last her captive audience – or watch over him as he lay in bed, drowsing or asleep.

She told him everything. Although he never answered, he was her confessor and her judge. She held nothing back. Quietly, in order not to be overheard, even in a whisper, she entertained him like Scheherazade: the difference was that Scheherazade told her tales to postpone her execution, whereas Celia told hers to postpone his. She reminisced about Thanet Steps, her childhood, her parents, Dot and Con. She described Owen Pennant, and the frenzy of their love-making at Biarritz, and becoming hardly more than his hostess and housekeeper at home, and then the horror of his adultery with that squalid woman, engaged in an act so extremely intimate, and painful for a wife to witness.

She spoke of her clean cuts, first by leaving Owen, then by leaving

Anthony himself at the Orchard. She had acted spontaneously, abruptly, but was still convinced she was right. Owen proved he was a traitor, and one betrayal was enough to convince her that she could never again depend on him: what sort of a marriage would theirs have been, what would it have been worth? People criticised her inflexibility: to keep your word, and expect the man to whom you had given yourself body and soul to keep his, was better than compromise, a marriage based on immorality or feebleness or money – she would rather be inflexible than degraded.

She was sorry, she said, that she had torn Anthony away from his sister and brother and that he had not seen his father since he was tiny. But she had acted unselfishly, for his sake, because the world would not understand him or treat him with respect, and to protect three other people, his father, Charlotte and Paul. Although she was a nurse, she could not have nursed him all day and all night: she had to be a wife, a mother of the other two, and keep house. She lacked the strength, it would have been impossible, whatever ignorance and the happy-go-lucky bleeding-heart brigade might think and say.

She asked for absolution. She asked to be forgiven.

He was more amenable when he was not well. Sometimes he let her hold his hand or lay her cool hand on his hot forehead. She could not kiss him with her mask on, but she pressed their foreheads together. His puberty had been delayed by the pneumonia, his voice remained half-broken, and he had not reached manhood in other ways. He was a boy still. Admittedly the beauty of his childhood had been replaced by features that betrayed his illness, frown-lines between his eyebrows, a sharp nose, tightly compressed lips, and always the anxious expression; but his eyes were bigger and bluer than they used to be, and they seemed to Celia to have acquired a beautiful new expressiveness. She thought he spoke through his eyes. She wondered if they had begun to communicate through their eyes.

The days passed, the months, a year, then another half-year – borrowed time. Celia did not tire of being with Anthony, tiring as it was in the ordinary sense. The kaleidoscope had been moved. Her love had altered. It was connected no more with guilt or uncertainty. It was unworldly, it was other-worldly, if such a word or state existed, she would say to herself. And the object of it was not the same as he had been, when she suspected him of malice. There was no more violence in him.

His health improved, and Celia was happy in a way when he was considered fit to rejoin the other boys. Her preference always was for him to be as normal and free as possible. Soon he would be back in the San, which, again in a way, was sad. Yet she loved to have him to herself, and his eyes seemed to register passivity and even perhaps acceptance of his lot. He surely listened to her autobiographical confidences, and she thought he at least appreciated the sound of her voice. She felt so close to him in their sessions in the San that she could not help imagining or hoping that he had comparable feelings. Could it be that he had served his time in the purgatory of disease? Could he be emerging from his chrysalis? She tried not to be both hopeful and fearful simultaneously – it was too contradictory – yet the emotions were combined since, if he rose from his form of being dead, he would not have time to realise his full potential.

Her love confused her. She was mothering her child, although he was nearly grown up. She was preoccupied by an affair of the heart, although it was unilateral as well as platonic. She was taking from Alan, Charlotte and Paul to give to one who had almost nothing to give her. Nevertheless, now and increasingly, her confusion was superseded by admiration of Anthony. He might only be a fragment of a person, but he had qualities – an individuality, an integrity – which she fancied had been acquired by some heroic psychological effort. He seemed wise to her, and in his presence, against all odds, she experienced peace.

She tried to explain it all to Edward Speed, who had been supporting her through the ups and downs of Anthony's vicissitudes.

He commented: 'I've heard similar stories before ... I wonder who is developing, the autistic child or the parent? ... Scepticism is all very well, but has its limits ... Anything can happen, and usually does ... Don't lose your nerve!'

Another assistant at the Orchard, Alyson, who was friendly with Celia, reinforced Edward's views. She inquired one day, while they watched the boys, Anthony included, mooning about in the garden: 'Do you ever think they're clever, cleverer than they look, cleverer than we are?'

Anthony's health had taken another turn for the better, which had side effects at The Homestead. Celia spent more time there. Alan was relieved. Charlotte and Paul received an extra share of attention.

She would praise Alan when they were alone in their bedroom at night. She said she had been too busy and tired to run through the whole list of her reasons to love him. She did so, bit by bit, while he tried not to go to sleep. He had caused her no tremors over unknown girls at the office. He had not beaten her. He had made bread for the family without fail. He had followed her into the maze of care of Anthony, and reassured her hundreds of times that they were not lost. He had been a gentleman and a brick. His only serious fault was that he kept on growing older.

Celia's fault-finding was lightly said, yet was no joke. Alan was old beyond his years, slower in all respects, more pedantic and harder of hearing. He added to her catalogue of dreads. Without him, to put it bluntly, her life would fall apart. She would have less time for Anthony. She would have no buffer between herself and Charlotte and Paul, who might begin to ask the unanswerable questions. And she would be doing all the practical things he had done.

As she ceased to concentrate on nothing but Anthony, who was apparently on a road to relative recovery, she was reminded that life was short not only for Alan. Her father rang to say that her mother was in hospital. Chrissy had been taken ill without warning, and had been diagnosed with rampant cancer. She was seventy-eight. She was aware of her condition. She was philosophical, not suffering intolerable symptoms, and was coming home on the next day. She would like to see her daughter and her grandchildren. Bernard was sorry not to have contacted Celia before, but everything had happened in a rush. He himself was okay, and could manage Chrissy with help from a District Nurse.

Celia rearranged everything, prepared a picnic lunch, and drove Charlotte and Paul to Thanet Steps. They spent half an hour with Chrissy between twelve-thirty and one o'clock. Chrissy was in the double bed in the Farrs' bedroom, and the curtains were partly drawn to shut out light. She looked bad, but behaved well, uttered no complaints, smiled with grace and courage, even laughed with the children. Bernard shared Celia's picnic lunch in the dining-room, and kept the children with him when Celia went upstairs afterwards.

Her mother spoke gratefully of the past. She praised her husband and even said that her daughter had become a fine woman. Her one reference to Anthony was not critical of his treatment.

She said: 'Poor boy! You've done the best you could for him, and borne your cross.'

Celia thanked her for saying so.

'We've had our differences,' Chrissy continued. 'Forgive me!'

'Of course, Mother. Forgive me, please!'

'Yes, yes. Perhaps I'll meet Anthony in heaven.'

'Perhaps, yes.'

'If I get there.'

They both laughed, and Celia kissed her goodbye in the dim room. She had a short talk with her father. He was sleeping in the spare room. He expected Chrissy to be admitted to a local hospice in a few days time. Her wishes were being observed. He said he was coping and that he would be all right. She promised to come to Broadstairs if she possibly could whenever needed.

Six days later she received the news that Chrissy had died at home. Bernard said she had gone to sleep and not woken − it had been more like a petal dropping than a death. They discussed the funeral. She would return to stay at Broadstairs for the night before her mother was cremated, and stay for that night too; also prepare tea for the mourners. She would notify Dot Tyler and Con Thornton. She would do all her travelling by train, so that Alan could drive the children down for the service and get them back to Highgate.

After it was nearly all over, and Alan and most of the guests had departed, Celia had a word with her father, then led Dot and Con upstairs, to her own room in the attic where they had conferred in the old days. The same posters were pinned on the walls, and some of her baby books remained in the bookshelf. Dot lay on the bed, Con sat on the ottoman in front of the window, and Celia on her little chair by the child's desk.

They spoke of death. They spoke of parents and husbands. Dot asked after Anthony Sturridge tentatively. Celia told the truth, and was sympathised with.

Then Dot said: 'Would it be better for all concerned...?'

'Probably.'

'What does that mean?'

'I've grown so fond of him. I'd miss him so much.'

'Is it horrid for you to talk of what happens after Anthony?'

'No − I don't mind − with you. I have nightmares about what happens then.'

'You'll be freed.'

'Will I? Alan's not very strong. You saw today how much older he looks.'

'But you'll have more time to be with Charlotte and Paul.'

'Yes. I hardly know them. We'll have to try to make friends from scratch.'

Con asked: 'Have you had any happiness with Alan?'

'Oh yes – not ecstatic – ecstatic's a caution, I was ecstatic with Owen – but Alan is slippers by the fire, and sweet and kind – everything in our garden was lovely until I realised Anthony was ill.'

'No happiness after that?'

'Rays of sunshine through storm clouds.'

'Can I ask you a really personal question?'

'You always do, we always do – and we're still friends.'

'Have you looked to right or left?'

'I was kissed and kissed back once – it was magical.'

Dot said: 'Only once? That's tragic – terrific kisses are the beginning of a story in real life – they're only the end in novels.'

'Neither of us could do adultery.'

Con said: 'You're awfully moral, Celia.'

'Is that a confession? Have you strayed?'

'A bit. No, more than a bit.'

'Happily?'

'It's been good for me and for dear old Ian. Actually, Ian's responsible without meaning to be. He bought a second sofa, and I fell for the delivery man. He's young. He's exciting. We meet in the back of his van – there's always a sofa there. He makes up for the change of life.'

'What's he called?' Dot asked.

'Vince.'

'You're not going to bolt, are you?'

'Good gracious, no! Ian is quite old, literally, and he'd be high and dry without me. I wouldn't have looked twice at Vince if it hadn't been for the change – I wanted to have some fun before it was curtains – I married too young – and there was no one else for donkey's years. Have you started changing?'

'I started and stopped, or seemed to – I haven't noticed symptoms lately,' Celia replied.

'What about you, Dot?' Con asked.

'I'm getting flushes. My naughty husband's gone to write a book in Alaska, he said he was distracted by having to open and close windows for me. Adultery might freshen up my marriage – isn't that what's said about it? But I can't be bothered. I've got my Adam, and I'm lucky to be rich – money can answer a lot of prayers, as Celia's discovered.'

'Largely thanks to you and your mother, Dot.'

Con said: 'I wish I'd helped you more,' and Celia replied: 'You would have if you could.'

They began to worry that they should go downstairs to be with Bernard Farr.

They talked about health briefly, Dot's migraines, Con's weight problem, and Celia's exertions.

Dot remarked: 'I've found out what would have happened to your Anthony if you'd kept him at home. You would have had to drug him, use tranquillisers and stronger stuff. My Adam's taught me how exhausting straightforward children are. You'd have been a dead duck if Anthony was let loose on you, and so would your other children, I guess. I hope Charlotte and Paul never forget that.'

Con asked: 'Was your kisser that doctor at the Orchard?'

Celia replied: 'You've got a memory like an elephant,' and Con commented ruefully: 'Not just my memory's like an elephant.'

Anthony Sturridge died five days after his Farr grandmother's funeral.

Late in the evening of the day of Chrissy's funeral, when Celia and her father were preparing to go upstairs and to bed, Alan rang through with the news that Anthony was in the San at the Orchard with a chest infection. Dr Speed had telephoned the information. Alan realised that Celia would want to know without delay, but was sorry to have to tell her in such already sad circumstances.

She was paralysed by the shock for a few minutes. She knew he would die – Edward would not have rung if the infection had not been terminal. That she had expected it seemed not to ameliorate the shock.

She had answered the telephone in the hall of 42 Thanet Steps. She rejoined her father in the sitting-room. He looked at her face, stood up, supported her to a chair.

'Is it Anthony?' he asked.

She nodded.

'Is he dead?'

'Soon will be,' she replied.

He made her a cup of tea with lots of sugar. He brought it to her and begged her to drink.

'How can I get to the Orchard?' she asked.

It was a tricky question. There might be a midnight train from

Broadstairs to London; but she would arrive upsettingly late at The Homestead, and the same applied to her arrival in the small hours at the Orchard – and how would Alan and the children cope without the family car? She did not want to ring Alan again – he would probably say he would drive to Broadstairs at once and transport her to the Orchard – leaving Charlotte and Paul alone. Her father offered to drive her there, but he was eighty-seven, or lend her his car, but how was he to recover it?

She agreed to wait for a morning train. The argument that convinced was that Anthony might be worried if she turned up at his bedside in the middle of the night.

She did her best to hide her frantic feelings from her father, told him she would try to snatch some sleep, reminded him that he was worn out and had better do the same. She would leave the house early without disturbing him.

He revealed that her face after she had spoken on the telephone had given him the jim-jams. He was okay now. They must both rest, at least. He would be longing for a bulletin about Anthony.

She left the house at five a.m. on the next day. She arrived at the Orchard at eleven, having been delayed by having to mend a tear in Paul's school blazer and to ring and explain why she was unable to work at St Hugh's. She spent hours in Anthony's familiar room in the San on that day and the four others.

He was paler, thinner, sleepier. He breathed with difficulty, yet could sleep through his feeble coughing. Sometimes an attempt was made to give him oxygen, but he hated the mask and nobody wanted to hold it forcibly over his nose and mouth. Apparently he was not in pain. Edward told Celia that he and Dr Timms, the GP in charge, had agreed that morphia as required, but no antibiotics, should be administered. She could not object.

She talked to Anthony, as before. She felt that they were communicating somehow. She was sorry to have been absent while her mother was buried. She said that his grandfather had stood up to the obsequies stoically. She discussed her parents' marriage with him, and Bernard's love of Chrissy, who drove most people demented. She told him that his father, Alan, had worked tremendously hard to pay for the Orchard – he had been too busy on Anthony's account to come and see him. She declared her love repeatedly, and now she removed her mask to kiss his forehead. He did not respond, or did he? She could not be sure if the flicker of his eyelids, or the slight opening of his eyes, or a jerk of his hand, meant anything much. It no longer mattered, she reflected.

In the evening of the fifth day she was convinced that her good night was also goodbye. She had to leave him – she had promised Alan and the others that she would be coming home.

Edward rang her there. The details of Anthony's passing were not too harrowing. Celia cried in Alan's arms, and his feelings of failure, because he had not braved the Orchard, came to a painful crux. They told each other that they had done their best for their ill boy, but neither of them seemed to believe that their best was adequate. Grief notwithstanding, Celia suspected that Alan was as nervous as she was of having to provide explanations for Charlotte and Paul.

Charlotte was at the awkward age in girls, between sixteen and seventeen. She was clever at school, but had not won the lottery for looks. She had inherited Alan's long face and high-bridged nose, and Celia's straight blonde hair that looked like rats' tails when Charlotte allowed it to reach her shoulders. She had an odd figure, big breasts and a fat waist. And she was greedy and overweight. Her lack of physical attraction was not balanced by the charm of an angelic character.

Paul at fourteen was giggly and cuddly, and better looking than his sister – his face was a masculine reworking of his mother's, and he had some of her agility; he was also bad at his books and had an unexpected obstinate streak.

Charlotte was close to Alan, they had always been close, and she was now critical of, rude to, and grumpy with Celia. Paul on the other hand was not very nice to Alan, he treated him like a relic of the past, while his manner towards his mother was indulgent and patronising.

Alan took it on himself to tell the children at breakfast.

'We've had sad news,' he said. 'Your brother has been very ill, and last night he lost his battle.'

Charlotte asked in a brutal way: 'Is Anthony dead?'

Paul asked with his mouth full of cereal: 'What's happened?'

Celia explained: 'Poor Anthony died.'

'Our Anthony?'

'Yes, Paul.'

'Well – I don't remember him.'

Charlotte chipped in sharply: 'Well, I do.'

Alan said: 'I'm afraid we'll have another funeral in a few days. Your mother and I feel there's no need for you to be there. Neither of you were able to know Anthony, unfortunately. I myself did not see him in the last few years. We'd understand if you chose to stay away. You've both got work to do at school.'

'Why did he die?' Charlotte demanded.

Alan hesitated, then said: 'He had an incurable condition.'

Celia interrupted: 'I'd prefer not to be dragged into Anthony's medical history. Please let's leave all that for another day. You two can think about the funeral. I must be off, I've many other duties to attend to.'

Paul said: 'I'm not going to any more funerals.'

Charlotte weighed in resentfully: 'Where's Anthony now? Where's he been? You might tell us that.'

'Please, Charlotte,' Alan said, 'please spare your mother – she's in mourning twice over.'

At this point Celia left the breakfast table. Later, without seeing the children again because they were at school, nor Alan because she had encouraged him to keep an appointment in Highgate, she drove to the Orchard.

Edward met her, and nurses and a few other mothers crowded round to console. She spent a little time with Anthony in a cold room that was new to her: but it was too sad to see him looking so well for a change and dead. The secretary in the office, Kirsty, talked to an undertaker who was willing and able to arrange a cremation. Celia chose two hymns, 'All Things Bright and Beautiful', and 'God Be in My Head'.

She was not sure what to do next: everybody was so busy. She sat in a lobby for visitors, and that kind acquaintance of hers, Alyson, passed by and stopped to commiserate with her.

Celia said: 'I mustn't keep you, you'll need to look after your boy.'

'Oh no, my dear,' Alyson replied, 'I lost my boy four years ago.'

Celia was sorry and sympathetic, she explained that she had assumed Alyson worked at the Orchard for the same reason she had done so.

'I couldn't stop coming here,' Alyson explained in her turn; 'I wanted to be where John had been, and help the other boys. The Orchard's been my saving grace as well as John's. I wonder if it would be good for you.'

They said goodbye.

For Celia, a ray of light tentatively broke through the darkness of recent days. She could reconnect with Anthony by working for autistic children. She could shelter under the wing of Edward Speed. She would be useful, occupied, and to some extent protected from her children. The stunning effect of Anthony's death wore off slightly. She had been exhausted before he died, she had years and years of exhaustion accumulating inside her, and when he was gone the remnants of her strength seemed to go with him. Now she sensed the possibility of recovery.

But driving back to Highgate in the car, in the autumn, she realised that if she were to work at the Orchard without the excuse of Anthony, she would have to tell her children the truth about his autism. She would have to confess to having told them lies. She might have to organise a tour of inspection of the Orchard, where autism would give a grim account of itself to ignorant youth. She foresaw misunderstanding, criticism, quarrels, and that Charlotte and Paul were going to be as difficult as their brother or more so.

The falling leaves were like a metaphor. Other metaphors occurred to her: pigeons were coming home to roost, she had sown a wind and had to reap a whirlwind. The idea that supported her was that Anthony had had worse luck.

His funeral was awful. Charlotte's mood took precedence over Celia's grief. Bernard Farr had offered to attend, but Celia had begged him not to. She had been afraid that he would scold Paul for obstinately hiding at school, and then she was thankful that he did not witness Charlotte's sulky demeanour. She wanted to keep Bernard and Charlotte apart for as long as she could – she was sure he would answer the questions Charlotte was likely to ask.

That evening she sought Alan's assistance in her new trouble. They were in their bedroom, he was already in bed. He said they should inform the children fully and without reserve, and that he would share with her any blame or aspersions that were cast on the struggle to provide them with a normal upbringing.

She replied: 'You won't be blamed, blame's reserved for mothers.'

He smiled at her nonsense. Charlotte and Paul would come round to appreciating all she had done for her three children.

'When?' she asked. 'I'll lose meanwhile or for ever. They're angry with me already for telling them half the story, and they'll be angrier if or when I tell the other half.'

'You exaggerate, my dear,' he said.

'And you don't know, Alan. What about heredity – they'll have that hanging over them – will they have autistic children? There's a money problem, there's public opinion –'

'My dear,' he interrupted her, 'it's late, you're tired, we've had a long wretched day – shouldn't we be thinking of Anthony rather than ourselves and what our other children might think of us?'

She did not answer back. She was silenced and crushed not only by the funeral, the attitude of Charlotte and Paul, the discordant atmosphere in her home, and Alan's unjust rebuke, but also the preceding years.

She kissed her husband good night. He had done his best for Anthony, but she was not in the mood to be lectured, and had to admit to herself that she was fed up with his limitations. His 'thoughts' for his dead son did not compensate for shunning that son when he was alive.

Alan slept while she lay awake, picturing her life as she had lived it, with marriages and motherhood included. Honesty brushed out illusions. Her husbands had not understood or loved her really, and two of her children were against her. As for the third, had she meant anything to his autism?

Day dawned, days were got through. Charlotte was occupied with her schooling and did not revert to the subject of Anthony, and Paul played football and cricket and seemed to have consigned him to oblivion. Celia explained to Edward Speed why she could not come to the Orchard for the time being, and had offered extra services to St Hugh's. She could not face being more at home: setting aside the deteriorating atmosphere, Alan was scheduled to retire in a matter of weeks and she was not looking forward to keeping him company round the clock.

One day she availed herself of Dot's standing invitation to join her for a bite of lunch. They ate sausages and mash with twelve-year-old Adam Tyler, a hungry type who left them to join in a friendly rugger match.

Dot inquired, 'Are you all right?'

Celia replied: 'No – yes – I'm so all wrong that I can't begin to tell you.'

'You have begun – go on!'

'I'm being eaten alive by doubts that I did well for Anthony.'

'What parts have they eaten so far?'

'Should I have had that operation on my Fallopian tubes earlier? Did I endanger my children by postponing it?'

'If you hadn't postponed, wouldn't you have had little Pennants, who'd now be racing about in Mercs and endangering the rest of us?'

'I suppose so. And I wouldn't have liked that.'

'Anthony was a mystery, luck's a mystery, and so's life – and the poor boy's story is water under the bridge, isn't it? Forgive me for being bracing. We relied on you because you weren't doubtful. You took a brave decision, and we've been proud of you.'

'Perhaps I wasn't right to spirit Anthony away.'

'Who's been telling you that?'

'My surviving children know more than they did – we had to let them come to the funeral – they have a little knowledge and it's being dangerous.'

'How?'

'Charlotte's angry with me, and Paul's not very nice. We haven't had a row or anything yet. Charlotte's at college, she hasn't time to pick a quarrel, and Paul only thinks of ball games – he's that age. The atmosphere at home is so bad, Dot! The air should be clearer, but I haven't the nerve to tackle the children.'

'You think they'll think autism's a stigma or a curse?'

'They're sure to think I was cruel to Anthony. But I wasn't – I loved him more than I loved them – and I was trying to be kind to everyone. Sorry to sound – and be – so feeble. Anthony's death has had a bad effect all round – Charlotte and Paul used to be biddable and on my side, and now they're my enemies.'

'Autism isn't a shameful thing – it's just frightfully difficult to live with – you can get doctors to confirm it. What does Alan advise?'

'Oh dear – Alan's at a disadvantage when it comes to Anthony – he only visited Anthony once at Orchard Grange.'

'Good grief! Once in all those years?'

'He couldn't bear it. He couldn't bear references to Anthony. Now he shuts up when I try to talk about Anthony. He won't be helpful when the crunch comes. It's not altogether his fault.'

'Why do you say that?'

'He doesn't know all. Nobody knows all.'

'What is all? I don't want to probe – but you know I can keep a secret.'

'The secret is that I haven't any defence against my children. Orchard Grange was my decision. It was based on my beliefs. My beliefs are arguable. Even the belief that swung my decision could be contested. I seemed to have reason to believe that Anthony had a killer instinct.'

'What?'

'You heard, Dot. I think he endangered the life of Paul. And I think he killed our canary – it was called Timmy. And he nearly killed us both in the car.'

'Oh Celia, poor you!'

'Apparently he showed no sign of that symptom later on. He was always supervised at the Orchard. I might have been mistaken.'

'You couldn't have kept him at home anyway. He'd have ruined all your lives.'

'That's a matter of opinion. You know what liberals are. I've told you my biggest problem, but it's bred little ones.'

'Such as?'

'Alan, for one – he's on the point of retirement – he'll be at home all day for seven days a week – and I can't rely on him to resist Charlotte's curiosity and stand up for me. He wasn't a broken reed when we married. He was broken little by little by Anthony. He'd have been dead long ago if I'd insisted on keeping Anthony at home – but that's only my opinion, again.'

'Are you postponing the evil hour of pouring out your heart to Charlotte and Paul?'

'Yes – roughly speaking – I'm postponing the possibility of another family disaster – just until the children are a bit older and wiser. Do you think that's another mistake?'

'Your situation's so tricky, everything you do or don't do could be a mistake. I'm not offering you advice – I just back you to solve your riddle, or rather riddles. I'm sorry for everything, Alan not least.'

'Oh – he's fine in himself – my other worry, in the same category, is my father. He's alone, a widower and aged, and I should ask him to stay in Highgate or take my family to Broadstairs, but I know there'd be talk of Anthony and I'd be in the dock ... I'll be miserable if he's ill or dies. Dot, I've bent your ear for too long.'

'That's friendship for old girls. Carry on if you want.'

'No – I've done – and thanks for listening to me. Are you as well as you look?'

'Fingers crossed! I married a footloose scribe instead of a wandering knight, but oddly enough Jason fits the bill, he lets me get on with my life, and Adam and I have so few interests in common that we can't disagree.'

'I'm afraid I haven't read Jason's books.'

'Don't worry. He hopes his books never fall into the hands of family and friends because they never read them – or buy them for that matter.'

'You do read them though, don't you Dot?'

'Of course – on pain of death – with torture thrown in if I criticise a single word. Luckily, Jason's books are good, and he can sometimes write them within reach of me.'

They laughed and kissed goodbye and Dot promised to pass everything on to Con.

Again time passed at The Homestead. The volcano continued to smoke, but did not erupt. Celia often wore black clothes to remind her children that she had been bereaved and was not fit to be taken to task. There were two celebrations, which, she hoped, were not turned into damp squibs by her half-heartedness. The first was Charlotte's eighteenth birthday. Her parents gave her a present of money and a dinner party for thirty, a mix of old school friends and the new friends she had made at college, who were dingy and eventually drunken.

The second celebration was to mark Alan's retirement. Carter Johnssen made a presentation of a silver rose bowl at a drinks party after work, to which Celia and the children were invited, and then Alan asked a dozen of his colleagues and business pals in for a buffet supper at home. Celia did her best to be sociable, and might have done better if Mr Carter had not told her to keep a sharp eye on Alan because he had been looking poorly.

In the ensuing days she noticed that Alan slept a lot. He dropped off over the newspaper and as soon as he had switched on the TV. He was looking his age, or even more than his age; but he had had a difficult life what with May and then an autistic son. She urged him to go for long walks and keep fit.

She had her father rather than her husband on her mind. Bernard had fallen over in Thanet Steps, the street, not in 42. He had broken no bones, only grazed an elbow and bruised a knee, but was feeling under par. She asked St Hugh's if she could take leave of absence for three days, bought supplies of food for Alan and the children, and escaped to Broadstairs.

She and her father were happy to be together again. They both said they had longed for a meeting. That led into why they had not met since the day after Chrissy's funeral. Celia's apology became an explanation, and gradually she also entrusted Bernard with her secrets. He urged her to grasp the nettle of telling the children the truth or a tactfully edited version of it.

She thanked him. She was inclined to agree with him. But when she left him and was in the train to London, she disagreed. Her father had failed to appreciate the intricacies of her situation and the characters of Charlotte and Paul. She could not teach them the history of seventeen extraordinary years in an hour or so, she would not try, instead she would answer the questions she was bound to be asked sooner or later. She would give the children the information they were seeking, but nothing superfluous to their requirements. She would wait to be asked. She was choosing now to hold her peace, whereas previously she was driven by fear to keep quiet. She trusted her father to understand and not to interfere.

She arrived at The Homestead at lunchtime. She was due at St Hugh's at two o'clock and to work there until ten at night. She found Alan asleep in his chair in the sitting-room, and no food prepared in the kitchen. She woke him and said she would cook scrambled eggs and bacon in the kitchen. She was depressed by her reception.

He came into the kitchen and said he was sorry. He slumped down in a kitchen chair and supported his head in his hand by resting his elbow on the table. She told him not to worry, she was glad he had got his forty winks.

'No,' he said. 'No, my dear Celia, it's not that, although I am sorry not to have provided lunch.'

'What is it then? Are you ill?'

'I've told the children everything.'

'You haven't!'

'They wormed it out of me. I believe it's a good thing, but I'm sorry because I know I've gone against your wishes. I'm convinced that in time they will see that you acted in everyone's best interests.'

'Oh dear! Did I act without your consent? Don't answer – it doesn't matter. I take it the children were upset?'

'Temporarily, yes.'

'How upset?'

'They've decided to stay with Charlotte's friends for a few days, the Timbles – Jane Timble came to Charlotte's birthday party. They wanted time to adjust to Anthony's illness and his fate.'

'You mean they didn't want to see me.'

'No, my dear, not particularly that, they wanted time together in which to adjust.'

'They walked out on me.'

'No, my dear.'

'How could you, Alan? I warned you. I knew what would happen. You've stolen my children from me.'

'Oh, no, no no...'

'Yes yes!'

She left the kitchen. She cried upstairs until a quarter to two. He had knocked on the bedroom door but she had said she had to be by herself. She went to the hospital. While she performed her duties mechanically, she posed and reposed the question, 'What next, what next?'

An answer of a sort was the news that her husband was in the hospital, in A and E, after collapsing in Paradise Street with a massive heart attack.

Alan Sturridge did not survive. He had been unconscious when he was stretchered into St Hugh's, and he did not regain consciousness.

Celia dealt with unavoidable paperwork at the hospital and was escorted home by Ellen, another nurse, a colleague. They drank cups of tea in The Homestead, and Celia had to account for the absence of the children – the two children, Ellen had no knowledge of the third.

'They're staying the night with people who live locally,' she said.

'Do you want to tell them about their father?'

'It's too late, it's nearly midnight.'

'Can I do anything? Would you like me to ring the people the children are staying with?'

'No, thanks. There'd be no point. I'm in no hurry to break the news.'

'You're so calm, Celia – I don't know how you can be so calm.'

'Forgive me for saying, that's what you think. But I could be getting used to death. Alan's the third person who was close to me who's died recently.'

'I'm very sorry.'

'So am I.'

'Would you like me to spend the night with you?'

'It's kind of you, but no, I'd rather be alone.'

'Well, I'd better be going back to work.'

'Shall I drive you to the hospital?'

'Don't bother, I like walking. How long were you married to Alan?'

'Nineteen years.'

'You'll miss him. I've been married to Jack for twice as long, and I hate to think how lonely I'll be without him. He's got a heart, as the cardiac people say.'

'Alan didn't seem to be ill. I was expecting my father to die, not my husband.'

'We all have regrets, don't we?'

'True! Thank you, Ellen.'

Celia wondered: what regrets could Ellen have? Surely none so sharp as hers!

Throughout the night she was tormented by waking nightmares. One was the memory of the reproaches she had heaped on Alan's head mere hours before his death, the hardest words she had ever addressed to him, that probably caused his heart attack. The other was Charlotte and Paul's rejection of and flight from their mother.

She rang the Timbles' telephone number at seven o'clock – it was not too early by normal standards. Nobody answered for many minutes. She was about to ring off when a sleepy froggy female voice came on the line.

'Is that Mrs Timble?' Celia asked.

'What's the time?'

'It's seven o'clock, Mrs Timble. I'm Celia Sturridge.'

'Oh God! Sorry, I was asleep – we were rather late last night – we had company. Hullo, Celia! I'm Gina Timble.'

'Are you Mrs Timble?'

'Not exactly, but you could say so. I've your kids here.'

'I know. Can I come and collect them?'

'Well, if they've surfaced. You come along, Celia. We don't stand on ceremony.'

'Gina, listen, I have to tell my children something serious.'

'What's that?'

'Their father's dead.'

'Oh hell! You can't get much more serious than that. Sorry, Celia! You come and tell them – I'll see they're up and making sense.'

'Where do you live?'

The address was distant enough to persuade Celia to drive there. She wanted to reach her children before they were involved in breakfast and preparing for school and college. The Timble home was in a terrace, grubbier than the other houses, and with a faded flyer in the downstairs front window advertising CND.

She rang the doorbell. Gina Timble opened the door – long dyed red hair with black roots showing through and a knee-length sloppy joe jersey.

'Come along in, Celia,' she said.

She led the way towards the kitchen, from which sounds of young voices and laughter issued.

Celia wanted to see the children alone, in a quiet room or in the car, but was too late to stop Gina, and found herself in the doorway of the kitchen.

They were sitting at the kitchen table, Charlotte, Paul, Jane Timble, an overweight girl of Charlotte's age with long hair in little plaits Afro-style and a bold expression, and a bearded and bespectacled youth. They all stared at Celia as the chat and laughter subsided. Gina pointed at the girl and said: 'Meet my daughter Jane,' and, pointing at the youth, 'that's Jane's boyfriend – we call him Tinker.' She added for Jane and Tinker's benefit, indicating the figure in the doorway: 'Here's Celia.' She had clearly not warned Charlotte and Paul that their mother was coming to collect them.

Celia said hullo and Charlotte piped up defiantly: 'Dad gave us permission' – meaning that Alan had allowed them to stay with the Timbles.

Paul said: 'I'm going to school' – his obstinate tone suggesting that he was not going anywhere with his mother.

Jane, interfering in a nasty tone of voice, said to Celia: 'And Charlotte and me, we're going to college' – reinforcing Paul's message.

Gina had the grace to address both Sturridges.

'You'd better speak to your ma out here.'

They exchanged glances and got to their feet protestingly. Celia retreated towards the front door and waited for them.

Charlotte, approaching, demanded: 'What is it now?'

Celia said: 'I'm sad to have to tell you your father died yesterday, last night.'

Neither of the children spoke.

Celia continued: 'I'll be in the car for the next ten minutes. Do come and join me. Then I'll be at home until lunchtime. In the afternoon I'll have to arrange the funeral with or without your help. I'll be back at home round about five.'

She opened the door and closed it behind her. Five minutes later Paul emerged from the house followed by Charlotte in tears supported by Jane Timble. Paul sat in the front passenger seat, Charlotte sobbed in the back seat.

'What happened?' Paul asked in his rough way.

'He died of a heart attack. He had fallen over in Paradise Street. He was brought into St Hugh's. I was there.'

'Did you see him?'

'Oh yes. I was with him, but he was unconscious.'

'You didn't let us know.'

'It was the middle of the night, and he was dead. If you'd like to see him, I'll drive you to St Hugh's. He's still in the Cold Room at the hospital.'

As an afterthought she said: 'I might have woken you and let you know if you'd been at home.'

There was no further conversation in the car.

In The Homestead Celia had to telephone Paul's school – Jane Timble had undertaken to inform their college why Charlotte was otherwise engaged. She made her children drinks of hot chocolate and carried the mugs on a tray into the sitting-room, where Charlotte was drying her eyes on the sofa and Paul sat frowning beside her. She was not thanked, and perched on a hard chair facing them – she felt like a criminal brought to justice.

'Did you have a row with Dad?' Charlotte asked.

Celia was taken aback – a raw nerve had been touched.

'What makes you think that?'

'Dad said you'd be cross with him when you got back from being with Grandfather, you'd be cross because he'd told us all about Anthony.'

'It wasn't a row – I'd planned to tell you myself – when I was over Anthony's death, and you were older and I had the strength. I was upset because I was afraid you were upset, and I was right, because you ran away and gave me the cold shoulder. I'm full of remorse for having reproached him – but none of us will ever know why he had the heart attack. His heart was in poor shape, he'd been threatened with heart trouble for ages.'

Paul barged in.

'Dad told us he'd had a pain in his heart ever since you put Anthony in that sort of prison.'

'Do you know what autism is, Paul?' she inquired.

'Not much,' he said.

'Do you, Charlotte?'

'I know it's an illness, not a crime,' she said.

Celia had another question.

'You've jumped to the conclusion that he should have been brought up with you, in the family, as if he were any boy, haven't you?'

'Well, yes, all right – we think so, and Jane who's studying psychology does, and Gina Trimble does too – and Gina rang a doctor friend of hers who said the same thing, that autistic children only have a chance of recovering if they're treated as one of a family, like an ordinary person.'

'Anthony wasn't ordinary. He was exceptional in every way from birth onwards. You don't remember – as I hoped – as your father and I both hoped, and why we took the necessary steps.'

Paul said: 'Dad wouldn't have had a pain in his heart for years if he'd done away with Anthony.'

Celia replied: 'Please mind your English, Paul – I won't be called a murderer even by mistake.'

'Sorry!'

'Far from being a murderer, I arrived at the decision to have Anthony treated elsewhere mainly to make sure that you or your sister or both of you and all of us wouldn't be murdered.'

Charlotte burst out, 'That isn't true,' and Paul chimed in: 'Dad didn't say that!'

'I feared it. I had reason to fear it. I didn't tell your father. I tried to spare him, and you and you, and Anthony, who might have been locked up for life in an asylum if he'd committed a terrible crime without meaning to – I tried to spare you all, and, in line with my worst expectations that made me secretive, you're not sparing me.'

'What did he do wrong?' Paul asked.

She described the French burn within inches of his jugular vein; the blow on Jake Thornton's nose; the death of Timmy the canary; the drama in the car. She described Anthony's speechlessness, which was never cured, and the malice of his character in childhood. She described his escapism, that he could not be allowed freedom of movement in an unfettered environment. She described his eating habits and his digestion.

'I couldn't manage him at home,' she said.

'Dad said the place he was in was expensive. You could have paid carers instead,' Charlotte pointed out.

'What carers?' Celia asked. 'A carer who was qualified to look after autistic cases, who had nerves of steel and could run as fast as Anthony, would have cost a terrific lot, and he or she would have needed a replacement for time off and holidays, and really a night nurse was also required. I had a husband and two "ordinary" children to see to, and would have had to work even harder to earn money to pay carers than I was working – four days a week of nursing – to keep Anthony at Orchard Grange, where he had a team of experts to care for him and myself seeing that he came to no harm.'

'Dad didn't like Orchard Grange,' Charlotte objected.

'I know he had reservations. Do you know how often he saw Anthony there? Once! Your father was a good man, you should be proud of him, and I was privileged to have been his wife. He was clever and dependable. But he couldn't cope with Anthony at all, he was defeated by the sadness of the Anthony problem, which you both seem to think you could have solved by carrying on as if it didn't exist.'

'Gina Timble –' Charlotte began, but Celia interrupted her.

'Tell me more about your Timbles – where's Mr Timble?'

After a pause Paul volunteered: 'There isn't one.'

'What do you mean?'

'Jane hasn't got a father.'

'Oh dear! Does Gina work?'

'She does sculpture.'

'What are her sculptures like?'

'She sticks bones together.'

'Whose bones?'

Paul had to laugh.

'Animal bones,' he replied.

'Where does she get them?'

'They're the bones of meat that people eat, cutlet bones and things like that, she gets some from the butcher.'

'What do her sculptures look like?'

'I don't know.'

Charlotte took over.

'They're interesting, and Gina's brilliant – you're not to run her down, Ma.'

'And you're eighteen, your friends are your business now, but I don't think it's right that you should quote your friends and their opinions against me and mine.'

'Gina wouldn't have chucked him out of his home.'

'How do you know that? Why do you say that? You may like Gina and her daughter, but they lead untidy lives and think they can save the world. Anthony in the Timbles' care wouldn't have lasted long. Who would have changed his nappies and washed them? He would have escaped and got lost or been run over. He didn't understand danger. He couldn't have joined in high-falutin talk. He wouldn't have appreciated sculptures of old bones.'

Charlotte persisted.

'He would have got love from Gina.'

'No, Charlotte. That's wrong. What Anthony got wasn't sentimental twaddle and impracticality, it was my life for seventeen years, and my mourning until I die. I do apologise for correcting you. And I do hate explaining myself and justifying myself and trying to, I hate it in others and hate it most when I'm the person doing it. But I must remind you and Paul that you were the cause of Anthony being in Orchard Grange. The proof of the pudding of my arrangements for Anthony is your objecting to them. You are so unmarked by the fate of Anthony, I mean his illness, that you think you could have grown up with him as you did without him. You enjoyed normality because your father and I sheltered you from abnormality. Don't flinch at my words, don't! Anthony did recover probably as much as possible in the Orchard. His anguish and jangling cries and irrational actions – all that subsided towards the end. I felt that he became a remarkable person in spite of his handicaps, and that he and I were close at the end. At least I admired him as well as loving him. That's all I can say about Anthony now, in the way I've had to say it, defensively – I rest my case, in legal language. This afternoon I'll go along to Coopers the undertakers to fix up your father's funeral, leaving here at three o'clock – I hope you'll come with me. There's food in the fridge for lunch and dinner. Meanwhile I'll be upstairs, thinking of your dear father, your dear brother and even my mother, and telephoning your grandfather and Mr Carter, your father's boss.'

In her bedroom, that had also been Alan's, she broke down. She was ashamed of having argued with Charlotte and Paul, and entertained a fear that she had presented them with something else not to forgive her for. But she rang her father, who comforted her for every reason and said he would motor over immediately. She also rang Mr Carter, who was sorry to hear the sad news and said he would bring Alan's will across on the day of the funeral.

Bernard Farr arrived in time for lunch, the family ate together, then walked to Cooper's. An armistice if not peace broke out. The children returned to their educational establishments. Celia and her father came to the conclusion that The Homestead would be too big for Celia to live in alone, when Charlotte and Paul moved out as children do, and even before then.

The funeral was followed by a modest wake at The Homestead. After it, Bernard had to return to Thanet Steps, and Mr Carter produced Alan's will and read it to Celia and her two children. It was simple, Alan's estate was shared out in quarters between his wife and his three children. Celia as Anthony's next of kin would inherit his share.

A month passed. Charlotte and Paul were nicer to their mother. Twice Charlotte cried on Celia's shoulder, once for her father, once for her brother, and both times by way of a partial apology for the awful scene on the morning after the night in the Timbles' house. Charlotte had changed, was losing her puppy-fat and promising to be quite pretty even though her face and her nose would always be on the long side. She was actually a soft-hearted girl, and perhaps the hard rude streak she had shown was attributable to a mixture of the anti-maternal phase of teenage females and the influence of the troublesome Timbles.

The obstinate streak in Paul resembled Charlotte's unexpectedly hard one. Celia wondered if they had inherited a version of her own determination. Paul at seventeen was handsome and good at games, which she hoped would compensate for his bad results in exams. He too had atoned – with a filial hug or two – for his part in the trial of his mother. He was somewhat inarticulate, but not a bad boy, Celia reflected.

She herself was neither happy nor well, physically well, in this period. She spoke to Dot and Con on the telephone: they told her she was run down, not surprisingly, and bereaved, and needed a long idle holiday, such as she had not had since she divorced Owen Pennant. Her father offered her time at Thanet Steps, alternatively an extended visit from himself. Edward Speed urged her to come back to help at The Orchard. She lay on her bed, drowsing in the day, worrying at night and often crying.

An unpleasant conversation with her children had a revivifying effect. It occurred about a month after Alan's death. The family of three was finishing supper in the kitchen of The Homestead. The children exchanged a conspiratorial glance, and Charlotte spoke up.

'Ma, are you thinking of moving from here into a smaller house?'

'I was, yes,' Celia answered.

'Are you still thinking about it?'

'Not seriously, not for the moment, no.'

'Is Dad's will in action yet?'

'I don't know. I suppose so. Why?'

'Well, if it is, Paul and I own half the house, don't we?'

'What are you getting at, Charlotte?'

'We'd like to sell it.'

'Would you? What for? Where would we live?'

Paul joined in.

'The Homestead's awfully valuable,' he said.

'Is it? How do you know that?'

'The father of a friend at school, he's an estate agent, and he told me it's worth a fortune.'

'He can't be right. We didn't pay anything like a fortune for it.'

'There's a property company after all the houses round about, Tom's father says, and we're part of the plan.'

'Fancy that!'

'Anyway, Tom's father says the house is worth a lot, and we should test the market.'

'Does he now! You sound like an estate agent yourself. I will think again about moving; but I'm attached to our Homestead. Your father and I sold our flats and pooled our resources to buy it, and it has sentimental value.'

Charlotte said: 'Dad put it in his will, all of it, I mean.'

'Yes, but he and I bought it together.'

'He thought it was his, legally, though.'

'Am I right to be worried by the way you're talking, you're both talking? I'm not sure I like it. I own half the house both historically and legally, because of Anthony's share, so it can't be sold without my agreement. I'm sorry if I'm disappointing you. Shall we change the subject?'

Paul said: 'Anthony's share should belong to us.'

'What?'

Charlotte explained: 'Dad left three quarters of his estate to his children.'

'I see,' Celia commented, and a momentary silence fell.

Her heart sank in the interval. Belatedly, she sensed animosity towards herself in these exchanges. But she knew she must not let anyone make a scene, she must not be involved in a scene about money, money of all things, in which she had never been interested.

'Can I have a little time to ponder your suggestions?' she asked.

'Of course you can,' Paul said.

Charlotte said: 'We're pondering, too – no more than that.'

'It's all right – you've made some good points – we'll work things out to everyone's satisfaction, I hope – I'm sure.'

The children thanked her, and she shooed them out of the kitchen to watch TV while she washed up the dishes.

In the next few days she made telephone calls. She spoke at some length to her father, also to Dot and Con. She spoke to Edward Speed, who drew on his experience of predicaments like hers to console her yet again by saying: 'Many of the troubles associated with autistic children can be traced to their siblings.' She spoke to friends at St Hugh's and Orchard Grange. And she had dealings with Carter Johnssen and her bank manager.

She and Charlotte and Paul were not getting on too badly when she wrote them this letter: 'Dearest Charlotte and Paul, You are the two people I love best in the world, but you have grown up now, you're adults, so I'm leaving you to make your own way and do as you please. I shall have left when you read this letter. I don't have to go, and I'm not going for fear that you would wish to be rid of me. No hard feelings on my side, only gratitude for the years you've spent with me. For my shortcomings, sorry! For our differences over Anthony, sorry! When we meet again, if we meet again, provided we're all willing to meet, I hope that you may have come round to seeing that we were caught in the trap of Anthony's illness, the whole family was. The trap was baited by choices, and every choice was harmful – my choice was harmful in your opinion, yours would have been harmful in mine. Anthony might have benefited from being at home, on the other hand I heard at Orchard Grange of a boy who was admitted because his brothers had tried to kill him. Your father's choice was not to choose, which I could not sanction because Anthony had to be removed before you two really noticed he had gone. My choice was meant to be protective of all concerned, believe it or not.

'Years do blunt the sharp edges of harm. I pray for that to happen, before we do harm to one another.

'Your destiny is in your own hands from now on – a truism, also a truth. I have signed over a power of attorney to you two – it means you own The Homestead and its contents and your father's money, and you will receive some compensation from my waiving my right to his pension from Carter Johnssen. I am taking with me

[300]

only the money in my personal account that holds my earnings from nursing. Your GranFarr knows what I'm doing, Dot Tyler and Con Thornton know – you will find telephone numbers in my address book, but I cannot guarantee that anyone will be able to contact me for the time being.

'My decision has been arrived at calmly. I would say my motives are twofold. I love you and want to give you time to decide whether or not to love me, and secondly because I believe in happiness, not misery. My ambition always was to devote myself entirely, without reservation, to the person or people I care for, and, according to my standards of happiness, I'm lucky to have realised it. Agreed, I could never be exactly joyful because of Anthony, but I knew he was well looked after and kept in reasonable health, and I believe he was as happy as possible, I have reasons to believe he was latterly, and that you two and even your father were happier than might have been the case. I dare to claim that I did turn great misery into at least a little happiness.

'I'm leaving now to give you the chance to search for whatever you think happiness is made of, and to seek it once more for myself. Happiness isn't everything, the modern cult of happiness is awfully selfish and usually counterproductive. We nonetheless do owe it to life to try to find and create something better than misery.

'Goodbye, good luck, and I hope it isn't too corny to add, *au revoir.*'

A DOCTOR'S NOTES

CONTENTS

PART ONE

Notebook One

THIS NOTEBOOK is the property of Dr Joseph Selaby of The Poor Cottage, Chantry Road, Maeswell, also of St John's Surgery, St John's Court, Maeswell. If found, please return it to one address or the other immediately. A reward for its safe return is on offer. The notes on these pages are private and confidential. Thank you.

The paragraph above is no doubt counter-productive. All the more reason not to lose my notebook. The medical records of my patients are kept in the Surgery, my notes refer to everything I cannot record, including personal matters. I am tempted to be indiscreet here. Probably another mistake, typical of me at the present time! I would read or at least look into a sort of diary if I found one. I would look into any document that I was told was private and confidential. I suppose I am more inquisitive than honourable. I am human, too, therefore might accept the reward. Yes – human – unfortunately.

Maeswell is a town in the South of England. It is large enough to support two doctors' practices. St John's Surgery, of which I am a partner, boasts three other doctors, Cunningham, Woods and Audrey Fletcher, a young lady doctor, and two nurses, Annie Miller and Nicky Benning. We treat an enormous number of patients from a wide catchment area of town and surrounding villages.

Two months ago I came to live in Maeswell in order to get away from overwork in a hospital, from an overcrowded city, from love that was over, and to be nearer my mother. I should rearrange those motives in the order of their importance.

Mrs Symonds brought me another ailment today, a bruised heel of her right foot, which caused her to hobble into my consulting room with aid from Nurse Annie. We are already more than acquaintances

– she has come to see me each week since I have had my brass plate on the door. She is a widow, an OAP, lonely but popular, and leads an active social life of the elevenses description. I have become a socio-medical port of call, as Drs Cunningham and Woods apparently were before me. I was about to speed her on her way this morning when she said: 'If I'm not careful, Doctor, you'll be thinking I'm a hypochondriac.' Wind was thus taken out of my sails. I paid more attention to her heel and diagnosed that it would soon be better. She was duly grateful and walked out with no trace of limp.

I am forty and unattached, my sister is older than me, my mother is seventy-five and a widow, and my father died ten years ago; but I prefer not to think about time and its passage. Besides, statistics lie. Here is a true statement: I am old enough – old enough to value my parents, be sorry for things, have regrets, and to know better.

My father was a doctor, and my mother a nurse – I inherited my profession. I remember Father when he was old – he would be ninety if he were alive today – white-haired, bespectacled, with a white moustache, upstanding, and a solid down-to-earth shape. He was not an intellectual, and had no culture to speak of. He was also obstinate, opinionated, impatient, peppery, and not easy to live with. He adored Mother and drove her half-demented, was devoted to his children and exasperated them, and was unshakeably loyal to all of us, and to friends, colleagues, staff, and political party. He was not quite what he appeared to be. He was English, perhaps Celtic, and comparable to an iceberg that is bigger beneath the sea than above it. He had two talents that are rarely combined, common sense and vision.

By 'vision' I mean seeing deeper than surfaces, and foresight.

I am glad to pay him overdue compliments here. I never praised him verbally.

Dr Frank Cunningham, the senior partner in this practice, is slightly reminiscent of Father. He must be past retiring age. He is the traditional 'country' doctor, rosy-checked, bluff, with a loud voice and usually attired in a tweed suit. He is a 'racing' man – he goes to horse-racing meetings with his sparky little wife. He inspires awe, and could scare the hell out of diseases.

Dr Denis Woods is the opposite type, plump, an accessible roly-poly, and a jokey family man who refers to his good-humoured wife as 'the Queen Mother' and to his four boys as 'the gladiators'.

Dr Fletcher differs from the other two not only by sex, but also because she is idealistic. She is not cynical about medicine and its limitations – she winces when Dr Cunningham in our rest-room announces that we doctors understand no more than twelve per cent of human physiology. She believes she knows more than that, she believes in science and its advances, she is a refreshing individual with energy, shining eyes, a husband and two children. She is not acquainted with failure.

Annie and Nicky are excellent nurses: you can tell they are because of their cheery attitude to their work – nurses cannot be noticeably sentimental or glum. Nicky is the younger one, and I find her propinquity distracting.

Three awkward sessions with this morning's patients. First, an unaccompanied child came into my consulting room, a teenage girl. I shook her hand, asked her name, sat her down, and returned to my chair.

'Are you here for your mother?' I asked.

Her name was Kathy Leonard and I had treated Mrs Leonard for blood pressure.

'Not really,' Kathy replied, blushing. She is a brown-haired sweet-looking girl.

'Do you need help?'

'Can I shut the door?'

'I'm afraid not. The rule is that I have to keep the door open if I'm alone with a member of the opposite sex.'

'There are people in the passage – they'll hear me.'

'I'll call a nurse in, then we can shut the door.'

Kathy looked negative, but I buzzed for Nicky. Rules apart, I thought she was going to cry.

Nicky joined us and the door was closed.

'What is it, Kathy?' I asked.

'Can I have the pill?'

'How old are you?'

'Sixteen.'

Nicky said: 'Think again, Kathy – I've seen you with your mother – you're younger than that, aren't you?'

'No.'

I said: 'I could ask your mother, Kathy.'

She burst into tears and blubbed out: 'I don't want a baby, and I'll lose my boyfriend if I won't let him. He's told me it's either.'

'My advice for you is get rid of that boyfriend without delay and find a better boy.'

She cried harder.

Nicky said: 'You're fourteen, aren't you, Kathy, you're underage?'

She shook her head.

'Dr Selaby can't prescribe the pill for you. Okay – you don't want your parents to be involved – you do want to cling on to your boyfriend. Tell him to buy a condom in a gents' toilet. Tell him to control himself and stop being selfish.'

She fled. Kathy ran out of my room, slamming the door. Nicky and I pulled faces at each other, and she ushered in my next patient.

He was a boy, ten or so, with shorn head jailbird-and-footballer style, and mother in attendance, who had made the appointment. She is Mrs Wilkinson and he is called Dylan. She is a hefty female with a loud voice.

'Dylan's fell on his head and I'm here so you can check him over,' she said.

'Where did you fall, Dylan?' I asked.

'Down the Rec.'

'Did you fall over or fall from a height?'

'He was on the swings,' his mother bellowed.

I examined his head and saw a swelling.

'When did this happen?'

Early, according to Mrs Wilkinson.

'When did this happen, Dylan?'

'Going to school.'

'You stopped to have a swing on the way to school?'

Mrs Wilkinson objected: 'What's wrong with that?'

'Did you lose consciousness, Dylan?'

'Saw stars.'

'Are you clear in your head now?'

'Yah.'

'Who's sitting on the throne of England?'

Mrs Wilkinson answered angrily: 'He won't know a thing like that – he doesn't do history.'

'Where are the Houses of Parliament, Dylan?'

He suggested on a querying note: 'New York?'

I said to Mrs Wilkinson: 'He seems not to know much.'

She replied: 'He wouldn't have known before he fell on his head

– we're not your sort, Doctor – and I didn't bring Dylan here for you to make him look stupid.'

'Well,' I replied, 'I think he's none the worse for his fall. His head's mostly bone in my opinion.'

Mrs Wilkinson was mollified. She thanked me for my opinion, and nudged Dylan into saying, 'Ta!'

My third awkwardness was caused by the mother of a third child. Mrs Wainwright, a woman even bigger than Mrs Wilkinson, led in Rowena, aged five. Rowena had breathing problems, a chesty cough and chronic wheezing.

I said: 'She needs to lose weight, Mrs Wainwright.'

'That's as may be, Doctor, but shouldn't you examine her?'

'I can examine her from where I'm sitting. She's pounds overweight. Come back when she's slimmed down.'

'You do surprise me, Doctor. She's got puppy fat. You're not kind to tell her to slim.'

'I was telling you to take more care of your daughter's health.'

'Oh, I am mortified. I am, Doctor Selaby. Come along, Rowena – you can have your ice-cream now.'

The Poor Cottage is a misnomer, it cost a lot. I had a fine flat in London, in St John's Wood, but I gave it away and started again from scratch down here. The Poor Cottage has two of the most desirable features of property today, it is within walking distance of my place of work and it has a garage. I also like its location, in a quiet side street, its age and charm. It is the last dwelling in a terrace of five, semi-detached, partly tiled on the outside, and inside has two receps, two bed, one bathroom, a kitchen and a small walled garden – the garage is a modern addition. The rooms are small and low-ceilinged, the walls are thin and damp rises; but I can make it warm and find it cosy. And being near my mother saves trouble.

Besides, it is nice for me and I hope for her. She has been an excellent mother to me, and to Jane, although Jane feels I was the favourite. I believe Ma always did her best to be fair and unoppressive: which is a considerable compliment considering her strong personality. She was born Catherine Weight, daughter of a Norfolk farmer. She must have been attractive, tall, good-looking, humorous. She met her match in hospital in Norwich – Father worked there. He soon set up in private practice. She became his nurse and receptionist as well as the mother of two children. She put Father first, and vice versa – their parental policy was to send Jane and me to boarding schools and give us as much time as they could spare in the holidays. No complaints, no regrets – I had a good boyhood and youth. The crunch came when Father died. She drew her own conclusions from the facts: Jane was married to Neil Proctor, also a farmer in Norfolk, they had two children, and were working night and day in order to make ends meet, and I was too busy to visit her. She sold the family house in Suffolk and moved down to Maeswell, where she had a friend. When the friend died, I left London and also came to Maeswell. Now I can look in on her often – her flat in Silver Court is reasonably close to my cottage. Today's visit was exceptional: she dredged up the subject of Iris. She said that The Poor Cottage would not have been a worthy home. I thought I showed she had given offence – she took no notice. Fear it may be a sign of her mind fraying at the edges.

My colleague Audrey stirs nostalgia in me. I used to feel as she does. I followed in Father's footsteps not exactly to please him or because he influenced me – those reasons were superseded by my own enthusiasm. I read about the 'first' European physician, the Greek Hippocrates, and was struck by the most famous of his *Aphorisms*: 'Life is short, Art long, Occasion sudden and dangerous, Experience deceitful and Judgment difficult.'

I still agree with every word of the Hippocratic oath, so-called. Professionally, after I had got the better of my squeamishness, my curiosity was satisfied by practice of the art of diagnosis and my philanthropic instincts by the aim of healing the sick. But London, my hospital in London, my life in London, reduced me to the point of wishing to be elsewhere, in a provincial setting, as far as possible from the rush and bustle and the old friends. I was able to buy myself into St John's Surgery – I had enough money for that, my cottage was bought with a mortgage. The change seems to be having some of the desired effect – I go to work every day almost willingly.

Frank Cunningham invited me to dinner. He is a dear old boy and has been kind to me. He lives with his wife Penny in a 1950s house in a garden at Larkspur, the swish part of Maeswell. The house is called Chandos. It is furnished like a four-star hotel. Penny is a dear of a different sort: she has not settled for being in her late sixties, has a curly blonde hairdo, is exuberant and flirty, and makes unmalicious jokes at Frank's expense. Dignified men often seem to drive their wives to ragging them in public. The other guests were our Protestant parson, William Wetherby, an OAP, with ailing wife Ada, and Patricia Deacon, thirtyish, unmarried, toothy and works for the Council. We ate in the dining-room – formally furnished with mahogany and a pair of prints of Montague Dawson yachts sailing the seas. I sat between Penny and Patricia: Penny said to Patricia and me as she indicated the seating, 'I hope you two get on together or even get off.' The food was soup, fish pie, prune jelly in a mould, cheddar cheese, and milk chocolates. It was served by a superannuated maid wearing a scarlet dress with pinny and odd upstanding headgear: Penny proudly announced that she had invented the uniform. We drank or at least were offered three wines, white, red and port. Penny jumped up to serve and replenish glasses: she said Frank had no palate and the amazing thing was that he was able to speak. The conversation was meant to be general, but Penny talked so much that she inhibited the rest of us. Moreover, the Reverend Wetherby's graces at the beginning and end of the meal discouraged jollity. We left early: Frank had revealed that in the old days of country entertainment carriages were ordered at ten o'clock. Both Cunninghams thanked us for having accepted their invitation. They clearly love Chandos and live there happily, but it is not convenient – they have to have two cars, one for Frank, another for Penny to reach the shops.

Ma has apologised for again delving into my past.

Dinner party food does not suit my digestion. Father used to say that amateur cooks were killers, and now almost everybody is an amateur cook, having a bash at esoteric sauces and mixing up flavours. Penny Cunningham's dinner was good, but I have reason to believe I can have too much of a good thing.

Mrs Symonds' heel has moved to her hip, so she tells me. She resisted my attempts to laugh it off. She demanded an x-ray, and, to save time, I referred her to Radiology in St Anne's Hospital in Tinbury. Poor NHS!

I dare to tell patients not only to eat less but also to drink less. I cave in not only to Mrs Symonds, but also to the people who seem to queue up to beg me to intervene on behalf of battered wives, bullied children, family finances and public safety. But the chances I get to do so are rare: the guilty parties run away and hide from doctors who might scold them. When I have managed to say my piece and wag my finger, I am forced to listen to the hackneyed record: 'My drinking is under control – I can stop when I wish to – I'm more amusing when I've had a couple – I drive better with a drink in me – it's not my fault – mind your own business, get out before I smash your face in, go to hell, I'll never speak to you again.'

Doctors, self included, are apt to respond feebly to such tirades, not just to avoid unpleasantness. They can make matters worse for those who have suffered and told tales. They cannot truthfully say excessive drinking is bad for everyone: some drunkards are kept alive after a fashion by pickling themselves in booze. Regrettably, it could be said, alcohol does not kill its addicts soon enough. And the fact is that 'cured' dipsos are often neither so healthy nor so nice as they were before the demon got its claws in them.

A surly girl barged into my consulting room and said: 'Smear!' When I said, 'I beg your pardon?' she repeated in a louder voice with the vulgar modern intonation, 'Smear, smear,' as if to a deaf person or a lunatic. I kept my temper, sat her down, dragged her name etc out of her, and again asked her to tell me slowly why she had come to see me. My assumption was that she was asking for the gynaecological test. She deciphered 'smear' for my benefit largely by sign language – pointing at her ear: she had been trying to say, 'It's my ear.' She had earache, which I was able to relieve.

The moral of a true story is that the government of this country or whatever is left of it – England, shall we say? – should urgently and forcefully teach elocution and deportment. The 'smear' girl spoke a language I could not understand, and she slouched in such a way that I could foresee her spinal and pelvic tribulations. Regional accents have been put in the shade by the inverted snobs who try to talk common, by a new type of pidgin that elides words and is spoken with an open mouth, and by the mystifying effect on verbal communication of Hollywoodese, Atlantese, popese, thugese, and the sloppiness of liberalism. And a large percentage of English people no longer deport themselves, they slouch or waddle, shuffle or strut or mince.

My notes were meant to stick to facts. Judgmental I did not want
to be, and the quagmire of politics I hoped not to fall into. Yet I
have to ask, if only to ask myself, if ignorance was always a defining
trait of the Anglo-Saxon race. The French think so, but may be biased.
A worrying number of my Maeswell patients fail to give me reassuring
answers to the question. They have no understanding of ill health or
probably of health, of my diagnoses and prognoses, or of how much
danger they could be in. They talk of heart attacks when they have
had strokes, and vice versa. Another possibly concussed boy was
brought in to me the other day, and I asked him if he knew the
name Adolf Hitler. The boy said Hitler had been Prime Minister
long ago.

I have a rich patient, who has offered to enrich me. Tucker Bee –
trade name or alias – was born and bred here, is now old and ill
and has bought a house in Larkspur. He means to live in it as long
as I can let him, and be buried with his parents in the graveyard
near my cottage. He made his money in secondhand cars. He has a
mistress/companion/secretary called Heather, who must be half his
age. He called me out for a reason that was new to me. He said he
was not ready to 'go' – 'I can play the market in bed.' He came to
the point. 'Here's a codicil to my will. I testify on this bit of paper
that you'll inherit from my estate one thousand pounds for every
week you will have kept me alive from this day onwards. Is it a
deal?' My reply was negative, and his comments were: 'You're no
businessman. I may have a year or two or three. You're kissing away
fifty-two thou per annum.' We parted on friendly terms. I think he
knew that I knew he had a shorter life expectancy, and if I had
agreed he would have demanded constant attendance. Tucker is a
rogue – his name is roguish – amusing too.

I work longer hours than Frank Cunningham because I am younger
than he is, and more hours than Denis Woods and Audrey Fletcher
because they have children and I have none. Our agreement is that
I shall work less if or when a fifth doctor is needed and joins the
practice. I had no objection to these terms – I needed to be busy.
And I am busy, if less so than I was in London. But spare time can
be hard to fill. I must recover my love of reading one day. There are
limits to how far one can walk. I hate most of TV. And I have no
close friends here. These notes fill gaps.

Winter is on the way – the nurses have been doling out flu jabs.

Dined with Denis and the 'Queen Mother', his wife Alyson, who is as jovial as he is. They are in their late forties, and a great contrast to the Cunninghams. They live out of town, at Deacon's Holding, a farmhouse in a few acres of land on the outskirts of the village of Clayburn. My fellow-guest was Nicky Benning, who seems to me too attractive to be a nurse. We were softened up with dry martinis in the sitting-room – Denis was proud of his recipe for martinis, two tablespoonfuls of Noilly Prat to one bottle of Gordon's gin thoroughly shaken with ice. The sitting-room is cosy with its blazing fire, sofa and chairs with broken springs, pile of children's toys in a corner, and friendly old spaniel. Alyson, off stage, shouted that dinner was ready, and we joined her in the kitchen and sat at the table laid for four – the Woods' 'gladiators' were absent at school or elsewhere. The food was Irish Stew cooked in and served from a pail-sized pot, apple tart with cream from Alyson's Jersey cow, and hot cheese straws – all very tasty. We drank claret in alarmingly large wine glasses. The atmosphere was relaxed, which was not surprising in view of the alcoholic refreshment. Alyson is fresh-faced verging on ruddy, Denis looked ever more rubicund as the evening progressed, and Nicky sparkled at me in spite of my attempts to regard her repressively. Denis said that Alyson would have preferred him to be a vet because of her farm animals, and she said the best thing about him being a doctor was that he came in handy at lambing time. Denis told a good story with apologies for it having no end. Friends of a patient of his, a married couple, were going on holiday in France with their caravan. They were taking his aged mother along. They drove from their house in North Wales to Dover, where the old lady discovered that she had forgotten her passport. They told her not to worry, she could shut herself into the lavatory in the caravan and nobody would be any the wiser. The two younger people got through Passport Control and on to the cross-Channel ship. But towards the end of the voyage the lady in the lavatory was taken ill. She was persuaded to stay where she was until they were through the French controls – they could contact a French doctor later on in France. There was no trouble in Calais, until they looked into the lavatory and were horrified to find that his mother and her mother-in-law had died. They returned to the *Douane*, confessed their crime, wringing their hands, and led the *Douaniers* back to where the caravan was parked. It plus the deceased and their car had vanished, they had been stolen.

On Sunday I took Communion at St Peter's, the church near my Poor Cottage. William Wetherby, whom I met at the Cunninghams' dinner, officiated with minimum fuss. Denis Woods had urged me to look at the stained-glass windows.

Referred two lovely people to specialists for tests, and wish I believed that the members of my profession knew more than twelve per cent of the science of healing.

Ma fed me yesterday evening. Mildly curried chicken mayonnaise and rice with cucumber in it, then oranges caramelised – she apologised for cold food in winter, but I said she had given me two of the best on her menu. She said she would like to cook for me more often, and in the next breath that she knew doctors hated to be pinned down for meal-times. I supplied reassurance, and she assured me that I was a good son. Her flat is one of fifteen in a block with a warden in attendance. Most residents are widows, one is an unlikely spinster, Miss Gabriella Shelby, a pretty soft-spoken septuagenarian, who is thought to have had her share of the spoils of the war of the sexes. Ma was funny about the latest arrival, a bachelor, George Mills, retired chartered accountant, no oil painting, and a shy mouse of a man. Obviously for the first time in his life he has aroused interest of a romantic nature. The ladies of Silver Court are courting him, quarrel over him, make scenes because he is nicer to one of them than to another, and invade his flat or try to at all hours. Consequently George has been transformed from one of nature's wallflowers into the cock of the walk. His head is held high, and he smiles at the world instead of trying to conceal his protruding buckteeth.

My oldest friend Robert, Robert Chimes, my age, like my brother, up and coming barrister, married and the father of two, stayed the night here. He was on his way to some Assizes, and was checking that I was still alive. He took me out to dinner at the King's Head. He does not approve of my 'burying myself in the back of beyond'. He sees Iris, and might have been hoping to remake our match. An unsettling visit.

Annie Miller, senior nurse, produced a casualty for me to look at before I began to see patients this morning. The man had a deep cut into his forearm, wound gaping but no longer bleeding. He asked me to put a stitch in it. He would not give his name. Description – mid-fifties, short, balding, wearing anorak, T-shirt, jeans, trainers, and walking with exaggerated limp.

'How was your arm cut?' I asked.

'Someone slammed a window on it,' he answered in words and accents that were almost impenetrable.

'What's wrong with your leg?'

War wound – he was an invalid – and 'on benefit' – paid a basic means of subsistence by the state.

'What's your name?'

He would rather not say – it was only the stitch he wanted. He also withheld his address.

I explained that the wound needed to be cleaned, that Annie could clean it and I could close it up, and he was in life-threatening danger otherwise, but that we would not treat a person refusing to identify himself.

He gave in. He was Jim Tye from a cottage in Clayburn. He had a wife who would be angry with him for having got in trouble in Maeswell, he had spent the night out so as to have the cut attended to before he returned home, and that was the gospel truth.

He was a liar. I saw through him. He had been on burglary bent. Nobody had slammed a window on his arm, he had broken a window, the glass had been thinner than he expected and a shard had cut his arm. He pleaded guilty to my charges. I insisted on examining his leg and could see nothing wrong there: Jim begged and besought me not to put his name on my computer as it might be spotted by his GP in Taylton, Dr Rees, who had certified that he was unfit for work and worthy of financial support by taxpayers. Dr Rees would find out that he had walked in from Clayburn, Jim said, and that he was walking the five miles back – he would lose his 'benefit' and might as well be dead.

Annie and I put our heads together. It was our turn to give in. Against our principles we did as we were told by the criminal. Alas, the Welfare State!

As Father was a doctor and Ma a nurse, strange that I did not become a revolting dropout.

Frank Cunningham's wardrobe tells a story. He wears a grey suit for work, a blue suit if he is lunching out or going out to dinner after evening surgery, occasionally a dinner jacket that seems to have turned green with age, a tweed suit for racing, a tweed jacket on Saturday mornings if there is no accessible race meeting, and a black suit for the funerals of his patients. The Cunninghams do not go racing at Ascot, but Penny dresses as if for Ascot's Ladies' Day when they go to a point-to-point. Frank's uniform as a punter includes a battered and stained brown Trilby and outsize binoculars in an old leather case.

Dinner with the Fletchers: how am I to return the hospitality of my colleagues? They live in Smith Street which leads to Larkspur, in an end-of-terrace Edwardian house, with carports at side and in the front garden. Andy Fletcher works in a stockbroking firm, was once a rugger-player, a forward, and maintains a connection with the game. He is short, broad and losing his dark curly hair. Their children are Kathy aged ten and Trevor aged eight. The other guest − not Nicky Benning, thank goodness! − was April, a friend and contemporary of Audrey, an anaesthetist by trade rather than in the social sense. My arrival must have been almost a last straw − it was a weekday, Andy only just ready after commuting homewards, the children probably complaining of having their hair brushed, and Audrey putting finishing touches to cookery and cushions; but I was greeted warmly after the family had caught its breath. Andy offered white wine or 'something more serious' − I took white wine, he took whisky. The food was supermarket, and none the worse for that − pâté, breaded bits of lemon sole with tartare sauce and peas, salad of foreign fruits with ice cream. We drank more dry white wine, then a sweet wine. We ate on our knees in the sitting-room − apologies for the ambiguity of sentence. Audrey did everything with help from the children, beamed, sparkled and did not flag, although she had worked her six hours at the Surgery. Andy is the pasha type, he snapped his fingers for service. He has a rugger-player's sense of humour: he said his missis was more doctor than housewife and that it was all he could do to stop her serving dinner to guests in a kidney bowl. Audrey is a fine person, but is not 'personal', at least she does not get 'personal' with me − her public persona is impersonal. Le Corbusier said that houses had to be machines for living in; Audrey's externals look like a machine for living in. Perhaps the point of Andy is that he can bulldoze through the machinery. His selfishness forces her to be the humble servant of her mate.

I need a woman – that is, a daily lady or housekeeper. More patients come to see me, and I never have time to clean The Poor Cottage.

Eureka! I made a sort of joke of the above at the Surgery, speaking to Mr Peele, retired builder, who looks after the fabric of our building and does the odd jobs. Thirty-six hours later Mrs Peele rang my doorbell and said she was willing to oblige.

Mr Peele is a gentleman of the oldest school, he introduced himself to me as Mr Peele. He is a strong-featured man wearing spectacles. Mrs Peele wore a hat the other evening. She is in her sixties, also bespectacled, with neat straight grey hair and charm of the reserved kind. She offered to help me – work and pay not mentioned. She arrives on Mondays, Wednesdays and Fridays at eight sharp, buys all the 'liquids' and dusters she requires, and leaves a note at the end of the week stating her expenses and earnings. She cleans and tidies everything, and begins to tell me the gossip of the town. For a change, I feel cared for.

Of course, my home is not homely without a kind wife presiding. But The Poor Cottage is a misnomer not only in a financial context: I am quite rich in luck – healthy, in work, a householder, in my forty-first year. And, luckily, I have started to read again – for the last year I have read nothing but advertisements of new drugs. The book that caught my eye and my attention is *The Journal of a Disappointed Man* by W.N.P. Barbellion. The author's real name was Cummings – he died young of Multiple Sclerosis in the early nineteen hundreds. The title of his book touched a nerve, although I am so much luckier than he was.

Heather rang today.
'Do I know you?' I asked.
'I'm Tucker Bee's partner. He's sinking, Doctor.'
'How bad is he?'
'Awful – he has been for days – he can't breathe, and he's sick – and won't let me ring for an ambulance – and won't have anyone else to help. I'm at the end of my tether, honestly I am.'
She was sobbing, and I said: 'Listen, when I last saw him he tried

to bribe me. I can't get involved with bribery and blackmail. I could ask my colleague Dr Woods to take over the case.'

'No – it's you he's after – I'm too tired to argue, but, Doctor, please! Tucker always was bad about money – he's still gambling and telling me he's losing the money he was leaving me in his will – and I don't want to be a pauper – sorry for saying so. Please!'

I caved in. For the third time I caved in against my will, first to Iris, then to Jim Tye, now to Heather. I was trained to temper science with mercy, not the other way round. I have disappointed myself.

Anyway, I saw Tucker and had him carted off to hospital. He was charmless even *in extremis*. Heather was embarrassed to have asked me to salvage her inheritance. She is a nicer woman than Tucker deserves, and she looked a wreck. She was grateful and kissed me goodbye, I hope not prematurely.

We are no longer a nation of shopkeepers, more's the pity. The 'little' shops are being squeezed out of business by cruel taxation and supermarkets. The Maeswell shops that sold useful merchandise are either being taken over by ladies selling cushions and trinkets in their spare time or turned into residential premises. Thank God for Bertha, my greengrocer, and Nigel, my butcher, and the strangely spoken girls who sell my baker's bread – all are close by The Poor Cottage. I risk being recognised by my patients when shopping locally in preference to driving out of town to the mammoth stores where the chill air-conditioning blows along the aisles.

Mrs Peele and my colleagues have been giving me a crash course in the social fabric of Maeswell. In a small town, society is easier to analyse than it is in the metropolis, although social life everywhere is roughly the same, levellers notwithstanding. Rank, down here, is represented by Lord Havior of Havior Place, his wife, surviving son and mother. The Cunninghams mingle with the Haviors, and Frank has told me of his affection for and sympathy with the family. The elder son of the present Lord and Lady died of cancer in his twenty-second year, and mourning him was aggravated by the fact that he had been given at least half the estate and they would be severely embarrassed by the cost of the tax on death, the death duty. There is a second younger son, but he is not altogether satisfactory for some reason. Lord Havior is apparently more or less incapacitated by his troubles; Lady Havior works in the Hospice of St Christopher where her son was nursed; and Lord H's mother, Helen Lady H, lives in the High Street and serves on numberless charitable committees. Mrs Gradwell-Taylor and such sub-grandees, Frank and Penny, for instance, are invited to Havior Place for occasional melancholy meals and functions.

Next best, after the Haviors, are the rich and especially the rich philanthropists. The anglicised Russian Minksofts, who, believe it or not, make their money by shipping coal from Poland to Newcastle, support worthy causes and sit at the top table; and another family of generous millionaires bearing a good old English surname, Sinopopolis, throw lavish parties at which all and sundry are made welcome. My various informants amuse me with their descriptions of those of us grubbing about under the upper crust. We are the 'classes', a term more or less invented by Karl Marx's teutonic passion for pigeonholes – I am quoting Denis Woods. Every creature of the human animal kingdom is struggling for status, and life is a bare-knuckle fight, according to comfortable peace-loving Denis, who has tried to read a Marxist tract or two. Doctors and other professionals are the top dogs, then come the politicians, then the middle-middle and lower-middle class, and then the masses, the class called 'working' although it has less ambition than the other classes and works less. Maeswell is not short of snobbery. Ma described a pretentious resident of Silver Court: Mrs De Villiers, living in a flat on the ground floor, was unwell, and another lady, who is unpretentious and lives in a flat on an upper floor, suggested a visit to the invalid, 'Would you like me to come down and see you?' The invalid replied: 'Not "down", dear, not "come down", "up" would be more appropriate.' Mrs Peele and her husband, who belong to the traditional artisan/craftsman class, have no respect for the lowest class. Frank said that his gardener, a peasant and proud of it, called the class he thought lower than his own 'rank Labour' – a slur on socialism. This gardener took exception to a contemporary and neighbour who won money in the Lottery and strode into the pub smoking a big cigar: 'You could see he was common.'

Doctors cannot be serious snobs. Illness recognises no pecking order. Pain is classless. A few exceptions, the inevitable awkward squad, prove the rule that patients in hospital are apt to get on well together. Health and strength make the difficulties. Leadership is a mixed blessing.

I have been entertained by my three colleagues. How am I to return their hospitality? Social life is a minefield.

Cold days, dark days, Christmas is coming.

Miss Shelby turned up at the Surgery, thanks to Ma. She is the Gabriella Shelby who also lives in Silver Court. She wanted a face-lift – another woman wanting one – and the name of a cosmetic surgeon. She made no bones about it and did not ask me not to tell my mother. She must have been a maneater, and I cannot be sure she is no longer on the prowl. She laughs a lot, has laughter in her speaking voice, and cheers a man up. She smiles, too, and shows an appealing set of her own teeth. She mocked herself and flirted with me simultaneously. 'Isn't it ridiculous, being so vain at my age? But God save us from women who aren't vain! It's no sin to be naughty if you still have something to offer. Women are capable of romance at any age – you'd know that because you're a knowing doctor – and I'm quite determined to be looked after by a male nurse on my death-bed. It's a woman's duty to be ready for love, isn't it? – ever-ready, say I. Now, would I look better with a little hitch behind each ear?' Her mannerisms were as good as a play. She hangs her head, then raises it and looks alarmingly straight into my eyes, then it was a sideways glance, an inviting movement of her lips, a full-throated laugh at some pleasantry of mine, a long warm handshake, a compliment – 'Your proud mother didn't exaggerate' – and a little grateful pat in the region of my breast-pocket.

I beg pardon for paying Gabriella Shelby back-handed compliments, and thank her on behalf of my sex for keeping her flag flying. Women also owe her gratitude, although the jealous cats would disagree: for she champions them against the feminists, who have done and are still doing them more harm than good. I remember Robert picking holes in Virginia Woolf's book, *A Room of One's Own*, an early tract that has influenced thoroughly modern women to desert husbands and abandon their children. Robert had been to the Woolfs' home in Sussex, Monks House in the village of Rodmell, and told me that Virginia's bedroom with the narrow bed and no creature comfort was the most effective passion-killer he had ever dreamed of in nightmares. That Virginia and her husband Leonard had intercourse there was unthinkable, Robert said. And he pointed out that in spite of having that room very much of her own, a wonderful thing for a woman according to her book, she had committed suicide. Feminism has won women rights, some needful, others self-destructive, for instance the right to drive buses and box other women, and the financial rights that put men off marrying them. Worst of all, the feminists have brainwashed women into thinking they are like men, can behave almost like men, and can fulfil their potential by burning their bras and acting macho. My experience would equate feminism with the contraceptive pill as good ideas that have had bad effects. Gabriella Shelby may be a little over the top, but she is more feminine than feminist and I love her for it.

Nearly all pills should carry a health warning, in my opinion, like packets of cigarettes. A wag spoke a true word about Viagra: that innumerable women of a certain age must be cursing its inventor. Another old fool wanted a prescription for Viagra a few days ago. I reminded him that his heart was none too strong and said that a resumption of sexual activity would be the death of him. He is or was a fox-hunting man and had recourse to the jargon of the sport to explain himself: he wanted to be able to kill his fox. I said the fox was as safe as houses, he would be killed long before he could catch it. He called me a puritan and said he would buy his Viagra in France, where love was legal.

These 'notes' could be called a meander through my mentality while I settle into a new life, or an aimless ego-trip. But who is going to call them anything? They are my 'dear diary' although dateless, my secret, safety valve and consolation. Here, I can express thoughts and emotions that a GP is obliged to keep to himself. Nowadays, when night falls so early, I am not tempted to take the country walks that I enjoyed on fine autumn evenings, and I sit and scribble by the fire.

I am in my consulting room from eight-thirty in the morning to eleven, then visit patients in their homes and in the Cottage Hospital. I am back in my consulting room between four-thirty and six-thirty. That is my basic routine for the five working weekdays. Every fourth night I am the duty doctor and emergency telephone calls from my patients come through to me at The Poor Cottage – each of the other doctors takes a turn at night work. Every fourth weekend I am in my consulting room on Saturday morning and on call on Sunday. About once every six weeks I attend at Accident and Emergency in St Anne's Hospital in Tinbury.

Treated my youngest patient since moving out of harm's way. She is called Laura and is nine months old. She was brought in to my evening surgery by her parents, a pretty mother and a father of the clean-cut English type who is a postman. Laura has croup and I prescribed a couple of ancient remedies – no antibiotics at this stage. She is a charming girl and looked blooming in spite of a cough and a touch of fever. She has fair hair, the bluest and whitest of eyes, an intelligent regard and a beguiling smile. Jenny and Paul Maxwell, the parents, will ring me at once if they notice any change in her condition, and anyway ring me early tomorrow morning. Jenny had come into my consulting room clasping to her bosom a bundle of swaddling clothes. She was the stereotype of concerned motherhood, a picture of love in action. Paul was the image of a supportive paterfamilias, trying his best to be stoical. Lovely people! They inserted two other words into my head: if only!

Laura is okay, slept most of the night and her temperature now normal.

Brutal doctors, heartless, misguided, unbalanced, stupid and unimaginative doctors, crooks too, I have come across them all; but they were exceptions. Most doctors have the nous to realise, they are trained to realise, that they have chosen to peddle strange merchandise, one as desirable and popular as the other is unpopular, namely life and death. They are dealing repeatedly, often on a daily basis for years on end, more often than soldiers and much more often than civilians, with the ultimate human predicament. They can be successful, but in the end are bound to fail, for death is incurable. Their work can patch up, prolong, postpone, and be brilliant and idealistic; but it can also be seen as quackery, a tissue of lies, disillusioning, disappointing, futile and heart-breaking. To be too logical is not good doctoring. To be too empathetic and sympathetic ditto. The emotional content of medical practice is serious stuff. Nevertheless I find my work addictive.

Two nights ago I was at the A & E at St Anne's Hospital in Tinbury.

I had done that duty in London; but there we had more staff around, including porters. And I think I only did it on week-nights; I was in Tinbury on Friday, pay day. The real trouble began at about eleven and subsided at about three the next morning. By then we had one lost eye, two or three broken arms, a broken leg, a broken pelvis and a broken neck – that is a list of the major casualties amongst members of the public, and does not include haemorrhages, cuts and bruises, hysteria, drunken incontinence and vomiting. Amongst the hospital staff and the police personnel trying to cope with the mob, there was a nurse with broken fingers, another with a black eye, others badly bruised, a porter concussed, a policeman hacked on the shin, another knocked out, a third with an injured knee, a fourth with a back problem, and I was hit on the jaw and the ear, spat at, sicked over, kicked and cursed. Cool Britannia! This is our 'culture'. This is the handiwork of our politicians and trend-setters. Are people worth curing?

I was not fit for work on the Saturday and Sunday because of the above, and took Ma to Matins at St Peter's Church. She likes it there not only because of the old stained glass, but also because gallant Parson Wetherby has resisted the abominable New English Bible and stuck to the poetry of the King James Version. I am not very faithful C of E, and feel shifty in the House of God. I wish I was an RC, the priests of which church are empowered to grant absolution.

Ma ranted and raged against the generation that cannot wait to blot out reality with drink and drugs, and had hurt me. I agreed, but had to say that the favourite entertainment of humanity has always been escapism and varying degrees of release from reality. That is what art has to offer, ditto the pie-in-the-sky aspects of religions and Marxism.

Ma is planning to spend Christmas with the Proctors in Norfolk. Jane has invited her, and Ma looks forward to seeing her daughter and grandchildren again – she has not seen them for nearly eighteen months. She would like me to complete the family reunion. No, no, not for me, I am not ready for days of exposure to a happy family. I promised to put Ma on the right train and meet the train that brings her home to Maeswell.

The courtship of parents amazes their children. Ma amazed me by relating that she had only begun to love Father a year or two after they were married. In the hospital in Norwich where they worked and met, she did not take to him, she thought he was just another of the young doctors trying it on with her. Gradually he had worn her down and forced her to change no to yes. Why? Because he was so kind. Was she not taking a big risk to marry someone she was not in love with? Yes, but ... 'He was steady, and patient when I flirted around, and women are born to be adaptable, aren't they? – and persistence usually does win fair lady.' I checked that Father was loving her while she was not really loving him: 'Oh yes – and sometimes I felt smothered, which was ungrateful.' How had she known when love hit her? 'Probably when I noticed that I was worrying about him as much as he worried about me. I wanted him to be happy and well more than to be happy and well myself. Love's lovely, but a life sentence. I didn't know what it was until it was too late – young people rush in because they're ignorant, not necessarily fools. We had become a team, you see, with our home and two babies and our own medical practice, and it was not a big step for me to see that we were inseparable emotionally.' She summed up their marriage: 'Your father was clumsy and an awkward customer, but he was straight as a die, he exasperated and amused me for all our years together, and I believe I was luckier than I easily might have been.' Her ending was philosophical. 'We were separated when he died, but only in one sense, and the comfort is that I don't wish my life had been different.' Ma certainly was lucky.

Notebook Two

TWO MISUNDERSTANDINGS: A Mr Deon Lucas kept an appointment with me. He was a new patient, fortyish, with shorn skull and heavy black moustache, wearing a T-shirt under a bomber jacket. His voice was high-pitched, his speech mannered, and he was a bit squirmy.

'Oh dear, where am I to begin?' he began.

He then said it was a very personal matter.

I asked for his address etc.

He brushed that aside, and said he had a more pertinent question to ask me: 'The point is, are you one of us or one of them?'

I replied that I was an impartial doctor ready to treat him.

'Well,' he said huffily, 'you are single, aren't you? That makes you one of us.'

'Are you unwell, Mr Lucas?'

'No, but I am unsatisfied, Doctor Selaby – you have not satisfied me in any way – so I shall bid you good day.'

With that, he walked out of my consulting room.

Two days later another new patient, Mrs Carsloe, consulted me at six in the evening: a big black-haired woman, talking non-stop, in her thirties, wearing a dress and scarves. She slumped in the chair on the other side of my desk, and between giggles and tears told me her husband had deserted her. She hung her head, covering her face with her hands, then looked at me flirtatiously.

'How can I help you, Mrs Carsloe?'

'Pat to you,' she replied. 'I'm lonely, Doc.'

'There's no medication for loneliness.'

'You're wrong there, Doc.'

I realised she was under the influence of something and caught her drift.

I said: 'You should see Dr Fletcher, our lady doctor, Mrs Carsloe. I suggest you go and ask for an appointment with Dr Fletcher now.'

'You've given me nothing for my pain, Doc.'

'What pain?'

'Here.'

She patted her stomach.

'Dr Fletcher will examine you.'

'A female doctor's not my type,' she said, and jumping to her feet she raised her dress and revealed a daunting nakedness.

I pressed the alarm bell under my desk and told Mrs Carsloe to leave my room. Mr Peele came to my rescue, but not before the lady who was no lady shouted at me: 'You don't like women, that's your problem, Doc!'

The Journal of a Disappointed Man plucks at a nerve. It charts the disintegration of a youth afflicted with life-threatening disease – he died in his mid-twenties. It is perhaps too sad to read for pleasure, notwithstanding its literary merit. I am ashamed to own up to a trace of fellow-feeling for the title.

Mrs Symonds has not deprived me of her company. No week of these last months has passed without her bringing me an ailment or two or three. Today they were pins and needles in one foot, pain in the other hip, a suspected frozen shoulder, and indigestion.

'I'm sorry to be a wreck,' she said with a disarming smile. 'And I rattle with all the pills inside me.'

As usual she twisted me round her little finger. We doctors are all deformed by having been twisted round so many little fingers. I was also impaled on the horns of Mrs S's dilemma. If she happened to be as wretched as she said she was, and either fell more recognisably ill or expired, the NHS might be sued for neglect by her relations and I might become a political football. I offered her sympathy and tentatively a referral to a psychotherapist. She was quite keen to have an opportunity to talk about herself to a captive audience at great expense to the taxpayer, but wondered if she should have an examination of her innards. I suggested a colonoscopy and provided details of what it involved. She was unshaken. She is a masochist, and I must be one to continue as her doctor.

But I like Mrs S. I do not like Mrs Quinn, an unmarried mother of three from the Haven Estate, run-down council-housing inhabited by no-hopers. She is in her twenties, dirty, tooth missing, braless, and a wheedler. She had bitten me once before with her wheedling. Today it was her head and the unbearable pain that was not alleviated by any OTC painkiller: could she have something stronger? I urged her to stick to Paracetamol – I knew her game and was refusing to play. She demanded morphia. I gave her a prescription without explanation and shooed her out of my consulting room. At least the pills I prescribed are not lethal. I wonder if these drug addicts have any idea of how disgusting they are. Apparently they complain to dentists of acute toothache in order to get a shot of anaesthetic into their gums.

St John's Surgery is housed in a Georgian residence with gracious rooms on ground and first floors. The ground floor has been divided into Reception, Frank Cunningham's and my consulting rooms, nurses' practice rooms and a rest-room for medicos.

The doctors drift into the rest-room for refreshments and are sometimes all together there. Occasionally we discuss problems posed by our patients. Otherwise we arrange duty rosters and gossip.

One day Frank Cunningham unbent to ask me if I happened to be a devotee of the sport of kings. I replied no, but that I was intrigued by his interest in the sport.

An interesting conversation ensued.

Frank explained, as I remember: 'I think it was formed by the contrast between my work with sick people and the health and strength of beautiful racehorses in the pink of condition. I'm not a gambler, but Penny enjoys losing an affordable fraction of family funds year on year without fail. Racing's our relaxation for different reasons. We'd be glad to take you to a race-meeting should the opportunity arise.'

Denis Woods was present when Frank was speaking in his kindly precise manner, and piped up to charge him with supporting the aristocratic principle.

Denis continued: 'Racing anyway on the flat is all about breeding and lineage, isn't that true, Frank? Perhaps you also like it for that reason – I do, in principle, although I don't go to race-meetings. It always amuses me to hear and read that the masses rush to Ascot and races everywhere on every day of the week, while the socialists and communists are doing their level best in the name of the "people" to polish off the toffs, pull down the old families, and preach that only they, no one else, are allowed to be more equal than others.'

Denis should have been a politician. But he might not have succeeded since he has too much common sense for that line of work. He is a thoroughgoing royalist and traditionalist. He produced a little list the other day, names on a card, which he aims to show to any republican who crosses his path. The list was of presidents and pseudo-sovereigns who have ruled nations in modern times, and he gave me a copy. Here are some of the alternatives for hereditary and constitutional kings and queens: Lenin, Stalin, Hitler, Mussolini, Chairman Mao, Pol Pot, General Amin and the other African despots, and the Middle-Eastern thieves and homicidal maniacs.

I have volunteered for the 10 am to 2 pm doctor-on-call duty on Christmas Day – not altruistically, but to have a reason to refuse possible invitations and not to have to celebrate publicly. I shall go to Early Service and eat and drink less.

There are still 'shopping days to Christmas', but I have already metaphorically wrapped my present for my colleagues. I am repaying their hospitality, and entertaining my new friends, by means of an office party. The 'Surgery Party' will be mine – I have booked and instructed caterers. The guest list will include wives, partners, children, pharmacists, and of course doctors, receptionists and Mr and Mrs Peele. The party will begin at six-thirty on Christmas Eve, after evening surgery, and finish at nine-thirty. There will be a buffet and wines, other liquid refreshments, and the 'venue' will be my consulting room and Frank's and the waiting-room – Frank and I will vacate our rooms early on.

The Poor Cottage has no central heating, and wind whistles through the space between the tiled exterior and the interior walls of lath and plaster. It is romantically ancient and historic, but I have no love to keep me warm.

Yesterday I paid Ma a compliment which she was not altogether flattered by. I told her she was good at growing old. The context of our conversation was that Susan Ledbridge, a chorus girl of yore, nowadays my patient, was attempting to show the other old ladies at Silver Court that she could still kick up her heels – do a chorus girl's high kick – and had fallen flat on her back and fractured her pelvis. Another patient of mine, Mrs Marlbury, suffers from the overweening ambitions of dotage: in her eightieth year she booked herself into a package tour of the Himalayas, the foothills thereof but the Himalayas nonetheless. Result – Mrs Marlbury fell down, was concussed, broke a leg and ribs, and had to be carried for five miles over rough terrain by Sherpas – she was in a blanket slung from a pole. She spent six weeks in a Nepalese hospital, and is now home, a very much poorer but apparently not a wiser woman. Ma, conversely, in her widowhood, moved into a sheltered one-bed flat in the warmer south of England, wears clothes with pockets instead of carrying a bag, gave up driving ages ago, and has savings which, she says, would cover the expense of a nursing home if she had to end her days in one. I thanked her for not worrying her children unduly.

A good example of how bad old age can be stumbled into my consulting room yesterday. He is a pseudo-gent called Tower, and was a new patient. He refused assistance and barked at my suggestion that he should have elbow crutches or at least a stick. He is in his eighties – would not give his exact age – had forgotten his address – and had clearly had a stroke, one side of his mouth was paralysed.

He wanted to know what was wrong with him: 'What's up? You tell me that!'

I did so.

'That's wrong for a start,' he said. 'I'm fit, except my legs aren't what they were. I'm A1 apart from the legs and a headache.'

I asked: 'What medication do you take, Mr Turner?'

'No pills, if that's your drift.'

'You'll have to take some in order to avoid a second more serious stroke.'

'I haven't had no stroke and I'm not having another – and I'm not here for pills.'

'You should take an aspirin a day.'

'No – they make my belly ache.'

'And I could give you another pill to ease the headache.'

'No – I'm not taking pills. You think again, doctor, and tell me what's up.'

'You're old, Mr Tower, and your arteries and veins are hardening. You'll have a stroke or a heart attack next.'

'You're as bad as my daughter.'

'You have a daughter?'

'Not your business.'

'Does she live with you?'

'Mind your questions! Somebody has to look after me. My old woman died twenty-five years past. The girl had to see to her mother first. That's the rule round here, that's what daughters are for.'

'It sounds as if your daughter would be fifty or sixty, and has looked after her parents for half a century or so.'

'Could be. Why not? I've kept a roof over her head. And she shouldn't speak to me like she does, and no more should you. Question is, can you do any good or not?'

'Answer is, sorry, Mr Tower. For your daughter's sake I'm not giving you a prescription. I don't expect to see you again. Goodbye.'

'What you getting at? I don't like your tone. Thank you for nothing.'

He dragged himself up and lurched out of my room, and surely returned home to torture his daughter – but not for long, perhaps thanks to me.

Missed church on the last two Sundays and regret it – duty took precedence. I would like to think the faith I had in my boyhood can be recovered. Science led me in an agnostic or even atheist direction; but now I see that science can only doubt and reject belief – it cannot consistently or logically scoff at or spurn faith, since science itself, its discoveries, its conclusions jumped at, are very often founded on faith. Remember medical science's changes of mind about the treatment of TB and mental illness, remember astronomy! Where are the fever hospitals of yesteryear, the laudanum for sale OTC, the Big Bang that was more believable than the Book of Genesis? Where are the Valerian drops, the bleeding cups and the leeches? Scientists used to subject mental patients to five or ten years of weekly sessions of psychoanalysis not necessarily because they were crooks, but because they had faith – faith that brushed aside the useless and perilous realities of life on the couch, and the waste of time as well as money.

The disappointment inherent in 'getting ideas' is that you are almost bound to find out someone 'got' your idea before you did. My 'ideas' these days boil down to truisms and platitudes: but so be it. Faith seems to me to rank in importance not far below air and water – you can hardly carry on without it. And you can choose to have faith in science or in music, in anything or maybe, unwisely, in anybody – or in religion. My faith aged twelve was mainly acceptance of the choice made by my parents and teachers. My stirrings of faithful feelings now are in response to experience.

Father told me this story. He was working in a hospital in London for part of the Second World War. In an air raid during the Blitz he and other medical staff had to take shelter in a passage on the ground floor – it was not a particularly safe place to sit, but they obeyed instructions and were sitting there, ten or twelve of them. They were used to bombing raids, they were dealing with the casualties, they joked about bombs, were a hard-boiled team, and probably brave to boot. The raid in question was vicious and the bombs began to fall uncomfortably close. Incendiary bombs fell in 'sticks' or 'sequences', and Father and the others suddenly heard such bombs exploding on the road outside the hospital, one after the other, nearer and nearer. And a doctor called Robbins dropped on to his knees on the floor and began to pray aloud, 'Save me, God, help me, God, please, God!' Father said that Robbins' action was more alarming than the Germans. There was no direct hit on the hospital – the bombs had left their craters in the roadway. I asked Father what he made of the episode and he replied: 'Robbins wasn't a coward, and he hadn't been religious. He was a good doctor and a scientist, but in an emergency he prayed.'

I sympathise with Robbins. When the chips are down, faith is better than none. Faith in God is chosen when people lose faith in people.

I met a woman in tears by my cottage. She had emerged from the graveyard of my church, and was hurrying to where her car was parked. I recognised Heather, the companion or concubine of Tucker Bee, and guessed that he had died and she had been at his funeral. I asked her in and gave her a cup of coffee with a dash of brandy. Tucker had died in hospital, she told me. I offered a few comfortable words, but said the wrong thing. She was furious, not sad. He had left her a pittance, not the house, and most of his money was divided between remote nephews and a football club. Why do so many women fall for rotters? Why do men marry viragos, for that matter? Heather has a thatch of colourless hair you could not easily run a comb through, her face is colourless too, and lined and creased. She had served him for ages, and did not know why she had bothered to be at his funeral.

Everything is our own fault.

Mrs Peele has invited me to tea on Christmas Day. I accepted gratefully.

The old widower who asked me for Viagra has died in the bed of another old boy's wife. A scandal and a fiasco, no doubt to be repeated *ad nauseam* thanks to erectile aids for men and the contraceptive pill for women.

Free condoms were offered by the government to the Headmaster of a Catholic public school – 'public' meaning 'private' in this connection in good old muddle-headed England. The headmaster said no. The bureaucrat was not amused and demanded an explanation. The headmaster replied: 'We teach a form of contraception that offers the safest sex. It's called abstention.'

A good doctor ought not to be too susceptible to the emotions of patients or the charms of the opposite sex. Women are apt to be naughty with their doctors. They make appointments for non-medical reasons, discuss their sex-lives in an inflammatory manner, strip off before they are asked to, complain of lumps in order to be palpated, and linger in meaningful positions. A few declare their interest point blank, and occasionally a woman pursues her doctor out of office hours, threatens and attempts to blackmail him. He should be resistant and immune.

Is the above wishful thinking?

Iris made it easier for me to ignore red herrings in London.

As the Christmas Eve party looms up, I am reminded of the local red herring called Nicky.

I fear my party was a mistake. Father said that doctors, ideally, should steer clear of such events.

It is Boxing Day. A week has passed since I scribbled Father's advice that I ignored. Now I have some free time until the year turns. The party was no fun for me. I had omitted to include Bob Clutter, our nightwatchman, a shadowy figure I had only met a couple of times; Bob, invited on the morning of the party, told me that he and Mrs Clutter were deeply offended. Then the champagne lacked bubbles, the white wine was sour, the red rough on the palate, and the caterer's finger-food solid cholesterol; one or two of the guests lit cigarettes in our strictly smoke-free zone; and our pharmacist's boyfriend spilt red wine on the carpet of Frank Cunningham's consulting room. In the middle of the party a tipsy yob gate-crashed, seized a glass of wine from a tray being carried round and demanded in a loud voice, 'Where's the poison cupboard?' He was ejected by Mr Peele and Bob Clutter after a struggle.

Goodbyes were mixed blessings. Frank referred to our 'first ever cocktail party' at the Surgery, suggesting that it would be the last if he had any say in the matter. Penny Cunningham urged me to find a nice little wife to be my hostess. Denis and Alyson Woods were both under the influence, he said he would cut off the wrong leg if he had to do an amputation, and she prayed not to be breathalysed as she drove him and their children back to Deacon's Holding. Audrey Fletcher was doing her level best to control Andy's intake of alcohol, marshal their children, and be nice to everyone. Annie Miller's husband made a lavatorial joke, saying that he could not wait to provide a specimen. The receptionists headed off into the night tripping and giggling. Mrs Peele reminded me of tea on the next day.

What was particularly mixed about the blessing of the end of the party was that Nicky stayed behind. I have already confessed to awareness of her attractions. She has a big smile and a firm figure. She is twenty-five, unmarried but seems very knowing, is good with men as well as with female patients, and her manner is sympathetic with sauciness thrown in. We had never spoken much except on business – no conversation – I was careful not to converse; but we had communicated otherwise, by ocular means, by meetings and greetings, on her side sartorially and on mine by evasiveness. She wore civilian clothes at work, T-shirts and trousers, tight T-shirt, tighter trousers and no panty line.

Somebody should write a booklet entitled, *How to Change Men's Minds*. More to the point, Nicky could. She wore a flimsy almost see-through dress, nothing to keep the cold out. She had half-pirouetted to show it and herself to me. 'Do you like it? ... Why not, it's Christmas Eve...' She was beautified by make-up – feminists, forget your naturalistic rules and regulations if you should weaken so far as to want a man! Her eyes shone and twinkled with the aid of mascara, and her teeth were whiter because her cheeks were as rosy as blusher could make them. She was ever ready to help with the party chores, taking coats, pointing out the lavatory, and continually caught my eye in spite of my attempts to avoid hers. She was flirting, she had come out of the closet to declare her interest, she was on the warpath. Even when she helped to clear up the mess in Frank's consulting room, she scrubbed the carpet in such a way that it became a proposition, kneeling there and smiling at me over her shoulder.

She lent the caterers a hand as they packed their equipment. Then Bob the nightwatchman said he would check the upper floors and switch out lights. The time was eight-thirty-ish.

'What's next?' she asked me, laughing.

I laughed too, a bit breathlessly because of excitement, also uneasily, since I had no plan for the rest of the evening.

'What indeed?' I replied, indicating that the party after a working day had been tiring.

She approached me and put her hand on the lapels of my jacket.

'It's still early,' she said. 'And my flat's round the corner. Would you like to come back with me?'

'I don't know...'

'Come back with me, Joe.'

Verbally she was taking liberties. She had never before called me by my Christian name, let alone its abbreviation. Nurses are meant to be respectful to doctors.

'Thank you...'

I had twice not finished sentences.

'I could feed you.'

She laughed again, perhaps at the double meaning.

I bent down to kiss her because I was nonplussed. I intended to kiss her cheek – or thought that was my intention. I did not know quite what I wanted or was doing.

Her lips met mine. She closed the gap between us. Words failed me, but actions spoke volumes.

In time she broke away and, holding my hand and looking up at me with sensuously heavy-ridded eyes, murmured: 'Come with me.'

'I must fetch something from my room,' I said.

She let me go. I sat at my desk without turning on the light. I sat in the dark and saw a little more clearly. Remembrance was like cold water. I rejoined Nicky, who was waiting in the Waiting Room, and said I was sorry.

'It's no good – it wouldn't be good for either of us – I can't – forgive me.'

She had a sort of wrap round her shoulders. Her expression changed from happy to inquiring to disbelieving to sad. She plucked at her wrap, rearranging it to keep out the weather.

'What a pity!'

She smiled and added: 'Some Christmas Eve!' and then, 'Night, Joe.'

I stayed in the Surgery for a quarter of an hour – I was afraid she might be waiting in the street. At nine I was back in The Poor Cottage.

In the night, and afterwards, in the next days, the question that dogged me was: could I continue to practice in Maeswell?

On Christmas Day I spent the morning in my consulting room, had a couple of hours at home, and went along to the Peeles' at four-thirty. Their sitting-room is warm and cosy, as they are. A coal fire burned in the grate, the room was filled with souvenirs of people, places, holidays, his army records, their Christmas cards. I sat in a plush covered chair facing the fire, they sat in their habitual chairs on either side of it. Plates were passed round and then a cake-stand with jam sandwiches to start with and slices of Christmas cake to follow. The tea was strong and reviving. The Peeles could have given many people who thought themselves upper class a lesson in good manners and the art of hospitality. We discussed my party, my family, their family, the Royal Family, and the scandals of the town, the overweight mayor, and the disgraced publican who had vanished with the Christmas Club money – the sweet evergreen clichés. Mr Peele related that he and Mrs P had 'walked out' for eight years before they could afford to marry. They had been husband and wife for just on half a century, and never forgot to be thankful that they had survived the war. They had a son who was a chartered surveyor, married to a good girl and living in Tinbury, and a daughter married to a sailor and living 'down Plymouth way'. They had eight grandchildren and showed me the photographs. They helped me temporarily.

I worried about Nicky, too. Should I ring her, and encourage or upset her all over again, or not ring her and behave like a chauvinist cad? Saying sorry often makes matters worse, but I do say it inside.

Three more 'free' days – I only have to be on duty at the surgery for a couple of hours on one of them. The new year beckons and should inspire me to begin again. Instead, I retreat into the past.

[341]

In those dark moments in my consulting room I saw writing on the wall, and drew an odious comparison. I could not bear to let history repeat itself. I could not compound my error. Iris was a popular person, we all 'loved' her – she was an occasional member of our 'gang' of medical students. We were all working hard and recreated ourselves as a rule in a cheap Chinese restaurant where we ate long-drawn-out meals and drank gallons of beer. Female hangers-on joined in, girlfriends, mistresses – Iris seemed to me to belong in that pigeonhole; whether or not she slept with one or more of us, I never knew. She was four years older than me, a stocky but smart young businesswoman – she worked for a pharmaceutical company. She had blonde hair, cut short and smart, a rather bony face, a wide white smile, and warm hands and well-manicured fingernails. Her parents were divorced; her father lived with a woman in the South of France, her mother in the North of England; she had a sister, married with two children, in Ireland; and she was a broadminded Roman Catholic. I found these things out later on, at first she was just an agreeable acquaintance, someone I sometimes linked arms with in the street, when a crowd of us marched home after blow-outs of crispy aromatic duck and crispy noodles.

I had had my share of girls on pedestals. I adored them in theory, not practice. For me, becoming a young doctor in a hospital was almost exclusive of dalliance, I was so overworked and exhausted. At long last I was granted leave, which, by chance or Iris's good management, coincided with a conference in a hotel in the country paid for by the company that employed her. She was to be in attendance there. She said I might like to string along – I could relax while she was conferring – and she wangled accommodation for me. On the first of the two nights of our stay she scratched on the door of my single room when I was reading in bed. I opened the door and asked what was wrong. She laughed quietly with a finger to her lips, let go of the skirts of her dressing gown, and showed me she had no clothes on.

It is eleven o'clock on New Year's Eve. Ten minutes ago the telephone rang. When I lifted the receiver the caller rang off. Could it have been Iris? Could I have telepathically summoned her by writing the above? Oh God, not that! Or could it have been Nicky?

On the first working day of the new year I asked Nurse Annie for news of N. Annie said N had not been well over Christmas, but would be coming in to work tomorrow. She said it stiffly. Annie, unlike everyone else, had not thanked me for the party. She must blame me.

I have seen N. She was at the Surgery, looking much the same apart from shadows under her eyes – no make-up, of course. We met on the stairs. I said, 'How are you?' She replied, 'Alive,' and then, 'Don't worry.' And she winked at me and laughed.

This evening, contrarily, I feel more depressed, and not up to writing the sequel to the true romance of Iris and Joe.

A disagreement at the Surgery, not quite a row, unpleasant nonetheless, although it does take my mind off my trespasses. The story is that a mother brought in her daughter, a girl in her late teens, and demanded an emergency appointment with a doctor. They were called Spade, Mrs Spade and May Spade, and were rude and provocative. Dr Woods agreed to see them. May had stomach pains, and her stomach was distended. Denis, after a cursory examination, told Mrs Spade that the cause of the trouble could be wind, pregnancy, a twisted gut or a tumour. I could imagine Denis giving his opinion in his throwaway style. The effect on the Spades was dramatic. They had howling hysterics. Denis managed to pass them on to Audrey Fletcher, who always treats our female patients with problems in their private parts. Audrey ruled out pregnancy and wind, but again dropped the word tumour and referred May to a specialist who would be able to knock that suspicion on the head. The specialist duly obliged: May had a blockage, largely due to diet, but nothing worse. The relief of the Spades took an aggressive form. Mrs Spade returned to the Surgery with Mr Spade, a builder. They broadcast the news that May had fallen into a decline since being warned that she might have cancer – could not eat, sleep, leave her bedroom, was terrified, frightened to death, and it was all the two doctors' doing, Woods and Fletcher. They threatened legal action. Frank Cunningham was summoned to talk to them, but he brought them into my room – we explained, argued, apologised and offered prescriptions of tranquillisers for May. At last they departed. Frank summoned a meeting of his colleagues in our rest-room. He put Denis and Audrey in the picture, and said that he foresaw no danger from the laws of the land – the Spades would surely not obtain financial compensation from our Surgery, however asinine the lawyers; but he deplored the medical fashion for doctors sharing their thoughts with patients. I sided with Frank – I have always thought it cruel to tell people they might have a life-threatening disease before the diagnosis proves or disproves it. Denis and Audrey spoke up for the modern attitude to our fellows and its rallying cry, 'We're all in this together'. They argued that the doctoral etiquette of the 'No cause for alarm' variety was outdated, untrue, euphemistic and risky. It put more pressure on the doctor and less on the patient, was not fair, and invited legal challenge and costs. They were not apologetic. They were not at all sorry for May. I can write here that I believe they were at fault.

Ma exploded at least a squib under me yesterday. She said after much preamble that she was thinking of moving up to Norfolk to be nearer her grandchildren. She denied that I had failed her. I tried to be objective and unselfish.

Perhaps I should go to Norfolk, too – uneasy at the Surgery.

Another upsetting experience: Mrs Thorner had an appointment with me this morning. She is a young woman, a girl, a child bride, twenty years of age, first name Norah. I called her Mrs Thorner, and she said, 'No, please, Norah's my name, Norah, please, Doctor.' She was agitated, pale-faced, all blue eyes and long blonde hair with a fringe. She explained that she is Audrey's patient, but had come to me because Audrey is on holiday. She is pregnant – early days – and wondered if I could give her a tranquilliser or something. Why did she think she needed a tranquilliser? She burst into tears. She and her husband Billy were not sure about the baby, they kept on arguing for and against abortion, and it was driving them crazy. She was not alone in being unhappy, Billy was unhappy, and I was not happy. She sobbed out her story. They were too young, they had nice jobs and were saving to buy a house, she had to live with her parents meanwhile and Billy with his, and they had taken care not to be stupid, but something must have gone wrong – and oh dear, oh dear! She would love a baby, but not yet – a baby would be their ruination – but they could not bear to be unkind. What was she to do? Could she have something to calm her down and let her sleep at night without harming the baby? I offered her my shoulder to cry on, and she clung to me in the sweetest way. I wrote her a prescription and apologised for not knowing how to stop people being sad.

Comparisons crowd in. More and more tugging at my heartstrings – or do I mean nerves? I now see Iris in a new light, as the subject of one of these notes and another shot at autobiography. No time for more this evening.

I told Audrey after she returned from her holiday about Norah Thorner, and she told me that between then and now a grandparent had died and left the young couple enough money for a deposit on a mortgage for a house. Apparently they are more inclined to have the baby.

Iris was my mistress for eleven years – no, I will not fracture English grammar to satisfy partisan pressure groups, the illiterates in particular. No, I was her lover, she was not mine, she was my mistress, and exclusively, I believed. She is a lovely normal woman. She did not seduce me so much as educate me. She was more or less my everything, teacher, guide, partner, companion and friend, and she was charming, tolerant, vivacious, good-tempered, good-humoured. She had a gift for getting on with people, women included. It was marketable, her popularity and her competence were appreciated by her bosses, and she kept on rising through the ranks of her colleagues at work. I introduced her to my family. Father and Ma liked her so much that Jane took against her. She was flirtatious with Father and brought Ma samples of vitamin pills. She was more of a success with my friends when they realised she was mine – my friends might have hung back before that – somebody else might have been involved with her.

We never lived together, which suited us. I had a flat near my hospital, she had one near her office. We were both workaholics, I suppose. We tired ourselves out and were usually in need of peace and sleep. We met at weekends, we were apt to cohabit then, and took our holidays together. At first, too, we snatched at extra helpings of love. I would go to her place in the middle of a night or vice versa – we had each other's keys. In due course, Ma scolded me for not marrying her, and Father shook his head over the permissive society. But she scolded me if I apologised for not marrying her, and put her hands over her ears if I talked of hypothetical children. She was not maternal, nor sentimental, nor pleased if I let her catch sight of the cloven hoof of possessiveness, and not in favour of our changing any of our arrangements: at least, that is what I understood her to be. Marriage and all the rest of it was the straw that would have broken both our backs. I was committed to striving to make sense of the out-dated idiocy of the NHS. The years of our thirties, Iris's and mine, slipped by pleasantly and satisfactorily, if in utilitarian style.

The surprise, shock, eruption, earthquake was her pregnancy.

Early spring, the season of snowdrops and infections.

Nicky is recuperating from our kisses quicker than me. She laughs and gets on with her work. When we meet in passages or on the stairs she looks at me with conspiratorially lowered eyelids. I remind myself that she was as much at fault as I was. If I had accepted her invitation, we would have strayed into the territory where fatal accidents happen. But I should not blame her for raising the spectre of the last act of the Iris drama – she and Norah Thorner.

Got to church at last. The Lord's Prayer fits my bill. Prayer for my patients, one MND, two MS, for little C and the other eleven cancers, for all the people who are ill for one reason or another, and that my diagnoses will not be wrong, and mostly for forgiveness.

My response to our baby was utterly self-centred to start with. To write that we both knew how the crisis came about is bizarre considering she was a woman of a certain age and I am a doctor. I mean that we both knew when and why it happened. On a Sunday evening in the month of July we motored out of London to dine in a country pub that was reputed to serve good food. It did, the food was delicious, wine ditto, the weather was warm and balmy, and stars winked and twinkled in the deep-blue heavens. The circumstances were designed by the mischievous fates for the pleasures of the flesh. When we left the pub one of us suggested that we might open the rear doors of my car – perhaps there was no verbal suggestion, we just tumbled into the back seat by common tacit consent. Afterwards, Iris returned to the pub to wash as best she could, and then I dropped her at her address so that she could use her douche and take other belated precautions. We had acted on impulse. We were aware of risk, but vaguely in my case, because of her customary preventive measures, and vaguely in hers inasmuch as she kept a business appointment on the Monday morning instead of going to a doctor. I must agree that I was irresponsible and should have known better; but my defence would be that my dealings with Iris were a kind of dream of sex, of relaxation, nothing so real or important as my life or death struggles in the hospital.

Her announcement was doubly volcanic: she was having our baby, and I had never been in love with her. When the soft-focus gauze was jerked up and away, our relationship was revealed with new and cruel clarity. The mix of my metaphors is descriptive of my state of mind. Perhaps the theatrical metaphor is the more accurate: the stage of our love was suddenly and starkly lit, the hiding places were illuminated, we were revealed in the altogether, and I suffered a great pang of revulsion. It was momentary. I did not know at once that it was also irreversible.

I behaved as well as I found possible. Iris made it easy for me not to pretend I was ecstatic. She too was distressed, and no doubt saw farther than me: women have a maddening talent for seeing farther into the future than their men. We did not have to do anything in a hurry, it was early days. That we should have carried on as if nothing much was different, or tried to, can only be explained by the pressure of our work and our self-supportive beliefs that her business and my career took precedence over everything else. We had no space in our lives for an intruder. She might have been weighing pros and cons, although she did not let me in on the process; I was true to my sex to the extent of subliminally leaving it to mother; when we met we giggled shamefacedly over our baby, and we procrastinated. Iris did not breathe a word about marriage. We were children of the age of permissiveness, and she probably sensed the change in me and that I would run a mile from being a husband.

I have not done us justice in the above. I do not deserve justice. And is it caddish to tell the unvarnished truth in a document that will not see the light of day? These notebooks already bear witness to my faults; Iris's, such as they were, jarred on mine increasingly. Her practical approach overruled feelings, her common sense was positively coarse. She had no patience with my attempts to honour my parents: although she was ready to charm them, she ignored her own, and once stated that parents were 'history'. She mocked my concern for patients: 'Leave your patients in the hospital,' she advised. She often called me a 'softie', 'not a man of the world', 'not streetwise'.

[347]

In good moods she spoke well of my sensitivity; when she was in a hurry, or simply impatient, she complained of my 'bleeding heart'. She minded her business even less than I minded mine: she was long-winded about her problems in the office, her climb up the greasy pole, her ambition and frustration. The act of love tells the full love story. I know I am contrary and ungrateful to acknowledge that her lips were too thin for kisses, her foreplay was brusque, sensuality was not given a lot of room in the beds we lay on, and her recovery time set records. Nakedness meant nothing but being unclothed to her – she paraded her body without aphrodisiacal discretion or shyness, and cooled passion with the misplaced enthusiasm of a nudist. The strength of her physique was more workmanlike than womanly.

I write as if I were Casanova or Don Juan. Truthfully, I had just enough experience of the opposite sex to have formed by means of elimination an ideal, that vision of the loveliness of the unattainable she. Iris and I made love over and over again, in several senses we filled vacuums for each other; but I have not yet got over the trauma of realising that I meant more to her than she did to me, and our eleven years were a mistake, a waste, and had not prepared me at any rate to pass the test that nature set us.

January has hurried by and we are halfway through February. Maeswell has not wiped the slate clean, after all. I cannot bear to look back at harsh things I have written about Iris, and shrink from writing the last act of our light comedy which gained a tragic dimension. Ma seems to have injected me with a yearning for greener grass.

A deeply embarrassing scene – Nicky marched into my consulting room after my evening spell of duty. She shut the door behind her ominously and sat down in my patients' chair. I had stood up, she asked me to sit down.

'Joe,' she said, 'why are you avoiding me?'

'Nicky,' I began, but she interrupted.

'You needn't be afraid of me – I'm not going to make trouble.'

'Nicky –' I tried again.

'I don't hold anything against you,' she said. 'You went off me, you ditched me – it happens – I wish you'd stop avoiding me, Joe – you're making my work difficult.'

I said I was sorry.

'That's the last thing I want to hear,' she batted back. 'Why can't

you be natural with me? You give all your nursing requirements to
Annie. I don't mind – I'm not complaining – I haven't lost my job
yet – but how can I stay on at this rate?'

'It's not like that...'

She interrupted again.

'We used to be friends. Why does a kiss after a party make such
a difference? It's ridiculous. I'd better go. You don't seem to know
what I'm driving at.'

She looked tearful and stood up. I approached her round my desk.

'It's all right, we'll be all right,' I said.

I would have liked to put an arm round her shoulders, but restrained
myself.

'Will it, Joe?'

'Yes – certainly – yes.'

'I shouldn't have come to see you.'

'Of course you should.'

'I'm not saying sorry – we can't say sorry to each other.'

'That's true.'

'Thanks, Joe.'

'Good night, Nicky.'

She laughed at me in a sceptical tone of voice, and walked out

Since then, thinking I may be the one not to stay on.

This is beside the point, but is comic relief and postpones the evil
hour.

Mrs Symonds called in again. She had an agonising pain in the
little toe of her right foot.

'What exactly do you mean by "agonising"?' I asked.

'Well, I had to take paracetamol in the night.'

'How many paracetamol tablets?'

'Only one, for goodness sake, Doctor – I'm not a drug addict.'

'And one common or garden tablet eased your agony?'

'Oh yes, I slept well after that.'

'Is it agony now?'

'Not quite so bad, but not good.'

'I advise you to take another paracetamol.'

'Aren't you going to give me a prescription?'

'No, Mrs Symonds. I believe your little toe will soon be hunky-
dory.'

'Is that all?'

'Yes, but come back to me if you experience agony that isn't cured by paracetamol. You could come back for a scan or invasive surgery.'

'Thank you, I definitely will.'

But I was wrong to mock. Doctors cannot be sure of anything except the fact that nobody knows. A pain in a little finger has been identified as the only symptom of a cardiac infarction.

Ran into Norah and Billy Thorner in the street. They had decided not to abort their baby. They have done the right thing, counted the costs and are being brave.

I was not, I was appalled by the prospect of parenthood, and I think Iris was, too. But we did not immediately settle on the final solution of our problem. We hesitated, toyed with various ideas, even shook the kaleidoscope to produce rosy pictures. Strange to relate and hard to confess, we let the weeks pass. It was not intentional cruelty, it was a sort of kindness – we were being kind mainly to ourselves. And we had no time to discuss and possibly set in train the complete restructuring of our relationship, lives and careers. Maybe we each hoped the other would pull the trigger. Two occurrences squeezed the trigger without pulling it all the way. Five months into the pregnancy, Iris was offered a directorship of her company, the seat on its board she had striven for. Simultaneously a localised epidemic of legionnaires' disease forced me to work more than overtime – I and other doctors were battling night and day to prevent the spread of the disease and not to catch it ourselves. Iris did not like to worry me with her dilemma, and I was unavailable anyway, snatching meals and naps at the hospital. My intention was not to sidestep the issue, but I lost track of time. In what would have been the beginning of the twenty-first week of the pregnancy Iris came and found me in a hospital ward and said something about an appointment with her gynaecologist. I did not listen, or perhaps hear – I have no clear recollection of the snatch of conversation. I did not detain, let alone accompany her. I was treating a patient who was near death, no other doctor was available – but that is only an explanation of why I caved in. My patient died soon after Iris and I had spoken, my conscience smote me, I rushed towards the wing of the hospital where the gynaecology department is located, and outside the operating theatre I saw a male nurse with a stainless steel bowl in which, partially covered by a paper towel, lay the corpse of my daughter.

I was always uneasy about abortion. The Hippocratic Oath that doctors have to swear states: 'I will not give a woman a pessary to produce abortion.' On the other hand I was uneasy about women who should not have a baby for good reasons being unable to obtain an abortion legally. The argument is beyond me here. I do not agree with the free love merchants who have implied support for, if they did not advocate, free abortions on demand; nor with Tolstoy, who had all that premarital and marital sex and then told the world that love was not to be made except for the purpose of procreation. These notes are meant to be autobiographical. I collapsed at the sight of my dead child. I collapsed in the corridor, was attended to by nurses, and taken to lie flat on a bed in a Recovery Room. I 'recovered' there from what I had colluded in doing – that is, I was able to seek Iris out in a ward and sit with her. She was not tearful. She was relieved that a stupid mistake had been corrected. She was tired and I was silent. Before long I was allowed to drive her back to her flat. She had food stored there, she said she had everything she wanted and just wanted not to make any effort, to sleep through the weekend, and get back to work in the week ahead. We parted without any meaningful communication.

It took place some days later.

Even on pages that will never be read I must draw attention to my consciousness of being in a glass house, and assert that I am not going to throw stones. No blame game! Abortion is a controversy, a difference of opinion, often a necessity, never a laughing matter, always a sorrow.

I was with Iris in her flat on a Saturday evening. We had not met since I drove her home from the hospital, and scarcely spoken on the telephone. Her flat is high up in a modern office-and-residential building. It has a balcony, great views, and is furnished in the minimalist style – almost empty, clinically tidy, cheerless and uncomfortable. You must be materialistic to live in such surroundings; but once I thought minimalism was smart. Iris welcomed me. She said she was fine, and that I looked worn out. She insisted on giving me a glass of red wine – 'It's the antidote to legionnaires' disease.' At this point she had apparently not noticed my state of mind.

'There's something I have to tell you,' I began.

'What's wrong? You're not ill, are you?'

'I need time by myself.'

'What do you mean?'

'I need to get away.'

'For a holiday?'

'To be by myself.'

'Without me?'

'Something happened, and . . .'

'Go on.'

'The baby happened, or, rather, didn't happen.'

'Are you backtracking on the abortion?'

'I raised no objections to it, and I'm not objecting now. But I have regrets, I do have regrets, and I can't shrug them off, and I need time to sort myself out.'

'You're deserting me.'

'Oh Iris!'

'Because I had the abortion – which you wanted but hadn't the guts to say so – and now you're sliding out – thanks a lot, honeybunch!'

'I saw our daughter.'

'What?'

'Don't force me to say any more.'

'Our daughter! It was an abortion. You liked doing what you did to make "our daughter". You owe me for setting you free from "our daughter". She's not the only thing that's going down the drain. I've given you eleven years of my life, and you never even offered me an engagement ring, not to mention a gold band.'

'Well – we live and learn.'

'You're not entitled to have more regrets than me. What am I expected to do?'

'You've always done what you wanted, Iris. You'll be a good company director.'

'What about you?'

'I'll carry on doctoring somewhere else, not in London.'

'Alone?'

'Yes. There's no third party. There's no party, if it comes to that.'

'I can't say I hate you, although I suppose I should.'

'You're not good at hating.'

'Or loving? Don't answer that question, Joe.'

Our conversation continued – no real row, no passion – typical of our love affair. She drank more red wine, and eventually said she had been hoping to have a nice dinner out with me. I offered her the dinner – we adjourned to the restaurant we had often patronised within walking distance of her flat. We talked of old times. She was hungry, but I had a brief attack of nausea during the meal. After I had walked her home, in the entrance to the building, she said she was not fit for copulation but was willing to try to give satisfaction if I was interested in one more for the road. I declined.

In the ensuing days my remembrance of my dead child kept on recalling me to the reality that had seemed to pass Iris by. I spent my odd half-hours off at the hospital in the chapel attached to the building. Grieving people came in to cry and pray. I benefited inasmuch as I realised I was more a religious than a scientific person.

Inevitably, when I came to live in Maeswell, Ma spoke of Iris. I told her we had split up, and she bemoaned the fact then and later. She said Iris would have been a nice wife for me – such a clever capable girl. She would have liked me to marry Iris and have children, grandchildren for her, in particular a grand-daughter – Jane's daughter Peggy was too rough and countrified. I told her that I had ceased to love Iris, and we had parted without acrimony. She scolded me with the oracular opinion of senior citizenship: 'Love's no excuse.'

A month has elapsed since I unburdened myself, and now it is more than a year after the events that changed the direction of my life. Iris has not bothered me – I no longer dread the telephone and the postman. I do not under-estimate all that I have to be grateful for. Wounds heal, although amputations can go on hurting: I still have pain in the space of my heart that was reserved for my daughter. I would love to love somebody else, but no such luck. Nicky, when I indicated that a few kisses were enough, minded more than Iris did when I indicated that I was bowing out after eleven years. Loves seem to have their different 'display until' and 'use by' dates.

Iris may have been as sick of me as I was of her. We were conveniences for each other. Her dragging matrimony into the argument amazed me. I was reminded of that girl we knew in Suffolk, a rebel who ran off with pseudo-gypsies, lived like a tramp, then got engaged to a childhood friend and hurried to Harrods to buy her trousseau and hand in her wedding present list. Iris had pretended that for her marriage, not rapine and pillage, was the fate worse than death.

[353]

Writing Iris 'out of my system' has had the desired effect, but the effect is double-edged. I have finally done the job I was waiting to do, brought down the final curtain, but now I walk home to The Poor Cottage more alone than ever.

I would have liked to call my daughter Rose.

Autumn is coming in, winds blow leaves off the trees, earth turns into mud, the days grow shorter, and I have decided to renounce self-pity. Life in Maeswell is not positively bad. My work is interesting. My colleagues are friendly, and Nicky and I have become platonic since she has 'gone out' with the man who delivers our pharmaceutical requirements. My cottage may be Poor but is my own, and I think I am healthy. At the same time I starve, my personal life is zero, a void, my work can feel like the treadmill. Ma thinks of leaving me in the lurch, and I never see any sign of a rainbow. Restlessness gains the upper hand. I cannot moon about like this for ever. In a big hospital I would at least have more nurses to choose from.

I wonder if I shall buy another notebook. The two I have filled with notes now look like the autobiography of another disappointed man. They were meant to be the preface to the second, probably last, and conceivably better phase of my life, but turned into my farewell to Iris and a memorial to Rose. My future must not be allowed to become a wasteland in the eyes of the Almighty.

Mrs Roecliffe in my consulting room today.

PART TWO

Notebook Three

I am still here.

A modern tragi-comedy, subject the NHS, main character Desmond Cochrane, Irish Englishman, a late-middle-aged drifter, drinker, punter, scrounger. He did jobs badly, sweeping pavements, for instance, and earned his actual living by milking the Welfare State. He used to be Denis Woods' patient, but Denis refused to sign any more sick notes, so Desmond told his hard line stories to Dr Austen of the other practice in Maeswell. Dr Austen was apparently a dear old fellow, nicknamed Jane by all and sundry and reputed to be gullible. He was persuaded that Desmond had something radically wrong with an ankle, which shot out in a weird way and was laughed at by schoolchildren, and referred him to Mr Stonebridge, the orthopaedic surgeon at St Anne's Hospital. Nothing happened for getting on for a year, during which Dr Austen retired to his villa in Malta. Desmond complained of the delay, but was told that Mr Stonebridge had more important cases to see to than a funny ankle. At last Desmond was summoned to St Anne's. He arrived with a plastic water bottle in hand – it contained vodka – and in the hours he had to wait got drunk. A nurse summoned him eventually, ushered him into a cubicle, told him to undress, gave him the garb for patients having operations, and in due course returned to look at his ankles. Both were dirty, and discoloured due to bad circulation: she was under the impression that he was in for amputation, some of his records had been mislaid, and she had to ask him which ankle she should mark with the blue pencil. He was too drunk to tell her clearly, and she said, 'This one, or that one?' he mumbled, 'Right, my dear,' and she marked the right ankle. A porter arrived, pushed him in a wheelchair into an anteroom, an anaesthetist gave him an injection, and Mr Stonebridge cut off the wrong foot. It was a scandal, blown up by journalists and politicians, blubbed about by do-gooders, and landed Mr Stonebridge in court. The hospital's defence was Dr Austen's retirement, Desmond's drunkenness, NHS bureaucracy and a computer fault. The taxpayer had to fork out a vast sum of money to compensate Desmond, who spent it quickly on slow horses, but was content to have rendered himself eligible for counselling, Invalidity Benefit, meals on wheels, home help, and regular visits by a trained nurse, a vicar and assorted ladies bountiful.

Mrs Roecliffe brought her daughter Melanie to see me. Melanie is eight and asthmatic, her mother beautiful.

Father forecast the fate of the NHS. He wrote to tell me why it was heading for trouble – I have the letter still. Here are his reasons: medical science would make advances that ill people would demand and the state could not supply free of charge; more people would live longer and fill too many hospital beds; people are easily over-indulged and spoilt, and spoilt people turn on and curse the spoiler for not giving them more expensive gifts, such as instant medical attention, services, care and so on; and the NHS was always bound to become a political football, done down by politicians. Father had no faith in politicians, most of whom have no professional qualifications.

The Roecliffe family has recently come to live down here, in a house called Wisteria Lodge, near the village of Taylton.

By way of contrast to Mrs Roecliffe, and somewhat ironically for me, Mrs Petty was back with the same complaint, yet another addition to her family. She is a cockney, forty-nine, her partner a road-worker, already mother of seven, heavily built, no oil painting, opinionated, humorous, and probably a diamond of the rough type. I scolded her for not taking the pill. She said she had no time to take pills. Another of her remarks would be of interest to sociology: 'He will get at me while I'm cooking the dinner.' Yet another summed up sex for lots of women: 'I'd like to put it on the windowsill and pull the window down hard.'

GPs are a repository for secrets, GPs have replaced churchmen. The generalisation that explains the inherent risks of heterosexuality is that sex for men is a miracle of mechanics, whereas sex for women is child's play, as easy as falling off a log. Religions and codes of behaviour aim to curb the activities of women and give a man some assurance that his mate's children are his own. I think, I prefer to think, that all societies respect fidelity, self-control, restraint, and I know that faithfulness is enforced by some. Love and sex are twins, but love that cannot exclude promiscuity is not up to much. I still have a pedestal ready for somebody to stand on. Have I found her?

A paradox: the more we are permissive the less sexy we are. Not immorality but morality is the aphrodisiac. I write as a doctor in practice, not a puritan or a prude. I have enough women patients to make me suspect that love in a cold climate is not so hot as advertisements, films, the pornographers and the sexologists suggest. Satyrs propose and nymphos are willing, rapists do their dirty work and sodomites wound one another, but I get the message that the British bedroom is mostly slept in.

A male baboon, as if to comment on the above, serves female baboons in season while he looks around with a bored expression on his face and seems to yawn.

Shortly before I started to write in this notebook I saw change and decay everywhere and wondered how and where to escape from all the decadence: different now.

Melanie returned, thanks be! Her asthma is responding to treatment, but she is a shy and nervous little girl and might suffer a recurrence. She has large bright-blue eyes. Her mother has grey eyes, quiet eyes.

Mrs Roecliffe startled me by saying her husband wanted a second opinion. I was doubly downcast. She said apologetically that her husband had heard of a London doctor who specialised in asthma in children. I said I quite understood and would forward my record of Melanie's case to the London doctor – it is the policy of my profession to co-operate with requests for second opinions; but my face must have fallen, for she said she hoped Melanie and her younger child, Tom, could be my patients on a permanent basis. The appointment lasted for less than ten minutes.

I hesitate to write down an absurdity yet cannot stop myself. At the age of forty-one I may have experienced the phenomenon of true love, potential love, theoretical love, love adulterous, immoral, unreciprocated, and obviously hopeless, at first sight. What it really is or was, scientifically, analytically, I cannot explain; but it happened when Mrs Roecliffe first appeared in my consulting room. It was unilateral for sure, it is almost certain to be another mistake – there is a father of the two children knocking about. I have become a 'don't know' late in life – I not only do not know a lot, as I had imagined I did, I know nothing – her Christian name, whether or not her first name is Christian, nothing to reassure me. How could I have changed in the blink of an eye from a despondent realist, a cautious practical man, into a certifiable romantic? There it is – the most hackneyed of clichés now apply – love is folly, love is blind, is brainless, reckless, incompatible with fear, and probably star-crossed. My prudent persona is horrified. What does she look like? Love casts its own light on the beloved. She is tall, slim, has dignity, has grace, has those illogically 'quiet' grey eyes, smiles more sweetly than other women. I could continue, but have to break off, not least to laugh at myself.

I should delete the above. No doubt I will have reason to do so one sad day. Meanwhile I should note down the side-effects of Mrs Roecliffe. I could not leave Maeswell while she is at Taylton, and had better tell Ma, who might have thought of Norfolk because of thinking I was not settled here. I should tidy myself up, have my hair cut, buy a new shirt, clean my shoes; and blitz The Poor Cottage, burn old papers, and bury the dead flowers in its garden – I must prepare for the most unlikely event of a visit. I would be wise to come out of my shell, revise my reclusive ideas, and seize any opportunity to meet my neighbours – society is a dating agency first and foremost. Nicky Benning and I can now be Platonists together.

I veer between dreams and nightmares. The latter preponderate. The thought that strikes me when I consider both is that happy beginnings are commoner than happy endings. A hard-headed estimate of my chances is daunting – years of frustrated adoration, failure odds on, success reserved either for when I am too old to enjoy it or post-mortem. I remember books that tell me cautionary tales: Flaubert's *L'Education Sentimentale*, the story of unconsummated love, the heroine modelled on a woman the author met when he was fourteen years old, and Balzac's *Le Lys dans la Vallée*, again a story of unconsummated devotion. The road stretching ahead of me is paved with question marks that cause bumps and damage. I am trespassing. Is it madness, or masochism, after Iris?

With Ma yesterday, she again brought up the subject of Iris. I said I had never fallen in love with her. Ma said the equivalent of nonsense, and how could I claim such a thing after living with poor Iris for all those years?

'I never lived with her,' I replied. 'We met and parted by common consent when we felt like it. And she was never poor financially or emotionally – she let me go without a fuss, and I believe she's drawn a line under our affair as I have.'

'Is that right, Joe?'

'It's more right than a charade and pretence. We haven't quarrelled over our bones of contention.'

'Was it ... was it only physical?'

'Maybe – but the physical side was never perfect for me – I'd call our affair friendly and lazy – we were preoccupied and didn't bother to disagree or look elsewhere.'

'I'm so sorry, Joe.'

'You needn't be.'

'But we thought it was love, your father and I always hoped you'd make a match of it, we couldn't understand your holding back.'

'Now I'll say sorry, Ma.'

'Your father and I wanted to be always in each other's pockets – that was how we described our feelings. We wanted to be close and have a family. Didn't anything like that come into your feelings for Iris?'

'No – yes – I thought so – and she too, I believe – but the fact is that love wasn't our top priority. Whatever our feelings were, they weren't strong enough to withstand strain.'

'I've never asked why you broke up. What sort of strain, Joe? Would you rather not tell me?'

'I don't know.'

'It was lovely for me when you came to Maeswell, but always a mystery.'

'We had a child.'

'Did you say...?'

'Yes – a girl – she was aborted.'

'Oh no!'

'I would have called her Rose.'

'Oh Joe!'

'Rose came between Iris and me, and Maeswell was to be the beginning of a new start. Iris wasn't more responsible for what happened than I was.'

'How did the abortion...? Perhaps I shouldn't ask...'

'It's all right, Ma. We dithered, we had other fish to fry – we were so busy and wrong-headed – and we took the decision late and in a hurry. And I couldn't go on living the life that had been the death of Rose.'

'I'm so sad for you, but thank you for telling me. Has being at Maeswell helped you?'

'I thought it would, I thought it did, then I thought it wasn't helping, and now I think it's given me a new lease – I shan't leave here for the foreseeable future, Ma. What about you?'

'I'm staying, too.'

'Not for my sake, not because of Rose? If you'd prefer to be in Norfolk, I wouldn't like to be stopping you.'

'No, Joe – the Proctors are rather too much for me – they're hard-up and frightfully hard-working, Jane and Neil are, and Tony and Peggy are young – I'd only be in their way.'

'We'll stick together, Ma.'

'I do hope so. Has anything else changed your mind?'

I had to laugh – she was as sharp as ever – Father always made a joke of her feminine intuition.

'Nothing to report yet, if ever,' I replied.

'Can I say good luck?!'

'Yes, Ma – thanks very much.'

I was thankful for the conversation as well as the luck. Ma will no longer imagine I abandoned Iris on a whim and left her broken-hearted. Later she spoke some words of wisdom that are worthy of note. She said: 'I was influenced to stay put in Maeswell by Ethel Harrop' – another resident in Silver Court. 'Ethel's a widow from London whose only son works near here – he's a solicitor, and married with children, he's called Timothy. Ethel fell over in her London house, broke her pelvis, lay on the floor for hours, and was discovered by her daily lady. Well, Timothy had a scare, and said it would be much better if his mother moved down to Maeswell, better for him because he could keep watch over her as he couldn't while she was miles away in London, and better for her because she would see more of her family, her grandchildren especially. Ethel followed Timothy's advice. The consequence is that she's lost all her London friends, locals and shop people and doctors, everyone she depended on, and has to try to make new friends at her age. She's very lonely and hardly ever sees Timothy or his wife or his children – they're all worn out by work and plans and exams and social engagements, and have no time for her although they do try to take her out to lunch on Sundays. She misses her old home, too, and can't settle in a two-roomed flatlet. Really, children shouldn't have those good intentions which make old folk miserable – the old folk would be happier to be lonely and die where they've always lived. We're all agreed about it in Silver Court. Anyway, I took the hint from Ethel. I moved to Maeswell just in time to adjust to it and settle down. Maeswell's my home, and to go back to East Anglia after all these years would be horrid, and far from helpful to you, Joe, because you'd worry and have to motor miles to check up on me. And I'd be a terrible bore to Jane, and the more so the older and dottier I became.'

First name, Mary – Mary Roecliffe. I consulted the grapevine: Sylvia in Reception told me that Mrs Roecliffe had rung for an appointment with Audrey Fletcher – that is, for a first appointment – but Audrey was on leave, and she agreed to let me attend to Melanie. Sylvia said Mrs Roecliffe had explained that she was acquainted with Audrey, and that Audrey had advised her to contact our practice if in need of medical help. I therefore detained Audrey in the rest-room as she scurried through it – she never rests – and extracted the information that Mary is married to Bruce Roecliffe and Bruce is a chum of her husband, Andy. Andy Fletcher is the rugger player, who struck me at the Fletchers' dinner party and again at the Christmas do as being on the chauvinist side. What would Bruce be like? Why did Mary marry him? But I know people should not be judged by their spouses.

We are being oppressed by the government. We are bullied by clerks in Whitehall. We are casualties of the Welfare State and squirm under the heels of the do-gooders. We are now bedevilled by so much paperwork, forms and questionnaires, that we are considering hiring a retired accountant to cope with them on three afternoons a week at our own expense.

Bureaucracy and chaos, the two seem to go together. The other day a woman and a boy came into the surgery both bleeding and sobbing: she was Ellen Thursby, Frank Cunningham's patient, a teacher at the state school down the road, and he was her pupil, Tommy Iles. Apparently a bad boy called Glen had been expelled by Miss Thursby, but had forced an entry into her classroom, crashed a fist into the side of her face and possibly dislocated Tommy's arm, been arrested at last by policemen, escorted off the school's premises, and then let go. We had to send the wounded ones to St Anne's Hospital by taxi. Miss Thursby declared that she would never teach again, nobody could, in schools and a country without rules, discipline, order or law. We have three similar grievances. Audrey had to press her panic button the other day when two young people threatened to 'cut her up' for refusing to give them drugs; then a man zonked out on cannabis obtained an appointment with Frank in order to ask him how to slit somebody's throat – Frank had to press his button, too. Thirdly, Denis Woods was off work for a week after doing weekend night duty at St Anne's: he was assaulted by a young drunk. As a result we are depressed to read that the liberals in and out of government are about to legalise 'soft' drugs and make alcohol available in retail outlets round the clock.

Robert Chimes wanted a bed for the night and I said nothing doing. I would have been pleased to see my dear old friend, but he is a barrister and would cross-question me. He met his wife Barbara at a children's party, married her, fathered a couple of children, and never looked to right or left – Fido should be his middle name. He nagged me for eleven years over Iris, compared me with bounders who sneak into gentlemen's clubs of which they are not paid-up members; and he would be equally disapproving of my having fallen for a woman whom I have met twice on other business, and is heavily married. Robert is down to earth to the point of being in it too deep to see the difference between a night with a beckoning star and a cloudy day with drizzle. I am not prepared to reveal myself full frontally to any satirical party.

Sorry to have missed Robert, and mortified to have caught an imaginary glimpse of my attachment to Mary Roecliffe through his eyes. He might have said I have retrogressed to the magic world of a premature second childhood. He might have suggested that I was like the lovers who pick on partners incapable of reciprocity for a variety of reasons and will never submit an embarrassing request for proof that they are beloved. Not so, not so! Something passed between Mary Roecliffe's eyes and mine when she followed Melanie into my consulting room, a message, if you like, a beginning, if you like, or the beginning of the end, as I would prefer to put it. The nothing that did happen, throughout the first consultation and the second, was much more dramatic and exciting than the loss of my virginity. And after all, there is magic, and there are miracles. I believe in the latter. How is life on earth and in the solar system explicable otherwise – nobody has explained it so far. Robert might scoff in spite of being a Christian, but which of us will have the last laugh?

Setting aside Mary Roecliffe for a moment, the farcical vicissitudes of Professor Lanskill have been something different – and a change is as good as a holiday. Philip Lanskill is old, eightyish, and eccentric, to put it mildly. He was a Professor of Eng.Lit. at some obscure University, is married to another superannuated academic, Una, and they live in a small house in Allende Terrace. Although they are both nearly bald, upstanding white fluff is their crowning glory, and their spectacles are like the bottoms of bottles. He has a deep voice, she squeaks, their home is thought to be unfit for human habitation, and they drive a vintage Hillman Minx. Not long ago they were due to drive to Tinbury, but the Minx was unco-operative, so the Professor went to crank the engine while Una remained in the driving seat. The car was in the garage. He inserted the crank handle and managed to turn it. The car started, was in gear, crushed him against the back wall of the garage, his right leg in particular. He recovered eventually from this accident, returned home, and again decided to go for a drive in the Minx. He sat in the back seat and fastened the safety belt in case of an accident. When the Lanskills arrived at their destination, Philip caught a foot in the safety harness, fell out of the car and broke his good leg. At last he was sufficiently strong to rejoin Una in Allende Terrace. But he was frail, felt insecure, and tried to wire up certain locks and door handles in order to repel burglars. Inevitably he forgot which metal surfaces were connected to the electricity supply, gripped a door handle, received a tremendous shock, was badly burned and broke an arm. He is still alive. He is the patient of Denis Woods, who has refused to provide certification to the effect that he is fit to drive an invalid buggy.

My goodness! Audrey Fletcher has invited me to dinner this evening. She has asked both Roecliffes, but Bruce is unavailable and she wondered if I would be kind enough to step in.

I am dressed and just off, dreading a rude awakening.

Dread unnecessary, disappointments nil, sighs numerous, regrets futile.

It was a 'business' dinner for eight. I was the last but one to arrive, Audrey was in the kitchen and called out to me. Andy greeted me without a handshake and told me the first name of the other guests, Alan and wife Tracy and Seb with partner Bubbles. Alan shook hands, Tracy said 'Hi!', Seb made a sort of bow and Bubbles said, 'Can I consult you?' Andy offered me a dry martini in a cocktail glass with a frosted rim: Bubbles explained, 'You drink the gin through the ice, isn't it loverly?' Alan was thickset with dark hair like fur, Seb was taller, bespectacled and with yellow hair reaching over the back of the collar of his shirt. Alan wore a grey suit, Seb a leather jerkin, and Andy a roll-necked jersey – Alan and Seb were tieless. Alan's Tracy was mutton dressed like lamb, Bubbles showed too much cleavage. The average age of the company was early forties. Audrey was having to cope with Kathy and Trevor, the Fletcher children, while she cooked.

The atmosphere was sticky. Andy is rough verging on aggressive, Alan was silent, Seb jokey, Tracy rather on her dignity, and Bubbles trying to live up to her nickname. We were to eat at a dinner table laid for eight in part of the open-plan living-room – the kitchen was behind a room-divider. The cocktails were strong, but the party spirit less so.

The doorbell rang and a moment or two later Andy led Mary Roecliffe into the room. Her appearance is like a blessing. She looks high class, discreet, open-minded, warm-hearted; reserved and friendly in my opinion.

She kissed or was kissed by the other people: were they linked by her husband? She bade me 'Good evening' – to my mind with a charming hint of intimacy or at least humour. She was offered and refused a martini. She hoped she was not late. She has rich dark-brown hair and the prettiest smile. She is poised and holds herself well.

Audrey had taken the children up to bed and now joined us, not looking as if she had been working overtime. Andy made a revealing remark when she and I confronted each other: 'Quack quack!' She shook her head at his witticism and asked us to come and sit at the table.

I was placed between Bubbles and Mary – later in the evening we got on to Christian name terms. She had Andy on her other side. The food was prawn cocktails – already on the table; then chicken casserole – Andy called it *coq au vin* to amuse his cronies – which was dished out with vegetables in the kitchen; then chocolate mousse and cheese. The wine was white throughout.

Andy talked to Mary to start with. Bubbles talked to me. She is a nice person and would be nicer if she calmed down. She treated me to her medical history, which is quite long although she looked to me as fit as a flea. Eventually I was able to talk to Mary. So far as I can remember I said nothing of interest, perhaps the same applied to her, but I thought it all wonderful. She told me about Melanie and Tom, Wisteria Lodge, her enjoyment of being near Maeswell, and I told her that I lived in The Poor Cottage and my mother had a flat in Silver Court. Whether or not she was gripped by these exchanges is a moot point; but I felt we were at least at ease together. The one exception to our humdrum conversation was when I asked if she was a reader, if she liked reading books, and she replied with enthusiasm that she loved it. I mentioned that I was tackling Gogol's *Dead Souls*, and she said she had heard of that book but was sad to say she was ignorant of Russian literature.

We were interrupted – Audrey was trying to get general conversation going – I suspected she was making heavy weather of Alan and Seb – moreover she was hopping up and down to deal with the dinner and could not converse with anyone for long.

Audrey succeeded, but her victory was Pyrrhic – Andy and his cronies took over, talked shop, and nobody else got many words in. This happened towards the end of dinner, round about ten o'clock, and after our host had replenished glasses generously. The shop that was talked was money – the three men worked in financial services, Andy the stockbroker, Alan a banker, Seb sold life insurance, and I understood that Bruce Roecliffe was an independent playing the same sort of game. Words that were double Dutch to me, and effectively shut Mary up, were batted back and forth across the dining table: macroeconomics, stagflation, bonds versus equities, dead cat bounces, toes in water, May and St Leger Day. I only raised my voice once, unfortunately to utter a howler. I requested a definition of a word often repeated, brick, which could not be a brick for building. They laughed at me. Seb said, 'Come on, Doc, you're supposed to be one of the makers of bricks,' which Andy and Alan thought funny. Audrey rushed to my rescue. She said: 'Take no notice, Joe – they don't know the names of the diseases you'll soon be treating them for – a brick is slang for a million pounds – which, as you and I are well aware, is not what we make.'

The party finished soon after ten. It was a weekday, people had babysitters to relieve, and early starts on the next day. On the way out I asked Mary: 'If I came across a Russian book I thought you'd like, might I send it to you?' She replied, 'Oh – thank you,' and we shook hands.

I could write a learned monograph on handshakes and kisses on cheeks. Some are good, some bad, judged by certain criteria. Mary knew that she attracted me, women know these things even before the men do. In the circumstances prevailing, I would give her handshake, the handshake of a faithful wife who is not averse to having made a conquest, ten out of ten.

It is two days later, and this morning Audrey and I met by chance on the stairs at the Surgery. I thanked her for the dinner party and said I had been going to write to her; she thanked me for turning out at such short notice, and told me not to bother to write. She said: 'I'm afraid it got a bit financial,' and I said it had been a most interesting evening. She asked: 'Did you fall for Mary?' I jumped, but managed an answer that was too affirmative: 'Absolutely, head over heels!' Audrey laughed and said, 'Well, she enjoyed sitting next to you.'

Love is not love unless it hides its face. I did not want to confide in Audrey, but regretted having missed my chance to ask her twenty questions about Mary Roecliffe. I was also suspicious of Audrey: what were the implications of her guessing that I would fall for Mary? Was she paying Mary a compliment, or casting aspersions? In short I was at sea – emotionally, nervously – since having been within kissing distance of my lady for two and a half hours. And I still am. My worst idea is that I have embroiled myself in a fantasy, and nothing will come of nothing; I have rebounded from Iris, and Mary belongs to a multi-millionaire and their issue.

Love at forty is not like love at twenty. It seems to me that the older you are the more impulsive and impatient, and the more difficulty you have in agreeing that the proprieties have to be observed.

A young man asked me to attend to a cut in his forehead. What was his story? He said the cut was a love-scar. I asked for more information, and he almost boasted that he was a bisexual. When I put on rubber gloves he called me a coward.

Frank Cunningham requested assistance this afternoon. I was at home, worrying about Mary, and in need of diversion. Frank drove me the seven or eight miles to the home of an old doctor, Dr Willy Monkton. I had heard the name, he had been a respected physician and was the friend of Frank and once upon a time his boss. Flora Monkton, the doctor's wife, was Frank's patient and had summoned him urgently: the reasons why were like scenes in a film. Burnside, where the Monktons had lived for half a century, was grim, grey and derelict. Creeper grew across the front door, windows were broken, paint peeled, and the verges of the driveway were virgin forest. We walked through weeds to a side door. Flora opened it – she was very old and hobbled, used a tall stalker's stick and spoke with a Scottish accent. She led us to a room that must have been a servants' hall in the palmy days. Dr Willy sat in a chair – a relic, hairless, toothless, and not all there. Flora asked us the following question: – what was to be done – her husband wanted to die and would be better dead, he was incontinent as well as insane, and she longed to take her own life? We drank tea and had no positive answer. There was no legal answer. Frank was depressed during our drive back to Maeswell. He chose to see the Monktons as living proofs of the decline and fall of our country. Dr Willy had volunteered for military service in the 1914 war and lost the sight of an eye. He had volunteered again in 1939 and contracted malaria that dogged him for years. He had bought War Loan, which was never repaid by government, and its capital value dwindled. His only child, a son, a soldier decorated for bravery, was killed. He had been burgled and mugged. He had sought medical treatment on the NHS and been infected with MRSA. Frank said that Dr Willy had been brought low by politics and taxation, bad medicine and lawlessness. Our drive took us through Taylton, near Wisteria Lodge, and my heart urged a far more optimistic line.

I wrote the above yesterday, and omitted a detail that affects me personally. Dr Willy Monkton married his patient – Frank Cunningham

reminded me that it was unethical and said Willy was lucky not to
have been struck off.

I am Mary's children's GP at present: is it unethical of me to be in
love with their mother?

To church this morning. My religion commands me not to harbour
the feelings I have for Mary. It may be splitting hairs, but I do not
expect or plan to act on those feelings in the meanwhile, perhaps
ever. The Lord's Prayer helped, as usual: I repeated 'Thy will be done'.

I seldom entered a church in the eleven years I was with Iris. She
was agnostic or atheist, or pagan. I was not brainwashed by her lack
of interest in religion, or influenced by her silly scepticism. The silver
lining to the death of Rose was that I rediscovered my religion and
derived most comfort from praying.

I would never again opt to be as uncomfortable as I subliminally
was with Iris.

A girl of twenty-two called Cherry is the daughter of non-smokers,
never smoked, has a non-smoking boyfriend, and has lung cancer. Ninety-
year-old Bertha called me out because she was suffering pain in her
foot, and in her cottage I was almost asphyxiated by the smell of cigarette
smoke. She did not have gout, the foot had nothing radically wrong. I
gave her a few painkillers, and in return she offered me a fag. Luck,
and how to bear bad luck, is why religions were invented. In church I
thought of the hostage I have given to fortune, and how risky my life
has become.

I spent another night in the A & E at St Anne's Hospital. As a result
I have a bruised calf of my left leg, where I was kicked by an
intoxicated female teenage nitwit, and am exhausted, disgusted, depressed
and the opposite of patriotic. Another doctor and I must have attended
to at least a hundred drunkards and drug addicts between ten p.m.
last night and seven this a.m., and we had four nurses to help us.
The waste of our time and energy, and of everyone's taxes, is in-
excusable: here, in my notebook, I refuse to play the game of hypocrisy
and can write the unspeakable truth. The liberal excuses for drug-
ging, binge drinking, yobbishness, hooliganism, violent behaviour and

criminal activities are poverty, upbringing, schooling, unemployment, racism, class and frustration. Stale buns! So what's new? What is new is lack of discipline. The words that cannot be spoken, the ancient remedies for sicknesses of the state, are punishments that fit the crimes. Forgiveness of offenders is all very well, but the prevention of offences by fear is more protective of the innocent. At present there is no death penalty for murderers, even serial or most foul, no corporal punishment which would keep people out of prison, no meaningful manner of controlling children allowed, no end to benefits or state money paid to undeserving people, and in fact no rebuttal by the establishment of the popular belief that money grows on trees. I know the decadence of our country is attributable to deep political errors, Marxist-communism-socialism and the pipe-dream of 'Welfare'; but attempts should begin to be made to rectify them. These weekend blood-baths in Tinbury and elsewhere should be abolished chop-chop. And ultimate deterrents are no bad thing, as the politicians of countries with weapons of mass destruction keep on telling us.

I am not a reactionary. I just wish England would stop sinking deeper and deeper into the mire. I could say I was not 'political' if my employer, the Government, would stop entangling me in red tape.

Some talk of holidays in the rest-room today. I said I would not be taking a holiday for the foreseeable future. Frank Cunningham said, 'All work and no play...'; Audrey said, 'You should, you know,' and Denis said, 'Well, I'll be extending mine in that case.'

No more of the nourishing coincidences on which love feeds. Four weeks have passed since the Fletchers' dinner. I would not mind being a fly on an interior wall of Wisteria Lodge, but Bruce and possibly Mary herself might swat me. Hunger gnaws.

Sad case: I had to break the news to Maurice Branyard that he has cancer. He is fifty-something, husband, father, an accountant, who recently lost his job with a large London firm – there had been a whiff of scandal. Maurice became my patient a few months ago – he had lost weight as well as his job. His reaction to the news of his cancer was surprising. He told me he had begun life in an orphanage, his parents had abandoned him, had then spent a few years with a cruel foster mother, and aged four or five had got his foot off a snake and on to a ladder in the home of a good fostering family. Ever since, he said, it had been a struggle to rise in the world. He had embraced the politics of envy and become a socialist. He was also dogged by the fear of failure and slipping back to his beginnings. That was why he had tried to do still better and had done worse. Yes, he confessed, he was guilty of juggling a figure or two, not quite of cooking the books. Why, why had he needed to, why had he done it? Because, he answered himself, ambition is habit forming, he had wanted more than he already had, more money, status, respect, security. He wound up by saying that the temptation for 'self-made' persons to take a last step on the ladder is almost irresistible; and that because of his illness he now wanted less and less, nothing but life on any terms. Perhaps his case was not so sad as I had initially thought it.

I begin to think that Mary Roecliffe is my wild goose. I can foresee no future in flapping along after her.

A case with similarities: I was able to read the letter from the Oncology Department at St Anne's to Constance Plym, who cried out, 'Hurrah!' The letter was addressed to Frank Cunningham. He had summoned his patient, Mrs Plym, but was called out urgently and asked me to see her. She is middle-aged and motherly. She said to me: 'For five years I've waited for the "all clear", and regretted the chances I had not taken when I was younger. Such a mistake! Now I've been given something I don't deserve – nobody deserves it but I've been given it – a second chance – and by golly I won't let it slip through my fingers!'

Contrary or not, this is a draft of the letter I might write to Mary.
    'It was a treat for me to sit next to you at the Fletchers', and to find out that you are a fellow-bookworm. I am sending you a book in hopes that you will enjoy it, *First Love* by Ivan Turgenev. I also hope to have a chance of discussing it with you one day, but please don't feel obliged to read it. The book is a gift, and second-hand, as you can see – it cost me about 10p so far as I can remember.'

I shall try again, here is draft 2: 'At the Fletchers' you gave me permission to send you a book I thought you might like, and you also said you had not read many Russian books. So I enclose Turgenev's

First Love, which in my opinion is lyrical and lovely, and surely very well translated by Isaiah Berlin. It's a gift – it cost me nothing – and a souvenir too. I hope Melanie is well, and you are too, and that we'll meet again before too long.'

A third draft, below, would tell the whole truth: 'I'm sending you *First Love* because it's good and because the title describes my feelings for you. I know I shouldn't declare myself to a married woman who has given me no encouragement, and who is unlikely to believe that she is the first love of a man of my age – but it's true. I was the "lover" of another woman for a long time, but that attachment cannot be compared with this one. Turgenev loved a woman who didn't return his love, he loved her all his life – is it my fate to suffer his experience? I don't care, and I do and will care, if you understand me. I aspire only to know you better, become your friend, be in your life – nothing more, realistically. Forgive me! Yours.'

I posted no book and no letter. I could not hint at, let alone explain, the significance of Turgenev's title in our circumstances, nor could she be expected to assume the role of Pauline Viardot-Garcia in a possible rerun of Turgenev's dramatic emotional biography. She would read *First Love*, if she read it, and simply follow the story of a boy in love with a girl and his discovery that the girl and his father were lovers. My drafts of letters remain in this notebook. But yesterday I remembered Mrs Plym and seized my chance for better or worse. My letter was as discreet as I could make it.

One consequence of waiting for a word from Wisteria Lodge is that I have given instructions to the girls in reception to assign Mrs Roecliffe to another doctor, Audrey preferably, or Frank or Denis. It was embarrassing – Bessie looked at me inquiringly. I could not supply reasons: which were that I remembered the Monktons, and Frank's comment that Doctor Willy might have been struck off for marrying his patient, Flora. Against my will, wishes, yearnings and hopes, common sense and the instinct of survival prevailed. If Mary should ever fall into my arms in my consulting room, if a magic wand should be waved for my benefit, I would not like to be disgraced professionally. That is a fact, the rest is fiction.

Nicky Benning is pregnant. She is going to marry her boyfriend, the pharmaceutical muscle-man, who delivers our drugs. He is called Nigel. Jokes have done their rounds in the practice: that Nigel proposed after spiking her drink with an anti-depressant. I congratulated her and she hugged me and said: 'He may not be a good fish but he's not bad' – a kind of compliment, I suppose.

Nicky is in her fourth month, and has told us she will be taking advantage of the new legislation affecting mothers: which means maternity leave and counting on getting her job back in due course. She has a friend, another qualified nurse, a delightful young woman who is able, willing and eager to take over. But the friend is youngish and recently married. We made excuses, we reduced her to tears, we angered Nicky, and instead engaged a grandmotherly nurse of fifty-five, who wishes to be known as Mrs Loft. Women of child-bearing age are no longer employable by small firms and probably by big ones; and I understand that men can also get paternity leave. The work-force will soon consist of children, old women and impotent men.

Mrs Pullen brought me a black eye this morning. The eye was hers, and it and the other one shed tears. She sobbed that Daphne, her daughter, little Daphne who was dim and pathetic, was the culprit. 'She hit me, Doctor, when I only said to her "Don't" – she reached up and hit me.' The worst of it was that Mrs Pullen had paid for Daphne to go to self-assertion classes.

Stunned!

I could not bring myself to write more than that word, stunned, yesterday. There were too many words, I was overwhelmed; I am calmer now, and with luck the hand that holds the pencil will not shake. Yesterday afternoon, about three-thirty, when I was at home between morning surgery, home visits and evening surgery, Bessie the receptionist rang me. Mrs Roecliffe had called in to return a book, Bessie said, and wondered if it would be convenient to drop it in at The Poor Cottage: yes, I said. Five minutes later she, Mary, knocked on my door. She was blushing, and no doubt I was. She had been bold although she was diffident. She was apologetic; but my welcome, however stammered out, should have convinced her that she had done no wrong in my eyes. She stepped into my house – my parlour, I could write, for it is my only sitting-room, but I would prefer not to suggest that I am a spider. She said she knew she ought not to be disturbing me – which is certainly what she had done, despite my assurance that she interrupted nothing. She said she wished just to have time to tell me how much she had enjoyed *First Love*. We sat on either side of my fireplace. She sat in the chair on the right, with the window behind her, and the light caught her hair as if to form a halo, and, when she moved, the side of her face and her eyes. She declined refreshments. She wore warm clothing, a skirt not trousers, and showed a well-turned ankle.

She said: 'I can't thank you enough for introducing me to Turgenev,' and I replied: 'I can't thank you enough for coming to see me and tell me that I'd chosen the right book for you.'

I did not tell her that I had meant the book to be a gift – I was benefiting from her regarding it as a loan – and the pleasant possibility crossed my mind that she was establishing an excuse for seeking my company.

We spoke of Ivan Turgenev. I referred to Pauline Viardot-Garcia, and she seemed to admire his lifelong devotion, almost dedication, to her – she did not find it foolish or odd. I mentioned other examples of voluntary enslavement, and the proven possibility of first love being the last for some men and some women. She agreed. Whether or not she took these exchanges in any way personally is not known. A strange thing had happened, our instant ability to talk to each other freely, in my case more freely than I talked to other people – stranger than it had been in my consulting room and at that dinner party. Conversationally, we crossed a frontier – we were in a world where words were precious and every sentence uttered by one was food for thought for the other. It was light stuff, feather-light, not ponderous at all, but she inclined her head as if to reflect on what had been said, and delivered her responses to me with excitement, as if they had just struck her.

We reverted to Turgenev and his book. She said he had conveyed the disappointment and disillusion of the boy to perfection. She sympathised with the pain of discovering that the object of love – the boy's love – was not so pure and good as he had imagined and believed. Was she convinced by Turgenev's description of love? Oh yes, she replied, but as if she meant to say, 'Of course!' What did she read? And when? I told her that I had done most of my reading before I was qualified and became an overworked doctor, but that recently I had again known the joy of losing myself in books. She said she had read *First Love* in one evening. She said she made time to escape into a book. What should she read next, she asked. I should have replied, *War and Peace*, but Tolstoy's book is long, if I lent her my copy she would not bring it back for weeks. I therefore said, 'Tolstoy's *Childhood, Boyhood and Youth* – it's at least as good as *First Love* – and you might like it even better.' She was dressed so nicely by my standards, informally, perhaps with the superior art that conceals art, and her complexion glowed in spite of her face being in shadow. She had a few freckles and wore a touch of lipstick.

'I should go,' she said.

'Please don't hurry,' I replied. 'I'm not busy.'

'But I've invaded your privacy.'

'It's the nicest sort of invasion.'

'The Poor Cottage doesn't really describe your home – it's so cosy and pretty.'

'Well – it doesn't feel poor any more – I might have been attracted by the name once upon a time.'

'How long have you lived here?'

'Getting on for a year.'

'I'm sorry you were ever poor.'

'I'm not now. Do you like living in Wisteria Lodge?'

'Oh yes. But...'

'But?'

'It's rather big, and I haven't got round to decorating it as I wish ... but I know how lucky I am to have such a home.'

I said, 'I want to explain something,' and she looked at me nervously.

I continued: 'I'm sorry I can't be your doctor.'

'Oh, that.' She sounded relieved. Had she thought I would go too far too soon? 'Yes, they explained at St John's Surgery that you were fully booked up, but could fit in my children.'

'It has to be that way, regrettably. I would take care of you all if I could.'

She looked at me. We looked at each other. It was nothing much, yet it was more than I expected, had dared to hope, had experienced before. Her eyes rested on me quietly – the metaphor or paradox or whatever is intentional. She reached for her bag, a shoulder bag made of soft material. But she stayed put, and I detained her by striking a less alarming note.

'We haven't discussed the Fletchers' party.'

'No.'

'Are you and the Fletchers old friends?'

'My husband has business links with Andy. Audrey's a sweet person. She'll be my doctor.'

'I was a bit taken aback by Andy.'

'A lot of people are. I'm not a very social person.'

'Nor am I. I see too many people every day.'

'And I've added to the number.'

'That's different.'

'Thank you. I'll have to go.'

'Wait a tick – here's the Tolstoy book.'

She put it in her bag, we thanked each other, and we stood in the brighter light on the pavement.

She said: 'I went to a service of carols at Christmas in the church over there. I took my children, and I liked the vicar.'

'He's called Bill Wetherby.'

'You know him?'

'I go to Early Service when I can. He likes the good old-fashioned Communion Service.'

'You're lucky. At Taylton the vicar asks us to shake hands with one another, which isn't easy because there are so few of us and we're all over the church.'

We laughed. Her laugh was spontaneous and infectious, and she has pretty teeth.

We said goodbye, and as she walked away I re-entered the cottage, not wanting to spy on her rear view or overload our parting with sentiment.

Coming down to earth with a bump, I was called out by Mrs Symonds. Her symptoms were dramatic even by her standards: she claimed she had dripped with sweat for twenty-four hours and was convinced her end was nigh. It was warm weather for April and I opened her front door, which was unlocked as arranged. A blast of heat greeted me. I was in Mrs Symonds' sitting room. She was in an armchair by an electric fire showing three red bars, fully dressed in clothes that looked wintry. And I had noticed that a central heating radiator was on and that all the windows were double-glazed and closed.

'Oh, Doctor, this heat is killing me,' she had the nerve to wail.

My remedial impulse was to switch off the electric fire and the central heating, leave the front door open because I could not open any of the windows, remove my jacket and scold her.

'But it's only April, Doctor, and April's a treacherous month, and I was determined not to catch a chill on top of everything else.'

I fanned the front door to get air into the house.

'Oh, I will say that's better, Doctor – you have helped me and your visit wasn't in vain.'

I said: 'You might have killed yourself – it was like a greenhouse in here – didn't you know how hot the room was? And why are you wearing that thick-knit cardigan?'

'Oh, Doctor, don't you be crisp with me, please – I'm an invalid.'

'You can't be an invalid to have survived in a cauldron.'

'That's not kind of you, Doctor.'

'Oh well, good night, Mrs Symonds.'

'Aren't you going to take my pulse?'

'It's my own pulse that worries me – you've put my blood pressure up with your shenanigans.'

She laughed in her disarming way, and then I laughed, too.

The point of this anecdote is that it links up with another. In the coldest March morning, frosty, gale from Russia, a juggernaut driver called Darren marched into my consulting room in a T-shirt and jeans. He had a heavy cold and asked for an antibiotic.

'You're not wearing enough clothing,' I said.

He said he never wore more.

'Don't you feel the cold?'

'Never,' he replied.

There is a class of persons who are born without thermostats.

Mary Roecliffe has established herself in my head. I think of her all the time, which is not to say second thoughts are excluded. Our ten minutes together in The Poor Cottage were for me rich beyond dreams of avarice, as a phrasemaker might say. I believe I enjoyed every emotion celebrated by lovers since Adam met Eve. But relations between Adam and Eve had a trace of ambiguity, and I had felt both at home with Mary and that I teetered on the edge of a cliff or a crevasse. I was safe and in danger. On reflection, realistically, probably, she called on me because she knew I loved her – I had made myself clear enough, anyway her intuition would have told her. She called on me because she needed support, reassurance, and knew I would supply it as best I could. I was not the only one to plot and plan, she asked for another book, she accepted the loan of one, she spoke of visiting my church. In short, she indicated that I figured in her future. We were in the same boat. But what future was that, and where were we drifting in our boat? I was in receipt of ominous hints in respect of her marriage, husband, even her child Melanie. I was not an accomplished adulterer, had not plumbed the adulterous depths with Iris, but I had treated patients who were and who had been; I had second-hand experience and book-learning. The fun of adultery is balanced by jealousy, the better the adultery the worse the frustration, and always the risk of becoming the adhesive that sticks a married pair together. Besides, it is often a mistake to marry your mistress or your lover. What was I walking into so blithely? Memories of Johnny-head-in-air haunted me. But then ... Then I realised ... Then it was too late. I have more ahead of me than to turn back to. I had committed myself and I renewed my commitment. Caring was reinforced by curiosity. And I am on the last page of this notebook.

Notebook Four

M Y MARK for morality is nought. One of the worst sins is mine, and that it is so far not physical is neither here nor there. For consistency my mark is also nought. I have been dead against the permissive society, yet had sexual relations with a woman who was not my wife for eleven years. I sanctioned the abortion of my child, blamed the mother of the child for aborting it, and deserted her. I am a man of my time, and ashamed of myself. Yet I cannot be responsible for another sort of abortion, I cannot do it – God should not have invented love if He wished us not to fall in it. Mary may prove to be my penance.

Nothing has happened, nothing may ever happen.

I go for afternoon walks in the Forest of Ashes, extensive woodland owned by the National Trust in the Taylton area, and fantasise about a chance meeting and love consummated under the trees.

Supper with Ma in Silver Court. She cooked me scrambled eggs and crisp streaky bacon and toast on the electric rings in her kitchenette, and afterwards we had tinned black cherries and cream. When I said she knew the way to a man's heart, she replied that I ought to find a woman who would cook me regular meals.

'Do you mean a wife?' I asked.

'No, no.'

'I thought I heard an old record being played in the middle distance.'

'Well, she could be your wife if she cooked well enough.'

We had a laugh, and the subject changed.

'Gabriella's had a windfall,' she remarked.

'Who?'

'Gabriella Shelby – you must remember her – she's the unlikely spinster, and my friend at Silver Court. Well, she's made quite a bit of money.'

'How?'

'No, dear – nothing wrong with it – she gave some money to a man who works in the City and she got back twice as much.'

'Is he a stockbroker?'

'Something like that – a financial person – and she's bowled over by him – he's so charming as well as clever with money. He lives part of the time not far from here. He's called Bruce Roecliffe.'

Adultery Without Tears advises us to learn not to emote when we hear the name of the beloved's spouse bandied about.

To church at St Mary's, the early service, spoilt for me by entertaining irreligious hope that Mary might be there. In the good old days of attendance at church for all and sexual frustration, the joke was that 'Let us pray' should be spelt 'Let us prey'.

I had to laugh when I attended the death-bed of my patient Jimmy Lovell. He was an alcoholic and divulged some of the secrets of his fun and games in days gone by. He thanked God for vodka, which does not smell on the breath. He said he must have drunk a million bottles of brightly coloured fruit-flavoured liquid laced with vodka. He had hidden bottles of vodka in his compost heap and drunk it hot. He had sunk bottles in his lily pool and drunk it cold. He had not drunk everyman's drinks since he was a boy: his beers, stouts, wines were always reinforced by spirits, and his gin was mixed with vodka, his whisky with brandy, his brandy with those high-alcohol-content French liqueurs, and his liqueurs were an absolute witch's brew. He had held down jobs in farming, in racing stables, in building works – whatever sober men would not dare to do, he did because he was half seas over. The turning point for drunkards, he told me, is when they get their headaches because they are not drunk – their hangovers are caused by drinking water. Propping up a bar had meant happiness for him, and he had had a grand life, even if it was a 'short'.

On the way out of the Lovells' home I commiserated with his wife Minnie.

'He loved his bottle best,' she said, 'he never looked at another woman.

Common sense is blowing away groundless confidence. She has a charming husband, who can turn dross into gold: why should she bother with the inhabitant of The Poor Cottage?

I doubt even that this notebook will be filled. My opinions and observations are beside the point, and I cannot continue to put my preoccupations in writing when they seem to be pointless.

A coincidence of a most peculiar kind has occurred. I was on duty at St Anne's Hospital the night before last. It was a Saturday, getting on for midnight, the A and E was inundated with drunken idiots and casualties of fights, traffic accidents, street crime and genuine emergencies, and my professional patience was just about exhausted. A man and a woman joined the queue in the waiting area. They were well-dressed although informally, looked well-fed and well-to-do, and were exceptions both classwise and inasmuch as they were sober. He also attracted my attention by standing up instead of sitting down like the other people on the chairs provided. I kept on passing through this waiting area. Injuries etcetera were attended to in cubicles, there was a surgery for small operations and a pharmacy doled out medicines. Moving from one cubicle to another I was aware that the arrogant man, now seated, was holding his left hand in his right. The next thing was that somebody in one of the cubicles was kicking against a partition and raising his voice – Oxford accent – swearing that he was in pain and had hung about for too bloody long. Against my principles and the rules of the department, which were that troublemakers should not be allowed to jump the queue or receive preferential treatment, I responded. I drew back the curtain across the opening into the cubicle and told him to mind his language and behave – behave properly, that is. He had angry blue eyes and looked at me with daunting hostility. He had two dislocated fingers, the third and little fingers of his left hand. He thrust his hand in my direction and said, 'Can't you bloody well put my bloody fingers back where they belong?' I summoned a nurse, Stella, and then asked him, 'How were the fingers dislocated?' He replied: 'Mind your own bloody business!' When Stella joined us I explained in an undertone: 'This bloke wants his fingers seen to and I want you to record our conversation' – the senior staff at St Anne's A and E carry small recording machines.

I then said to him: 'The relocation of your fingers is possible, but painful. You are in a hurry evidently. I can do the job here and at once, or you can take your turn in the operating theatre and have a numbing injection or a whiff of pain-killing gas. It's your choice, sir.'

'You get the bloody thing done, so that I can go home.'

'You've chosen to have the two dislocated fingers of your left hand repositioned without anaesthetic, is that correct?'

'Yes and to hell with it!'

I mentioned the date and time, and he confirmed them. I sent Stella to collect the forms he had filled on admission. I then did the dirty work, causing him to squeal when I yanked the longer finger, to ask me to wait while he prepared himself for the little finger, and to squeal again and shed involuntary tears when I had to waggle it and push as well as pull.

He uttered a few more expletives of the fashionable kind, mopped his brow with his handkerchief and blew his nose, and remarked, 'What a performance!'

I replied: 'Everything you have said has been recorded, including your choice of treatment, and you are still being recorded.'

He pouted and shrugged his shoulders in an almost Gallic manner.

'The nurse will bind your hand,' I told him.

'Oh God,' he complained, gracelessly yet with a touch of humour.

I left the cubicle and met Stella out in the passage.

She said to me: 'That was tough stuff.' She meant it had been tough of me to do the operation in the antediluvian way.

'I hope it teaches him not to make a nuisance of himself.'

She handed me one of the forms to sign. I glanced at it and saw the name, Bruce Roecliffe.

Setting aside my reaction to that name, the story continues. I watched from a distance as Bruce Roecliffe emerged from the cubicle with his hand strapped. He was good-looking with his thick blond unruly hair. He walked like an athlete, lithely. He signalled to the woman, his companion, not Mary, and she stood up. Her hair was brown and long and hid her face, and she followed him towards the exit. They did not seem to be on very friendly terms.

He and that woman were not just friends. He was too masterful, she was too furtive. How were his fingers dislocated, in a row? Had that woman dislocated them? The news was not good for Mary – better for me.

Some days have passed since I wrote the above, and I have still not sorted out the pros and cons of my entry into one of the most disagreeable of relationships. Bruce Roecliffe wields power over Mary and, vicariously, over me. I am at his mercy as I have never been so at the mercy of any other man. I disliked him for good reasons before I knew who he was, I may also have disliked him at the urging of a sixth sense, and I took much more against him when I realised that Mary had at least to live with an errant husband, a spoilt brat, on whom my happiness depended. I shuddered to compare her wide-apart, wide-open, wide sweet eyes with those furious ice-blue eyes of his. I thought of him handing her a fat cheque, and her kissing him by way of thanks, and him demanding a more convincing proof of her gratitude. I thought of her humiliation, of her having to make do with the left-overs of other women, of the bribery and corruption involved. I pictured him padding along the passages of Wisteria Lodge, bent on teasing and torture. But I had done my bit of 'torture'. I had made him wince and squeal. I should not have broken with various codes of medical practice and relocated his fingers as painfully as possible. The irregularities multiply. Adultery is not a fairy story, nor a bedtime one as yet; but my aspirations in respect of Mary might turn out to be not the wildest of dreams. I have found myself not on the path of virtue, and waste my time on wondering if the end will ever justify the means.

My thought for this day is that work is good, leisure bad. We go to pieces if we have too little to do. I speak for myself – or write it, to be precise. I would not like to add to the difficulties of ill or disabled people, or the involuntary unemployed.

My MND patient died. Motor neurone disease is terrible, but in my experience is reserved by fate for the most heroic people.

May Day, the first day of the month of May, traditionally the time of village maidens dancing round maypoles in England, now the communist-socialist holiday that celebrates the murder of countless millions of class enemies.

Bank Holiday, no surgery, not much to do except count my mistakes; but the sun shone, so I drove out of Maeswell and walked in the Forest of Ashes. I seemed to be alone there, which was nice if not what I foolishly hoped for. I walked along a path or ride dappled by sunshine. Flowers showed off their colours and the young leaves on the trees boasted every shade of green. Birds sang, twittered, cawed, cooed, scolded and squawked. The rites of spring and regeneration were forging ahead. I sat down on a bank of mosses and buttercups, and these words formed in my head: 'I want gets nothing'.

However, curiosity refused to be renounced. I pinned down Audrey Fletcher in the rest-room and gave her a potted account of my brush with Bruce. Could she shed any light on it?

'Naughty Bruce,' she commented, frowning.

Then she asked me: 'What did she look like, the woman he was with on a Saturday night in the A and E?'

My answer was brown hair, a great deal of hair, and Audrey exclaimed: 'Oh dear!'

'Do you know her?'

'Not for certain, but she could be somebody as naughty as he is.'

'I see,' I said.

'No – you don't – any more than I do – and I'm not going to cast the first stone, and you mustn't jump to conclusions – please!'

Audrey had spoken sharply.

I said okay, okay, and that I was sorry, because I liked Mary, and sorry I had lost my rag with her husband.

'He deserves it,' Audrey said, bustling out of range of further discussion.

The NHS, ruled by an unscientific temporary political boss and a vast bureaucracy, resembles China in the days of the Dowager Empress.

She rang me. She is returning the Tolstoy book tomorrow afternoon. My life is all believe-it-or-not.

Mary Roecliffe arrived at The Poor Cottage at four o'clock yesterday. She was shy with me, we were both shy. It was my fault, I showed too much emotion, greeted her too effusively, and had prepared tea with cucumber sandwiches.

'I'm sorry to bother you,' she began, and when she saw the sandwiches she said, 'You shouldn't have – it's very kind of you – but I didn't mean...'

'How are you?' I asked.

Oh, that cliché, that platitude, the question which elicits answers that people in general seldom listen to, that question fraught with deep meaning for lovers, who pose it with fear and trembling!

'I'm well, thank you,' she replied. 'How are you?'

'Fine,' I said, wishing it could have been, 'All the better for seeing you.'

She looked lovely, a lovely lady, a lady who was lovelier because of her blush; and agreeable, ready to respond to me, at once composed and eager, and not without humour, good humour.

She had read the book. She had not been able to stop reading it, and was grateful. We discussed it – she refreshed my memory – I had forgotten details. She was set on reading *War and Peace* and would buy it in London if it was unavailable in Maeswell. I said I hoped she would come to tea with me again even if she had no book to return, and we both laughed. Then I made the tea and we ate sandwiches to cover our confusion. She seemed to enjoy the two small sandwiches she ate while we spoke of her children and I revealed that I was a bachelor without any.

She said, breaking through some little barrier and forcing herself to say: 'You know you've written in the beginning of *Childhood, Boyhood and Youth*, there's something written in the front end-paper, and I thought it must be in your writing.'

'Because it's illegible?'

She saw the point, that doctors are supposed to have handwriting no one can decipher. I was anxious for a moment – could it be something scribbled by Iris? – and reached out for the book in order to look and see. It was the following quote from Tolstoy: 'The hero of my tale – whom I love with all the power of my soul, whom I have tried to portray in all his beauty, who has been, is, and will be beautiful – is Truth.' I remembered where Tolstoy had written it, and when I had, for that matter.

'Oh yes,' I said, and looked up from the book.

Her eyes were glistening.

'I'm sorry,' I said.

I was apologising for whatever it was that had made her sad.

'No, no, it's nothing – forgive me – that sentence is so moving. Truth is such a wonderful rare thing, isn't it?'

I agreed, and she continued.

'If you're a truthful person, you think when you're young that other people tell the truth, but they don't, often they don't, and it's a shock. You don't know where you are. Do you? Do you know people who don't tell the truth?'

'Oh yes. My patients lie like mad. I can never find out if they've taken the pills I've prescribed or how much they drink in an average day.'

She laughed and brushed away a tear with the back of a pretty index finger.

'I'm afraid I bore my children by begging them to speak the truth and nothing but. And I shouldn't, really, because they have enough to put up with.'

We talked for a few minutes, but I was not concentrating, had other things on my mind, and have forgotten what we talked about. Had she been referring to her marriage? Who had shocked her? Unexpectedly she announced that she should be going.

I over-reacted. I felt responsible, and a failure, and probably showed my feelings as well as asking if she had to be in a hurry.

'My daughter – Melanie, who you know – will be finishing her dancing lesson, and I must be punctual or she'll worry.' Then she added: 'It's so peaceful in your home, and cosy with your books.'

'Will you come back one day?'

'Yes ... Yes,' she repeated, as though she could have said more.

She stood up and we moved in the direction of the door.

'Is Melanie well now?'

'Thank goodness, yes, she seems to be. That doctor in London, he had nothing new to say about her asthma, and she didn't take to him.'

We were veering in the direction of her husband, who had insisted on withdrawing Melanie from my care, and I inquired: 'Have Mr Roecliffe's fingers given any more trouble?'

She was either forgetful or puzzled.

'His dislocated fingers,' I jogged her memory.

'I don't understand,' she said.

But I did understand that I had dropped a brick and been indiscreet.

'It's nothing important, I did a running repair at the A and E the other day,' I said.

'What sort of repair? And what is A and E?'

'The Accident and Emergency Department at St Anne's Hospital. I work there on some weekend evenings. We all take turns to work there.'

'But what had happened to my husband?'

'I don't know – he'd dislocated two fingers – it's easily done – and I put them back where they were meant to be. I only saw him for a minute or two, and we had no personal chit-chat.'

'Was he alone?'

'I don't know.'

'Did you say it was a weekend?'

'Yes.'

'Which day?'

'Saturday.'

'And when was it?'

I supplied the date.

'Oh,' she said or she sighed, and looking straight at me with a pained expression, she put an ironical gloss on the mischief I had inadvertently made: 'You're sure he wasn't attending a meeting in Paris?'

We managed to laugh.

She held out her hand for me to shake, but I clasped it in both of mine and said: 'Please come back soon, I'd love to see you again.'

She murmured, 'Thank you,' turned away, and I opened my front door and she walked into the street.

I cannot stop thinking about my brick and every thought enlarges it. Not content with clashing with the husband of darling Mary, I have drawn attention to the fact that she has been betrayed.

On second, third or fourth thoughts, it must have happened before. I mean, Mary would not have dismissed Bruce's infidelity with half a joke if she had not been aware of or even used to it. Owing to her disappointment and disillusion, she did not react to my news with incredulity, horror or hysteria. Self-interest is not moral: I was pleased to believe her marriage was unhappy. On the other hand, honesty reminded me that tears had flooded into her eyes because 'people', a 'person' maybe, her husband more than likely, told lies.

I gave Mary a couple of examples of the lies I am told by my patients. I could give her hundreds. Our Welfare State leads us into temptation, and money for jam does not deliver us from the evil of lying. Patient after patient has tried to convince me that they should receive handouts from the government because they are 'invalids' or 'incapable' of work. They want me to fib in writing that they are 'sick', should be allowed to park their cars where they please, deserve to be sent to a convalescent home, need cosmetic surgery, and so on. As a race, were we always so dishonest? Am I just getting older than I believe I am? Tolstoy was not wrong to love the truth – think of what befell his poor country, the Union of Socialist Soviet Republics, which ruled by lies.

Politics and sex go together, politics and love do not.

Here is a sad story or a cautionary tale. Bessie in Reception rang through to me during evening surgery to say a man wanting an emergency appointment seemed to be a phoney. He had said his name was John Smith and his home was in Yorkshire, but spoke with a West Country accent. Did he look mad or violent? Bessie answered no, so I told her to send him along. He was a mild-mannered man in his thirties, wearing a clean open-necked shirt and jeans. He asked for Viagra. He was very sorry to say it would help to keep his marriage on the rails. Yes, he was a married man. And he was the father of a son, a toddler. But he was squeamish, and he had yielded to the pleas of his wife, who was a nervous woman, to stay with and support her while their baby was born. It was traumatic. He was not meant to see everything, but he saw too much, and heard too much, his wife cursing and screaming her head off, and the doctor's and nurses' earthy exchanges. The consequence for him was that he left romance behind in the Labour Room at the hospital, and, worse, sexual desire. He was proud of his son, he was devoted to his wife, but he was unable to rise to the occasion of her marital overtures. I wrote the prescription. What would Mary think of Bruce Roecliffe and John Smith being almost bracketed together in my notebook?

I took tea with my mother at Silver Court before my surgery this evening. Walking there, I noticed a woman in the car park and, as doctors will, thought she must be or have been a patient of mine. I partly recognised her and cudgelled my memory. She was young-middle-age with a good figure, and was approaching her car. I suppose I stared at her, and she seemed to catch my eye, bent down to unlock the door of her car, and got into the driver's seat with her back turned to me. I remembered. She had a lot of straight brown hair, shoulder length, like a hedge – a hedge to hide behind. She was the woman in the A and E with Bruce Roecliffe – with or without Bruce, to be precise and imprecise simultaneously. She had hidden her face from me both in the waiting area and again in the car park at Silver Court. Did Ma know a woman who fitted her description?

'Oh yes,' Ma said. 'She's Vera Martin's daughter Pansy. She's often here. She's got that sort of hair, and at her age she should have it cut shorter and thinned.'

'Does she live nearby, is she married?' I asked.

Ma had beans to spill. Pansy was accident-prone. She married a man called Egbert Doughty, an unsuccessful engineer and really, as Ma put it, 'ditchwater'. She produced two children, a delinquent boy, and a spiteful girl. The Doughty home was poor and miserable by all accounts. But Pansy made matters worse by picking a lover who was even worse than her husband. Apparently he is rich and spoilt, had taken her up and soon dropped her, and she had pursued him and come in for rough treatment – he was married, of course. There had been a bust-up not long ago, when she attacked him physically and he had beaten her black and blue. Vera Martin worried rather publicly about her daughter – she feared divorce was in the offing, and Pansy would have no means of support. Her lover had promised her the earth, and that was exactly what she would be left with.

Ma asked me: 'Why are you interested in Pansy?'

'I'm not,' I replied. 'But I always wonder what women mean when they speak of being beaten up. Some patients of mine consult me if their hair's been pulled or their faces have been slapped.'

'It wasn't like that for Pansy. She had to have her breast scanned because he'd hit her there, and she had ribs broken by his kicking.'

I obtained this information under false pretences. In London I treated half a dozen women with serious injuries inflicted by their so-called lovers who were drunk, drugged, sadistic, moronic, or inadequate and feeble. I had not told Ma, had misled her, because I was keen to know more about Bruce Roecliffe and the sort of husband he might be to Mary. He had been nasty in the A & E; but he spoke the Queen's English, was not a pleb or a prole, and dressed expensively. That he could torture a woman and risk giving her breast cancer, and break her bones, was bad news. Mary was married to a violent bully. The extenuating factor might be that Pansy née Martin had infuriated him. When had the beating occurred? My guess is that she and Bruce had a row and a wrestling match, she bent back his fingers and dislocated them, and after he had been treated at St Anne's Hospital with her in attendance they had driven somewhere, indoors or outdoors, and he had caused her GBH – Mary, meanwhile, labouring under the impression that he was in Paris.

More summer colds than life-saving crises. I suffer nonetheless from a double 'whammy'. First, George Mills, the antediluvian heart-throb of Silver Court, was taken ill and I attended: nothing much wrong, mostly the ailment known as *anno domini* – perhaps one of the romantic female residents had gained access to his bedroom. Anyway, he revived and shook a knarled finger at me. I was not a 'proper' doctor, he said, because I looked in my computer instead of practising the art of 'diagnosis by the eye', and I did not examine his tongue, tonsils, glands in the neck, sound his chest back and front, or test his reflexes, as was always *de rigueur*, part of the etiquette of medical practice, in the good old days. Secondly, Robert Chimes came down to stay the night at The Poor Cottage – I could put it another way, he came down on me like a ton of bricks. He scolded me for not surfing the internet, not doing emails, not having a modern mobile, not text-messaging, and not having the wherewithal to play videos, CDs or DVDs. Unwisely I had let him in on the secret of Mary Roecliffe, and he roasted me for loving a woman who should not love me, for my masochism and addiction to failure, for having stuck in the rut of Iris and for not letting the dead bury the dead, and for not realising that *les belles dames sans merci* were no longer on the menu and the twenty-first century is not the age of chivalry.

My reading has gone phut recently. It is again restricted to pill-makers' adverts and newspaper headlines. My literary leanings boil down to imagining Mary's reactions to *War and Peace*. And nothing has happened worthy of a note in this book – no maiden imprisoned in a Gothic castle has let down her golden tresses for me to fondle.

I wrote the sentence above too soon. Today, Saturday, this afternoon, there was a sale of work in our church hall and Bill Wetherby had asked me to put in an appearance. I walked through the churchyard in hot sunshine round about three. The hall, like the church, is Victorian, but has been given some sliding glass doors facing west, which were open wide. The trestle tables displaying goods for sale were inside the hall, some tea-tables with chairs were outside, on a grassy lawn away from the graves. I had a few words with Bill, then with his wife Ada, who presided over the arts and crafts exhibits, mostly daubs by children and wooden mice with leather ears and tails. There were other stalls for clothing, jam and cakes, fruit and vegetables. A good many people had turned up, and many of them were my patients. I was talking

and shaking hands, and refusing offers of cups of tea, in the sunshine
on the lawn, when I saw Mary. She was with her two children and
two older people. She wore that seductive thin light-coloured summer
apparel for women, and a broad-brimmed straw hat at an angle. We
saw each other at the same time. Her face lit up – or I chose to
think it did – as mine certainly had. We met in the crowd. She gave
me her hand more to hold than to shake, and she smiled at me
warmly enough to melt hearts colder than mine. She indicated Melanie
and introduced me to Tom, and then introduced me to her parents.
Tom is a wan child of seven or thereabouts, Melanie seemed scarcely
to recognise me. Mary's parents are called Warden – she would have
been Mary Warden. Her father is a tall handsome polite man, her
mother has a friendly smile. Talking was not easy. She said that two
of Tom's paintings were for sale – they had been viewing them – and
I said something about *War and Peace*. Her parents mentioned the
lucky weather. Then Bruce Roecliffe appeared. He was shouldering
his way through and called harshly to Mary as if she had been a dog.
He was still at a little distance. Mary ignored his summons – she
commented on by ignoring it – and said: 'I've finished the book and
wish I hadn't.' Tom interrupted. He was tugging at his mother's clothes
and pleading with her: 'Dad's waiting for us, Dad's waiting.' Mary said
to him, 'I know.' But Bruce had not waited. He stormed up and
expostulated, 'For God's sake, Mary, come on!' She introduced me
cleverly, that is non-committally, for she cannot have wanted him to
know that she knew about his fingers and philandering. She said,
'This is Dr Selaby.' He flashed a glance at me, mumbled, 'Hi!', turned
his back and strutted off, calling, 'You kids, get a move on!' Mary
asked me, 'May I ring you?' I answered, 'Please!' Mrs Warden said as
she passed me, 'We have our marching orders,' and Mr Warden raised
his eyebrows, signifying a mixture of disapproval and resignation. I re-
entered the hall, crossing to Ada Wetherby's trestle table, and bought
the pictures by Tom Roecliffe.

It was an unsettling encounter. Bruce Roecliffe is or has an unquiet
spirit – how did he marry a woman with quiet eyes? I know the
type – doctors have to try to diagnose souls as well as the diseases
of bodies – and I see signs of the warlock stirring in Bruce. He sets
my teeth on edge. Such people merit scientific investigation: what is
it that forces them to create bad feeling, jagged edges, exasperation,
antipathy?

For the record, I have shuffled awkward patients out of my consulting room and into a colleague's, and the colleague in question has noticed nothing untoward or disagreeable. Yet there seems to be an antonym or counterpoint to love at first sight. Personally, I would avoid Bruce like the plague if I could, if it were not for our interdependency.

Tom's paintings were upsetting, too. One was of a house on fire, the other of a tree falling down. The subjects were fearful and the colours used were lurid. Tom had not looked like a country boy in the church garden – no touch of sun, no freckles. Melanie was pale and shrinking. I suspected they were frightened by their father; but I was frightened of mine at their age – and the vogue of calling fathers by their Christian names and not being frightened of them has cost modern mothers dear. The psyches of children defeat analysis more thoroughly – if possible – than adult psyches do. A distressing comparison struck me: Melanie and Tom were reminiscent of the children in Henry James' ghost story, *The Turn of the Screw*.

No telephone call from Mary in these last days.

Another resolve not to break up a marriage. Another attempt to justify my hypocrisy. Another prayer to be forgiven. Again, and almost, I dare to reproach God for enabling us to love even in vain, also for giving some of us a monogamous instinct; but I blame myself for Iris, for Rose, and potentially for Mary. The Hippocratic Oath, which I swore, is all for morality, and I have stumbled into the amoral modern jungle. Actually, the Age of Chivalry produced a code of love – I remember reading a list of its rules – including one that would answer Robert and comfort me if my memory could be relied on. The love that is dedicated wholeheartedly and without self-interest to the service of the beloved, the rule goes, transcends other undertakings and bonds.

Life is cheap nowadays, yet nowadays modern states levy crippling taxes to pay for the welfare of the people and the prolongation of life. The dearth of logic compounds confusion. Bombs turn out to be easy to make, nitwits queue up to be suicide bombers, and governments drop bigger better ones while legislating against the death penalty for heinous murder. It seems that governments only kill innocent people. No wonder morality is a muddle and the end is probably nigh! If time is short, I would like to state here and now and without a doubt that I loved Iris in haste and regret those eleven years at leisure, and will regret their outcome for ever. I mean my love of Mary at least to be different. The idea of love without self-interest would worry any red-blooded man of my age; but the empathy and sympathy between me and Mary promise that our interest in each other could be fully satisfied when our circumstances and scruples permit.

Trouble at mill: Denis Woods may be sued. Conscientious Denis may be sued for negligence. The story beggars belief. Denis had a troublesome middle-aged patient who had a troublesome daughter of twenty-three: mother a well-to-do divorcee called Anne Collett, daughter called Micky, short for Michaela, and father of Micky an expat. Micky drifted in and out of relationships, jobs, dwellings, psychiatrists' clutches, rehab clinics and financial scrapes. One night she went out with a new boyfriend, got drunk or drugged or both, agreed to go back to his flat, undressed, got into bed with him, changed her mind, said no, and he had his way with her. She returned home, to her mother's house, said she had been raped, and her mother summoned Denis, who turned out in the middle of the night and drove ten miles to where the Colletts live.

Micky told her tale reluctantly, she was honest enough not to blame the boy exclusively, and only concerned in case she would have a baby. Denis gave medical help and his opinion, which was that rape had not occurred, since Micky had gone too far to have the right to draw back, and she had not left the boyfriend's bed after saying no for two subsequent hours. Mrs Collett raged at him, but he could and would not change his mind, and he departed. Mrs Collett then summoned the police; the next day the police contacted Denis and agreed with his reading of the evidence; and the case seemed to be closed. However, a feminist organisation took a different view. It paid a solicitor to write Denis a threatening letter stating that he was negligent to have influenced the police in the matter of the rape victim Michaela Collett, who was denied a thorough investigation of the crime. Denis wrote back that the lady in question failed a breath test several hours after the alleged rape. He had also taken a blood sample, so far untested, which, he was sure, would show traces of illegal substances. Both tests were authorised by Miss Collett's signature. He added that if legal proceedings should be instigated, he would cross-petition that the feminists were challenging his professional integrity on behalf of a contrary over-age nymphet and tease, guilty on several counts. Denis still fears the feminists – they have money to burn, he says, and the militants have no better understanding of right and wrong than male chauvinists.

The Cunninghams again invited me to dine, I accepted the invitation, and now I already feel their food sticking in my throat. Penny issued the invitation. Since then Frank has told me the names of the other guests. My opposite number is as yet unknown. People called Perry are coming, Victor is a dermatologist with a practice in London as well as in Tinbury, and Shell is a pretty young woman with an interest in the arts. The other couple, who will make eight of us in all, are Bruce and Mary Roecliffe.

Bruce will be the guest of honour. He has apparently given money to St Christopher's Hospice, where Frank is one of the visiting team of doctors. Frank thinks Bruce is a philanthropist and good fellow.

This dinner party preys on my mind. Romance relies on privacy. Romantic love is the opposite of 'social' love that has to show itself off. Society, high and low, is a waste of time and energy for a person in love – and almost the same applies for a teetotaller. Society is a marriage market or a dating agency for ungregarious souls, or it is nothing but a bore. It also serves as a business forum, where useful contacts can be made and insider deals done. I write as an overworked doctor, a man in love, and a temperamental recluse – three good reasons not to go to dinner with the Cunninghams and have to endure the company of my beloved together with her legal lord and master.

Life seems to have been simplified by a generation younger than mine. I refer to four of my patients in their twenties, all occasional churchgoers, who have supplied me with autobiographical information. Molly Prentice justified her desertion of her hard-working husband, who was devoted to their children, by saying she had always wanted to be a single mother – she was awarded custody of the children. Jane West justified her divorce proceedings by explaining that she was fed up with having to ask her husband for money, she was hoping the courts would grant her a fat capital sum and index-linked alimony. John Walker walked out of his marriage because he was tired of his brood. Adrian Lucas left his wife at the airport where they were catching a flight to their honeymoon destination. The common excuse for bad marital behaviour is 'I no longer love him or her' – which is a contradiction and retraction of everything they have said and done in the period of courtship, and of all they have solemnly sworn in church.

We congregated on Saturday evening at the Cunninghams' in Larkspur. We had been asked for eight. The evening was grey and rainy, English summer weather. I was the first to arrive, and was greeted by both Frank and Penny – she powdered and painted and wearing a dress that revealed too much crinkled flesh. She hugged me, Frank was gravely welcoming, and they told me that Mrs Minksoft would be my neighbour at dinner – I would be between Mrs Minksoft and Shell Perry, the dermatologist's mate, whom Penny said I would adore. The Perrys were the next arrivals, he a bald benevolent tough-talking sixty-year-old, she a fortyish redhead with wet-looking lips. Mrs Minksoft was late, and blamed her chauffeur. She is small and dark, rotund, and looks as rich as she is supposed to be. The Roecliffes were late – Mary apologised, he did not.

When Frank introduced me to the Perrys, he – Victor Perry – passed a remark I had heard annually since my childhood: he said, 'Not very promising weather for Wimbledon.' Shell Perry had a racier line in small talk. She said: 'Are you a gynaecologist? ... What a pity, I have a laugh with gynaes ... Not married? ... And no partner?' Mrs Minksoft is a Hungarian chatterbox. She said: 'A doctor, my dear! My husband is a doctor, too. He has a doctorate from Oxford – in literature, my dear – but he writes nothing except cheques, he is a doctor of money, which is good luck for many people, but especially for me.' She laughed at her own joke loudly and showing the gold crowns of her mouthful of teeth. Frank introduced me to the Roecliffes. Mary and I shook hands for longer than was necessary and two words were exchanged along with smiles: she said to me, 'Hullo,' and I said 'Hullo' to her. She then reminded Bruce that he had met me at the fête in the grounds of my church. He said, 'How are you?', and waved a hand at me dismissively but not exactly rudely.

I cannot describe women's clothes; suffice it to say that Mary was well-dressed for dinner in a town in the country in summer, and that her appearance qualified for those sweet unfashionable compliments, fresh, clean, dignified, ethereal. Bruce wore white trousers, a blazer, an open-necked shirt and a scarf or handkerchief loosely knotted round his neck. He had dash, I give him that, he was also flash; and, although men are supposed never to know whether or not other men are attractive to women, I could see that with his thick tangle of golden hair, aquiline features, bold blue eyes and carnivorous smile, he exuded sex appeal.

Bruce and Mrs Minksoft were acquainted. He addressed her as 'Minx' and she called him 'wicked'. Bruce and Shell Perry were more than acquaintances. He was her 'sweety-pie' and she was his 'Poppet', and they kissed cheek-to-cheek, laughing as if at a charade. We drank our dry martinis – Mary, talking to the dermatologist, refused hers – and Penny bustled in and led the ladies into the dining-room. Shell Perry walked ahead of me. In view of later events, I must record that her flimsily clad back view was pleasing and that she wore no discernible knickers.

The Cunninghams' dining-room is oblong, and we sat as follows under the Montague Dawson prints of great yachts racing in wide seas: Frank at the end of the table near the window, Mary on his right, Victor Perry next to Mary, Penny Cunningham next to Victor and near the kitchen door, Bruce Roecliffe on Penny's right, Shell between Bruce and me, and Mrs Minksoft on my right and Frank's left. The important thing so far as I was concerned was that I could look across the table at Mary – I was not sorry not to be sitting next to her, I would have been shy and we would have had to make polite conversation.

Whatever the laws of social etiquette appertaining to dinner parties, the Cunninghams broke them, probably unconsciously. Each chose to talk to his and her more attractive neighbour, Frank to Mary rather than to Mrs Minksoft and Penny to Bruce rather than to Victor Perry. As a result, for quite a time, Mrs Minksoft on one side of the table and Victor the dermatologist on the other were left out conversationally and sat in silence, eating the bridge-rolls on their side-plates. More difficulties were caused by Frank rising to his feet to pour out white and red wines, and by Penny leaping to hers in order to give orders in the kitchen.

However, alcohol and food generated good will. We had avocados with vinaigrette to start with, sole in a white sauce with grapes as main course, prune mould and vanilla ice-cream for pudding, and cheese straws. Shell Perry told me that Australian men were even worse lovers than Englishmen, she said the corks dangling from the brims of Australian male headgear distracted women from the matter in hand. Mrs Minksoft aired her opinion that her husband Rudolph must have given more money to Frank for his Hospice than Bruce Roecliffe could have done, and therefore she should have been sitting on Frank's right instead of Mary. Victor Perry roared with laughter at a joke he had cracked with Penny Cunningham, Mrs Minksoft shouted down the table at Bruce, Frank was passing round a decanter of port, and Mary and I exchanged a conspiratorial glance or two.

We were still there, but sitting less formally. Shell Perry had half-turned to Bruce Roecliffe and he – on her left – had also half-turned and had his right arm resting on the back of her chair. They were laughing – others were laughing, but Shell and Bruce were laughing in a nearly lascivious way. All of a sudden I guessed, realised, that as his left arm was under the table and her legs were extended in its direction, he was caressing her where a more respectable woman would have worn knickers. My reaction was to look at Mary. I saw, at once, that she had seen. Her countenance had somehow solidified, was stony, like a sculpture. Then her eyes met mine, beaming at me a message of pain and misery. A moment later, deliberately but as if by accident, she pushed back her chair. Penny had the tact to stand up and shepherd all the ladies, including not much of a lady, out of the dining-room.

Frank is old-fashioned, he believes in giving his guests for dinner the chance to 'wash their hands', and each sex to have a chinwag without interruption by the other. We four men were alone in the dining-room, Frank, self, Bruce and Victor Perry, and the decanter of port was rotating clockwise. Frank thanked Bruce again for his donation to St Christopher's Hospice. Bruce's answer was an unexpected diatribe, and to the best of my memory went like this: 'Thanks for feeding us, Frank, but – sorry! – I'm here to complain. Having two other captive quacks is all to the good. I want to blast off at the National Health Service. You lot let the bloody politicians create the bloody monster – hadn't any of you ever heard of Dr Frankenstein? Over fifty-odd years the monster's grown way beyond control. Politicians are windbags, they're not competent to run anything, countries or a health service, they're the puppets of bureaucrats, and bureaucrats are like rabbits, only good at reproducing themselves. You'll tell me the monster's beautifully dressed, but I'm telling you it's stark naked. To hell with pious hopes and downright lies: politics can't beat nature. No legislation can stop people being ill. No society should presume it can keep everyone healthy and alive, and no society can afford that sort of nonsense. Our hospitals are fever-pits – if you go into hospital relatively well you come out ill or dead. They're filthy. And who are the cleaners and the kitchen staff, are they taught hygiene, are they disciplined by being hired and fired freely by a matron or a leading doctor? Tell me another! And in the A & E, drug addicts and drunks shouldn't be treated as if they were decent people, they should be thrown in a cell until they're sober and a doctor or a nurse has the time and inclination to deal with them. Better late than never, why not withdraw your labour and force the politicians to think again? Wake up! Make people pay if they can for your services – pay if they can, pay at least a deposit, pay up for missing appointments, pay in full for misbehaving! Stop conniving with the criminals milking the benefits system! Cut the hypocrisy – people never will be equal – let the rich and the poor be what they are and wish to be! No sharp intakes of breath, please – I'm not being original or saying anything extraordinary! It's common knowledge – free health services ruin a country – the idea of free health is tempting fate – and the Welfare State's a slippery slope. You doctors should damn well pull yourselves together and start cleaning out the bloody stables!'

We rejoined the ladies briefly. Because I could not help Mary, I only longed to be away and at home. The sight of her suffering towards the end of dinner, and the thought of her living with a man so randy and shameless, so dogmatic and oppressive as Bruce Roecliffe, got me down. How could he, how could she? That he talked some sense about the Health Service did not compensate for his abrasive delivery. The dermatologist, Victor Perry, had two good reasons to remove Shell from the scene of the party: he was unamused by Bruce and had called him a vandal and a hooligan, terms perhaps also applicable to Bruce's friendship with his wife. Bruce himself took his leave brusquely, he seemed to have shot his bolts in the dining-room; Mary followed him out, and I followed Mary.

Frank and Penny stood in the lit doorway, bidding us good night in crestfallen tones. The dinner had gone wrong, and they sensed it. I waved goodbye to the Perrys, and Bruce nodded at me, and Mary addressed me in an undertone when I opened the passenger door of the Roecliffes' car.

'Can I see you?'

'Any time.'

'Tomorrow at four?'

'Yes!'

She got into the car, and Bruce drove off fast, scattering the Cunninghams' gravel.

Today is the next day. It is evening now. At four o'clock I saw Mary passing my sitting-room window, and opened my front door. I closed the door quickly, and we faced each other in the dark little room. We smiled, were relieved, were almost happy, were together and safe.

She had not seemed to be hurried, but there was urgency in our exchanges.

I thanked her for being with me.

'No – thank you – but I shouldn't be here – I'll have to leave you soon.'

Would she not have tea?

'No – don't worry.'

'It's Sunday, not a day for dancing classes.'

'They're having tea with friends, my children, and I must go and join the party. I must be sure to pick them up and take them home before...'

'Before what?'

'Can you tell me something? What did Bruce do when the men were alone last night?'

'He made a speech.'

'What about?'

'About the NHS and its failings. He wanted us to put it right.'

'Was he rude?'

'Not quite – rough – and excitable.'

'I don't want him to collect the children from their party. He scares them.'

'Won't you sit down and rest?'

'No – I can't – it would have been nice, if I'd come here to discuss *War and Peace*. I just wanted to see you again and be in your soothing atmosphere.'

'It's the same for me.'

'No – no – what I've told you isn't the whole truth. You ought to know it's a mistake to be friends with a woman who's having matrimonial problems.'

'I can't help being your friend.'

[401]

'No – thank you – but you mustn't, we mustn't – you're on quicksand – and I want to rescue you while there's still a chance – I came to say goodbye.'

'Please don't say it.'

'Yes – we're a might-have-been, you must see that.'

'But I ask very little, I expect nothing much.'

'It couldn't be, it wouldn't work.'

'Please, Mary.'

'We're strangers – in one way we are – you have no idea of the trouble you could be getting into – honestly, I'm thinking of you – only of you.'

'I know – I do know that – and it's why I can't help loving you.'

'Oh God!'

She uttered the words in the form of a small scream, and headed for the door. I touched her arm, a touch not a restraint, our first physical contact since her arrival, and she stopped, almost froze.

'Can I write to you? Can I ever speak to you?'

'No – no, definitely.'

'Mary!'

'Give me time,' she said.

'How much time?'

'A month.'

'Will you communicate after a month?'

'I promise.'

She reached for the door handle, but I stepped forward to open it. We did not speak again. I watched her walking away until she turned the corner where the churchyard ends.

PART THREE

Notebook Five

WHEN MRS Peele told me that she was engaged to her future husband Ron for nine years, I took it personally. A long time to wait, I remarked. She explained that they had been saving in order to buy a home of their own.

Mrs Peele cleans my Poor Cottage on Mondays and Fridays, removes my dirty washing and brings it back clean, changes my sheets, copes with refuse, and buys household necessities. I seldom see her, but by her works I know her. She does not bother, nag, ruin or bore me. Why should I want a wife?

We both happened to be at The Poor Cottage the other morning, Mrs Peele and self, and, following on from her revelation about the length of her engagement, I ventured to ask if Ron was worth waiting for. She said: 'Well, we've been lucky because of knowing we were comfortable together.'

Mary is obviously not comfortable with Bruce. I am and believe I would be comfortable with Mary. The moot point is whether or not she would be comfortable with me in the longer term. On Sunday afternoon she was very distressed, and I passed one of the acid tests of courtship, I was not completely undone, nonplussed, infected with or defeated by her distress.

But I am sad, although a few days are not nine years. And I worry for her with more reason than she has to worry unselfishly for me.

The pains of romantic love are not much fun for mature persons. Shakespeare was not wrong to make Romeo and Juliet children.

To pass the time, my free time which is not much but seems longer because Mary is not on my horizon, I again picked up *Dead Souls*. The gloomy title matched my mood, but it is misleading, a misnomer.

The first 'book' of three is comedy, fun, joy and delight, an exception to every rule, a fantasy of genius, non-stop entertainment of the highest order. Gogol, the author, refers to it as a 'poem' – and so it is. The other two 'books' are as peculiar as the first in that they are dull, stupid and unreadable – Gogol is thought not to have written them although they appear under his name. He was born in 1809 and died in 1852, aged forty-one. He published his first writings at his own expense. He was extremely prolific in his short life, and became one of the great writers. He was not a 'normal' man, and never happy. I wonder if Mary would like his book.

A doctor's work is never done. However sad or unwell he or she may be, he or she is almost bound to have to treat a patient who is sadder and iller than he or she is. The real doctor's dilemma is how to be always more sorry for patients than for himself or herself.

The telephone is a blessing for old people, but a curse for those who are older than old, and for their relations, friends, tradesmen and doctors. Ma was telling me that Joyce, the daytime 'warden' at Silver Court, was driven almost to drink by nonagenarian Laura Henbey, who has developed an aversion to returning the receiver to its cradle: result, Joyce is rung in her office repeatedly by Laura's cronies wanting to know if she is alive and, if so, why is her telephone dead or emitting the engaged signal. They have fixed her up with an antique instrument of the kind used by Laura in the 1920s – it stands twelve inches high; but I understand the improvement is not great.

A pile-up on the main road, a 4 × 4 driven by a youth crashed through the barrier between two carriageways and ploughed into a small car containing four members of a single family, OAP car owner, his wife, sister and sister-in-law. I was called out to help to revive the youth, but he was already in an ambulance when I arrived. He was not badly hurt, the four other casualties were dead. A female journalist buttonholed me and spoke of the 'tragedy'. I returned, 'Why do you journalists insist on getting everything wrong? This isn't a tragedy, it's a crime scene.' The youth is a local criminal aged nineteen. He stole the 4 × 4 from a yard of secondhand cars for sale. The vehicle was not roadworthy and had no Road Tax and was uninsured. The youth, who had no licence and drove it too fast, was drunk and drugged by cannabis. The other car was in the slow lane when it was hit. Its driver was a retired Minister of the Methodist Church. His descendants and those of his sister and sister-in-law will receive no money from any insurance company. The youth will be sentenced to a rest cure in prison. In my opinion he should pay the ultimate penalty for his offence and the harm he has done. If or when the politicians reinstate capital punishment by one method or another, I will gladly pull the hangman's handle or administer the lethal injection.

Love is blind, but should I be straining my eyes to see the trap that Mary warned me not to fall into? She referred to her marriage: I have assumed all along that it is problematical – she would not have reciprocated my overtures to any extent if she had been exclusively occupied by wifehood. That Bruce is a serial adulterer would not surprise me – I witnessed his pass at Shell Perry under the Cunninghams' dining table at which his wife was sitting. He can be grouped with the cohorts of horrible husbands, and might be a horrible father too – she said he frightened his children. He is certainly a bully – he tried to bully three doctors, one of which was his host and old enough to be his father. In short, Bruce Roecliffe is not perfect, but had Mary meant that he was insanely jealous and might try to murder me?

From my glass house I ought not to throw stones at Bruce for being an adulterer, and I have no proofs of the extent of his promiscuity. However, loving another man's wife is a novelty for me, and I cannot resist the urge to analyse it. The main difference between a love affair and adultery is the legal aspect – legal in innumerable senses, according to the laws of God, of the land, of tradition, etiquette and human nature, because the adulterer is trying to steal somebody from somebody else, alienate someone's affections, hurt someone's feelings, appropriate a possession of more or less value, take advantage, cheat and win the game. Are there extenuating factors? Surely the unhappiness of a wife would excuse a readiness to be rescued and released from durance, duress, and violence of one sort or another. Mary's morals are irreproachable, I believe, but is she a wife battered and brainwashed by Bruce who has a screw loose? How I yearn to be able to speak to her, hear her voice on the telephone, ask if she is all right, or pour out my feelings on paper, in a letter, in letters!

My dreams of love that is pure if adulterous are rudely interrupted by battles of the war of the sexes waged in my consulting room. Women's ailments I pass on to Audrey Fletcher or to a specialist if I can, but often I am too late to stifle a tale of woe or terror. Women are apt to book an appointment for one reason, pain in a toe or a congested cough, when they really want to see me for another. They are bewildered by their partners' sexual requirements. A woman asked me if it was right and proper of her husband to wash her from head to foot with Dettol before and after intercourse. Women have asked me if the following were acceptable and should be accepted: a white honeymoon, a partner with satyriasis, perverse practices, sex exclusively on the kitchen table, oral sex that goes too far, his arousal by her pain, physical assault? Several women have described marriages and even partnerships that were never loving, sex that was rare and disagreeable, pregnancies that were simply awful, and motherhood that was drudgery. For all classes of persons, upper, middle or lower, to be the weaker sex is dangerous. Admittedly men have consulted me about women who, with cruel words, sarcasm, mockery and contrariness, have virtually castrated them. But I dredge up these dirty memories because of Mary and my suspicions of Bruce.

Today Frank Cunningham and I found ourselves together in the rest-room. I had written to thank Penny for dinner, and I now thanked Frank. His gesture conveyed the message that thanks were out of order. He was dissatisfied by his evening of entertainment and expressed his dissatisfaction characteristically.

He asked me if I had been acquainted with Mr Perry. When I said no, he said that he had never before met Mr Perry's wife, Shell, who seemed to be a lively lady. I indicated agreement.

'Yes, well,' Frank continued, 'Penny tells me she was not behaving in a modest manner. Were you aware of anything of that sort?'

I did not mince my words in reply, I was unwilling to protect Bruce.

'Good gracious,' Frank exclaimed.

He continued: 'Bruce Roecliffe blotted his copybook twice over in that case.'

We discussed his – Bruce's – post-prandial opinion of and advice to the medical profession. Frank was against all of it, and squashed my tentative support of one or two of his ideas.

'However,' Frank changed the subject. 'However, I have a third concern in respect of Bruce Roecliffe. He has given money to St

Christopher Hospice, he did so before he came to live down here, and he has since then. He's been generous, I grant, but recently I've heard of a case of possible malpractice. He wangled money out of an old friend of ours, who lives in Silver Court and is acquainted with your mother, invested it in some speculative scheme, and, when it was lost, informed her in an off-hand and casual manner.'

'But isn't he a stockbroker? I thought he was, and that his business dealings were regulated by official bodies in the City of London.'

'No, he's a financial adviser, and seems to have the right to do as he pleases.'

'I suppose your friend was rash to hand over more money that she could afford.'

'Yes, but Bruce was wrong to have obtained her money by saying he could increase it, by investing in a speculative way, and wrong again to react to the loss as he did. Our friend needed income, she's too old to hope to benefit from slow capital growth. He acted at least irresponsibly, and has broken laws of natural justice. I wonder why he donates to our Hospice – how guilty is his conscience? The pressing question is whether or not we should continue to accept his donations.'

I had no answer for Frank, and many new questions for myself; but meanwhile I paid an urgent visit to Silver Court.

In reply to my cautious questions Ma told me that Lisbet Tinnislea as well as Gabriella Shelby were friendly with Bruce Roecliffe. Lisbet is another resident at Silver Court, pretty in an old-fashioned way, according to Ma, and Austrian by birth – I have not met her. Whether or not Lisbet has entrusted money to Bruce, she has not publicly complained of losing it; and Gabriella still seems to be pleased with him both financially and personally.

'He's an odd man,' I commented carefully.

'I was introduced to him the other day. He's good-looking, I can see why the ladies fall for him.'

I could have done without the last remark.

I asked: 'Was he after your money, Ma?'

'Well – he gave me his card.'

'Don't ask him to invest your money, don't on any account!'

'Is he a crook?'

'I don't know that, I don't know it for certain, but I'd prefer you to play safe.'

'He has a glittering eye.'

'You always say that's a bad sign.'

'It's not a good one.'

'What does it signify, Ma?'

She shrugged her shoulders, and asked: 'Are you friends?'

'Acquaintances.'

'Is he married?'

'Yes.'

'With children?'

'Yes, a girl and a boy.'

'Are you a friend of his wife?'

'You're too sharp, Ma!'

'Is she your special friend?'

'Maybe.'

'Now it's my turn to tell you to play safe. I wouldn't like you to be on the wrong side of him.'

'No ... I wouldn't like that either. He's so odd he could do anything, and I feel protective of Mary Roecliffe.'

'Clever women protect themselves.'

'Thanks for the advice, Ma.'

'What advice am I to give Lisbet and Gabriella?'

'If he's got their money they should try to get it back. They could say they need it for a young relative's wedding or an old relative's funeral. Don't mention my name, please!'

'I won't. And I mustn't alarm them. What has Bruce done that you don't approve of, apart from marrying Mary?'

'He made mistakes for the friend of a friend of mine. I'm not saying he stole the money. He probably bought shares that went down instead of up.'

'Is that serious?'

'Serious enough.'

'Anything else?'

'I think he's dangerous.'

Robert Chimes again stayed the night. When he had stopped making mockery of my dedication, I asked him if he had ever come across or heard of Bruce. He tapped his forehead with his fingers and supplied the following. There had been some financial jiggery-pokery that landed Roecliffe in a court of law, and then he was cited in an unsavoury divorce case – Roecliffe had seduced a wife, the husband divorced her, and she came to a sticky end, in a car crash or by suicide.

'When was that, the divorce case?'

'Oh, five or six years ago.'

In other words, Bruce had been unfaithful to Mary not long after they were married, judging by Melanie aged nine and Tom aged seven.

I have not lost my nerve or my patience. Something precious and priceless passed between me and Mary at once, when we first set eyes on each other, an emotion unique inasmuch as I had experienced nothing like it before and expect never to experience again – for lightning does not strike the same spot twice – and convinced me that she is my fate, come what may. I remember with a surge of gratitude the awareness that my search for the other better half of myself was over, and my recognition of that commitment which is the sole agent of peace. But the 'buts' have raised their ugly heads. To mix my metaphors, the sharp points of common sense puncture and deflate. How long, oh Lord? I have nothing whatsoever to count on. Unhappy marriages have connections with creaking doors that never fall off their hinges. I have no knowledge of what I am up against, the history, the past, the characters, the future. I do not like to think of my relationship with Mary as a siege, yet I begin to consider a future of digging myself in and sitting out the time it will take for her to surrender. I must not pollute love with obstinacy – love is above trying to prove Ma and Robert wrong.

It is the middle of the third week of the month of our semi-voluntary 'separation'. I have not yielded to the temptation to break in on Mary largely because I do not know how to, and she has not relented – War and Peace remains undiscussed. This afternoon I went for another walk in the Forest of the Ashes. Nature was celebrating summer. I saw young rabbits with flirty white scuts, grey squirrels played hide-and-seek with me, a weasel sprinted by like a hyperactive toy, and magpies chuckled murderously. Adult creatures were being run ragged by the demands of their babies, and the trees were heavily pregnant with leaves and fruits. The scene could be called happy, if happiness is a feature of the wildlife experience with its non-stop struggle to survive; but I felt sad on account of a patient. Alec Whitehead was a new patient – he limped into my consulting room yesterday, looking dreadful. He is a scholar, author of biographies, dignified, polite. He was so sorry to bother me. He told me he had AIDS, and how long he expected to live. His hometown was London, he had been treated there for several years, and had come to Maeswell to be nursed by his mother, who has a house in King Arthur's Terrace. He showed me his medication, and wondered if I could think of any medicine to make his last days either more bearable or fewer. He was precise, not emotional. He was not only new to me, he was my first AIDS case – in my London hospital those patients were directed to a specialised department. I offered him a few strong painkillers. He was grateful, and seemed to want to unburden himself. He said he had probably contracted the infection without knowing it when he was thirty-seven, thirteen years ago. It had cut short his career, also finished his love life, and forced him, who had lived openly with a man, to keep the secret that he was ill and potentially infectious. He had been his mother's blue-eyed boy, he said, he had been going to win fame for her sake, but she understood him, she understood everything.

At this stage I asked if he had ever been bisexual, and he answered, 'Never!'

'Thank goodness for that,' I said.

He reproached me gently.

'I would have liked to be bisexual, but I wasn't. We think bisexuality's natural. We think there's very little difference between homosexuality, bisexuality and heterosexuality. We use words like copulation and fornication to describe our acts of love and passion.'

I tried to express sympathy.

He said: 'I'm lucky to have lived for fifty wonderful years.'

I urged him to come back for another prescription of the painkillers if need be.

'Oh, I don't think I'll need more,' he replied with his wisp of a smile.

Acquired Immune Deficiency System, AIDS, is a viral disease, spread by bodily fluids, apparently not by kissing. Incubation does not affect health and takes eight years on average. There are then two phases, Human Immunodeficiency Virus, HIV, and ARC, Aids-related complex. The disease can stop at that point and disappear; but more commonly it develops into AIDS, with its life-expectancy of three years at most.

Alec Whitehead chose to cut short his terminal period.

Several quiet days, patients exceptionally thin on the ground, Ma visiting Jane in Norfolk, no word from Mary; but not a holiday, more like marking time, tension on the increase as we near the end of our month which bears a secular resemblance to Lent, the celebration of the fast in the wilderness.

I wrote too soon. Yesterday evening at about ten o'clock I received a telephone call. The caller began it thus: 'Joe...' The voice was female, tremulous, a sort of cry. I refrained from asking, 'Who is it?' – my heart was telling me. 'It's Mary,' she said, and I replied, 'I know.'

Those Christian names, let alone my nickname, how aphrodisiacal they are! Modern English manners, which scarcely use surnames, have stolen one of the great thrills once reserved for lovers.

'Melanie's ill,' Mary said.

'Shall I come out to you?'

'Could you?'

'Of course.'

'Do you know the way?'

'Of course. I'll be with you in fifteen minutes.'

It was a rush. I had to fetch medicaments from the Surgery. Then I drove flat-out through the roads and lanes, past the Forest of Ashes, and in through white wooden gates, along a gravelled drive, and stopped in a turning circle in front of a house with Gothic-style windows. A light was on above a Gothic front door, and electric light emanated through drawn curtains.

I rang the doorbell, and the door was immediately opened by a grey-haired elderly lady who said, 'Madam's upstairs.' I was in a staircase hall, and now Mary called down from above in a beckoning tone, 'Joe...' I mounted the stairs, met her at the top, and followed her into a large pretty bedroom with full-scale dressing-table and mirrors and a single bed, on which Melanie lay wheezing.

Mary said, 'She's a little better,' and Melanie tried to smile at me.

I gave her an inhaler and the mildest sedative, I did not want to frighten her with hypodermic syringes and oxygen masks – she was already on the mend. I talked to her as reassuringly as I could, putting my finger on my lips when she looked like talking. After five minutes or so she was breathing almost normally. I told her I would leave the room with her mother, in order that she could be quiet and settle down, but we would remain close by until we were sure she was okay. I happened to have brought a buzzer, which I put in her hand and explained that if she squeezed it we would hear the buzz.

Melanie is a sweet girl. She smiles through tears, and gradually was able to take deeper breaths. Her mother rearranged her pillows and sat on the edge of the bed smoothing her hair and stroking her forehead. Before too long her eyes were closing, and Mary and I left the room and sat together on a sofa on the landing – we were some ten yards from Melanie and the sounds of her breathing were audible through the open door.

Mary thanked me in an undertone, and I said to her: 'I'm sorry you were worried. Melanie should be all right now. I hope she'll grow out of her asthma. She's in the care of a London doctor, I know, I remember, so I've been careful not to administer any controversial medicine. I could leave you more pills and a flask of oxygen, but I'd rather you rang me in the unlikely event of another crisis during the night.'

'Would you mind?' she asked.

'Not at all – I'm used to it – and Melanie's a more worthwhile patient than some – and I'd do anything to help you.'

Her eyes filled with tears, and she said: 'I feel responsible.'

'For Melanie's asthma? God's responsible for that.'

She produced a handkerchief, dabbed at her eyes, said sorry, and then: 'Not God's fault this time.'

I was surprised, but had no sense of being in the vicinity of quicksand. Although she was wrought up, and had reason as a mother to be so, she was fundamentally composed, poised, and her composure transferred itself to me. There was an intimacy between us, and assurance that we could solve problems.

'What happened?'

'Her father frightened her.'

'How?'

'They're close, you see – she loves him, and I think he loves her.'

'Do you want to tell me what he did?'

'He put on a balaclava helmet.'

'What?'

'He wore it for skiing in his youth. It's knitted and dark blue and has holes for eyes and a mouth and covers the whole head. They were used by soldiers in the Crimean War, used for warmth. Bruce pretended to be a criminal when he went in to kiss Melanie good night.'

'Not a good joke.'

'No. I don't understand him any more.'

'Where is he now?'

'I don't know. He was upset by the screams and then the asthma. He might have driven back to London.'

'Are you going to be alone in the house?'

'No – Ursula's with me – she looks after us all – she began by helping me with the children – she let you in when you rang the bell.'

'Is Melanie in your bedroom?'

'Yes.'

'Where will you sleep?'

'With her – in there – in a big armchair – if I sleep; but that doesn't matter.'

'May I ask you one personal question?'

'Yes.'

'Can you cope with your husband?'

'I'm not frightened of him. He has a better side. He's changed a lot.'

'The month you asked for – you remember? – that month still has days to run.'

'I know,' she said. 'I turned to you because you're a doctor, but I would turn to you if I was in any trouble.'

'That's music to my ears, but ... But could we meet sometimes anyway? We still have to talk about *War and Peace*.'

'Yes ... Yes...'

'You'll have to contact me.'

'Yes.'

'Will you?'

'Yes.'

'Thank you so much, Mary.'

'No – thank you – you've made such a difference for me.'

'Same here.'

'Perhaps...'

'All right, I'll leave you. I'll let myself out of the house. Ring if you need me.'

We stood up. She held out her hand and I clasped it in both of mine. Then I walked downstairs carrying my medicine chest and out into the night. I was glad she had not offered me only a cheek to kiss.

My recollections of Wisteria Lodge are vague – I did not have architectural matters on my mind. A light shone over a front door in two parts – the Gothic doorway and windows were probably Victorian. The house is family size, and no doubt the greenery clinging to the façade is wisteria. The hall was wide; doors opened into rooms right and left; the landing where I sat with Mary was a square space; and her bedroom had a high ceiling.

The single bed was of extreme interest to me. Considering that the Roecliffes were hardly middle-aged, and she was so desirable and he was unable to keep his hands to himself even at a dinner party, that bed must tell a sad story, but I was not crying.

My account of the episode is abridged. It cuts out or anyway loses the full romance of the long-awaited call in the late evening, the arrival at her home, admission into it by the traditional abigail, the ailing daughter and my successful attempt to ease suffering, and then our talk on the landing, hushed, grateful, my reward, her beauty that was mine for the moment, her compliments and pledges, and the myriad implications.

The sequence of scenes had perspective and depth created by the shadows cast by Bruce Roecliffe. He was there, with us, in every way except in person. He was the agent of the summons I received, he had scared Melanie. His cruelty was the agency of our kinder acts. I hurried to his house, to treat his daughter, for the sake of his wife – I was the puppet on his string.

At my age and in my profession, as a reader and a student of the social comedy, I had theoretical knowledge of the eternal triangle, the *ménage à trois*. I knew it all when I first looked into Mary's quiet eyes in my consulting room, knew that she beckoned me from beyond the obstacles and thornbushes, the razor wire and minefields, barring the distance between us. Now, it would be almost as difficult to turn back as to carry on, setting aside the fact that I have no inclination or intention to change direction. Yet practically, in practice, I continually seem to touch the electrified wire that is Mary's marriage. She belongs to Bruce, and one of the links in the chain of my love of her, which she may or may not reciprocate, is that I do too.

Mrs Symonds, who enjoys ill health, brought me a sort of bouquet this morning, a fungal infection of a toenail, an irritable bowel, a suspected carbuncle, and a tic or twitch of her left eyelid that makes people think she is winking at them.

Old Sam Thomson, in my consulting room this a.m., cried despite his fighting fitness. His wife Nelly had been ill – cancer, chemotherapy. Tears were his response to strain. He has been so worried about Nelly, and he cannot believe she is cured. What is worse for him is that she refuses to 'take care of herself'. She does not let him do the housework or the shopping, apparently she does not go to bed early or get up late in the morning or sit still in between. He spoke of women in bitter-sweet terms. 'There's no controlling them for their own good, they won't be protected, not they. I see her running herself into trouble again, and I can't stop her.' I comforted and calmed him down as best I could. I referred him to a priest. But in my heart I was agreeing with him. Iris was a proud career girl, who would not brook 'protection' or 'interference' from the man she slept with. I never saw myself as a bridegroom standing by Iris attired in a virginal white dress before a priest and an altar. My daughter's death might have been my fault because I postponed an offer to marry her mother, and as a result Iris, in spite of her feminist attitudes or owing to her pride, rushed to have the abortion, which led to the parting of our ways and tears all round. I pine to protect Mary, but I know she would not let me, not yet, if ever.

Another extraordinary occurrence. I write in the evening – it is evening, nine days after my time at Wisteria Lodge – and this afternoon I had visitors, the Roecliffe family, minus Mary. Yes, Bruce came to call. Melanie and Tom were with him. I was taken unawares and aback – I had been having a nap in the chair beside my new wood-burning stove.

'Are we disturbing you?' he asked.

'No,' I lied.

He sat in the chair I had been sitting in – symbolical, since I had sat on his furniture in his home, including the bed he might have shared with Mary notwithstanding its single dimensions.

The children stayed close to him, touching, leaning on him, affectionately maybe, but they reminded me of the young offspring of predators, stroking and wheedling their parents who might be tempted to eat them.

'We're here to thank you for saving Melanie's bacon,' he said.

Melanie squirmed a little at this description, and Tom giggled rather sycophantically to please his father.

'You know my Melanie, have you met Tom? Let me introduce

you – Doctor Selaby, Thomas Roecliffe – shake hands with the doctor, Tom – don't disgrace me!'

The boy shyly extended a limp moist hand: why was he sweating, why was he so nervous? They are fine-looking children, Tom handsome, his sister pretty, but pale – they are pale-faces, reserved, restricted. She has her asthmatic tendency, what is the matter with him?

Bruce was saying: 'Melanie's womanly, she'll marry young and have issue – you understand "issue", don't you, darling? She sides with her mother. Tom's a tomboy, he likes to kill things – we shoot sparrows with our catapults, don't we, Tom? He's going to have a gun soon and we'll shoot pigeons in the Forest of Ashes. He's a chip off my block, we're bloodthirsty.'

He was not exactly informing me, he was addressing his children and teasing them. They were noticeably unresponsive. They looked as if they had gone limp.

I offered them refreshments, and Bruce refused on their behalf: 'I won't have them growing up to be nuisances.' I then initiated them into the mysteries of my stove, which can run hot on maximum draught and many logs, and on minimum draught burn a single log for many hours. I next suggested that they might like to look around my house – for a start I indicated the staircase behind a cupboard door winding to the upper floors.

When Bruce and I were alone he said quite viciously: 'I'll tell you one thing about children, you can't do right in their bloody little eyes.'

I said I had neither children nor wife, and he commented: 'I envy you,' which was a bit hard to take considering that I wished his wife was mine. He continued: 'You don't need a wife to be lumbered with children – women are so bloody casual.'

I referred to the dinner at the Cunninghams', but he seemed to have forgotten it, he ignored me and said: 'How do I pay you for turning out to cosset my daughter in the middle of the night?'

I corrected his errors: 'Melanie was in pain and in danger, I administered suitable treatment, there was no cosseting, and your wife called me out at approximately ten p.m.'

'Okay, but how much?'

'I don't practice privately, and I don't know the NHS rate for a night-call, and I won't accept money for this one – expect further calls to be pricey.'

'Fair enough! What about that dinner party? I lashed out over the port, I was tight and bored – did I cut you to the quick?'

'No.'

'What a pity! I meant to let off a bomb under the Welfare State, which you lot collude with and support.'

'I support it unwillingly – I'm not in favour of change. You said that medical staff shouldn't tolerate the bad behaviour in A and Es at weekends. I agree. I agree wholeheartedly.' He showed no sign of appreciating my reference to himself. 'And,' I continued, 'I'm inclined to agree that we should isolate the drunks and druggers until they sober up and until proper patients have received treatment.'

'In great discomfort – concrete floor, concrete benches, one lavatory and unisex.'

'Well – warnings would have to be issued and widely publicised. St Anne's Hospital in Tinbury would have to see the point, the police ditto, and money would have to be raised for a poster campaign and so on.'

'I'd contribute.'

'Thank you. I'll see if I can set the ball rolling.'

The children reappeared. They approved of my home – children like people and things to be their size. Their approval was expressed more by wan smiles than by words. Tom tried to explain to his father that the attic room was reached by a ladder, not stairs, and his father showed impatience with the halting delivery by turning his head away and frowning. Bruce is good-looking and so on, yet it struck me, when his cheek caught the light through my sitting-room window, that his skin is not a good colour under the suntan: wishful thinking?

'Come on, kids,' he said, standing up abruptly.

The 'kids' jarred on me: I object to inverted snobbery, people who talk common for effect, and I plead guilty to being a pedant – a kid is a young goat, and its parents are a billy and a nanny.

He opened my front door and stood on the pavement. I held my door open, and the children were behind me.

'If you've got any money to invest, contact me,' he said.

He was entitled to say so, he is a businessman, but I have inside information about his business. And I must add to my descriptions of his eyes: I would apply an adjective to them as metaphorical as that which describes Mary's eyes, his are 'hot', indicative of inner fires and dishonesty.

'Shake hands,' he said to Melanie, although he had not offered me a handshake.

Another limp hand touched mine.

I said, 'Goodbye, Melanie,' and she glanced at me fugitively and mumbled thanks.

Tom said to me when we shook hands: 'I don't think your house is poor.'

At evening surgery yesterday, a couple of hours after Bruce and the two Roecliffe children had left me, James Bolt brought his son Jimmy into my consulting room. James is a smallholder, he and his wife Aggie grow asparagus and other unusual vegetables on a few acres near Clayburn. Jimmy is nine, red-checked and sturdy. He is a cricketer, had been batting, and received a bouncer that connected with his temple rather than his bat. He told me: 'I was trying to hit the ball to square leg, but it swung in and caught me.' The boy was amused, his father worried by the egg-shaped swelling: 'Is it okay?' he asked me. My advice was to take the casualty home, get Aggie to put a cold compress on the bruise and a bandage, then early to bed and, if the swelling had not subsided by the next morning, more medical examination. Jimmy was pleased not to be fussed over. He thanked me for not giving him an injection and shook my hand hard. He and his father went away laughing. They made me feel sorrier for Melanie and Tom.

Supper with Ma. She is concerned about Lisbet Tinnislea, who has fallen mysteriously ill and is losing weight. Her doctor is called Hemming and belongs to the other practice in Maeswell, and in Ma's opinion is hopeless. I could not ethically, and would not like to, step in for all Ma's urging. Bruce is Lisbet's friend, he might help her.

At last – at least it seemed to me to be at last – a call from Mary.
'Can we discuss *War and Peace*?'
'When?'
'Now.'
'I'm waiting.'
She arrived. We looked at each other in a way that was better than shaking hands or a mutual peck. She excites and calms me simultaneously. We began with the refrain of the song of love: 'Are you all right? ... Are you?'
'Come and sit down!'
'I can't stay long.'
'Is Melanie dancing?'

'And Tom's in the gym.'

She continued: 'I'm not here because Bruce was, I'm not following in his footsteps.'

'I hoped you weren't.'

'What was he like? I didn't know he was planning to visit.'

'He was pleasant. I've no complaints.'

'He can be pleasant.'

'He was not so pleasant at the Cunninghams'.'

'I know that.'

'But he made a suggestion there – we discussed it the other day – it's about the management of the A and E at St Anne's Hospital.'

'Where you treated his dislocated finger?'

'Exactly.'

'I'm not meant to know that – he's kept it dark. Never mind! You're not getting involved in a business venture with Bruce?'

'Oh no.'

'Don't, don't – I don't want you to be involved – it'd be a great mistake.'

'I won't – I'm well aware of what a mistake it would be – and because of my friendship with you.'

'Yes ... Yes ... I must talk to you...'

'Likewise!'

She laughed, we both did – our conversation was like gliding over a surface of humour, good humour, notwithstanding its urgency and gravity.

She said: 'My marriage isn't normal – I mean it's open to some extent – but not really for me. Our friendship, yours and mine, might become difficult.'

'I expect so.'

'No – more difficult than you expect – Bruce is a strange person – I don't understand him after being his wife in name for many years – he ties everything and everybody in knots.'

'Does he know you're here?'

'No.'

'Is it difficult for you to meet me like this?'

'No – easy, lovely, but complicated – my marriage – I couldn't leave Bruce, not even completely emotionally – I owe him a debt, and have to accept his waywardness and faithlessness.'

'Is Melanie his daughter?'

'Tom's his son.'

'I see.'

'You see so much, but not the whole picture. I wonder if anyone in the world sees into Bruce's heart, or if he has one. No matter! I shouldn't meet you for your sake.'

'Not true!'

'I'm sure to disappoint you.'

'Nobody can take decisions for another person.'

'I came to say...'

'You haven't said it, I can't hear it. Listen to me! I'm forty-one years of age. I had a mistress for a long time, but it's over and done with. I'm not promiscuous, I never have been, and have loads of experience, I know myself and my own mind. When I met you something irreversible happened to me. I'm sorry, I'll try not to be a drag on you, but there it is – I'm a healthy man, but I'd rather love you near or far than compromise elsewhere.'

'Oh dear ... Oh, my dear...'

'That sounds nice.'

'We hardly know each other.'

'I've known you well enough ever since we met, and perhaps before.'

'You're saying wonderful and terrible things.'

'I'm rushing in, yet I'm not an absolute fool. Where are you going?'

'To fetch my children.'

'It's too soon.'

'I'm wrong to sit with you.'

'Not very.'

'I've told you anyway – I've put you first – think of it – remember!'

'You're a beautiful woman, Mary, beautiful through and through, and adorable and exciting.'

'I'm stopping my ears!'

'Well, listen again – take your hands away from your ears! I shan't talk to you so frankly again, unless you wish it. Can't you stay a little longer?'

'I don't dare. Goodbye, Joe. How does your door open?'

I stood up and opened the door. We stood facing each other for a moment. She leant forward and touched my lips with hers, then hurried down the street without looking back.

Thanks be for her contrariness!

But which is meaningful, the goodbye or the kiss?

I can see the outline of the tale of Mary, Melanie and Bruce, and could have a shot at colouring in the rest, the fears and tears, the ceasefires and the resumption of hostilities, the relief, the regrets. I bow my head to Mary, who behaved better than me. She sacrificed herself rather than her child, assuming that it was a sacrifice for her to marry Bruce.

Winter is on the way, season of colds, coughs and pointless consultations, heydays of hypochondriacs and self-obsessed neurotics, fatal for some and not good for the doctors still on their feet who have to shoulder the extra burden of colleagues on sick leave. Moreover, night falls early, mothers in general are not keen to drive their children anywhere in the dark, and one mother in particular may not take her little girl to dancing lessons and her son to gym in the late afternoon. Will we ever get down to *War and Peace?*'

This notebook is a new 'economy' format, it has half as many pages more than the other four notebooks – a bargain, the makers proclaim, although the price seems higher. I doubt that I will use the extra pages. My life is again in the doldrums, nothing is worthy of record.

In the rest-room at the Surgery, I spoke my piece about the mayhem at weekends at St Anne's, and our possible response in order to ameliorate it or at least to provide protection for the medicos on duty. It was a flop, no takers, and in fact Denis Woods disappeared before I had finished speaking. Frank Cunningham was dead against the incarceration, the kidnapping, however temporary, of drunkards and others of that ilk. Police had powers to lock up offenders, doctors and nurses had none. He said that bad behaviour used to be the prerogative of the upper classes who could afford it, now the lower classes could afford their turn to make beasts of themselves. My proposal was illegal and impractical, he said, and he was surprised that I had advanced it. Audrey Fletcher shook the feminist tambourine at me: although she is strong for women's rights, and women doing men's jobs, she recoiled from the notion of drunken women having to use the unisex lavatory. Neither Frank nor Audrey are realistic. The former is too old for night duty at St Anne's, the latter as the mother of two young children is excused. I was at St Anne's last Saturday night from ten p.m. to two a.m. on Sunday morning. A youth screamed abuse at us for one and a half hours for not giving him drugs: in the end we forcibly administered a sedative. A nurse had her arm badly twisted, a porter was punched and stamped on. Natural functions took a lot of clearing up. I did not become a doctor to be a nursemaid and a punchbag for the aggressive new-rich on the razzle. The world has changed more than Frank and Audrey know: the laws of the land discriminate against law-abiding people – blinkered liberals and cock-eyed do-gooders are paving the way for an iron man, a martinet, a cruel despot and tyrant.

I suppose I feel under the weather because it rains non-stop, my country is badly governed and decadent, Ma has been unwell, I am lonely and have received no word from Mary Roecliffe.

Oh hell! I wish I was not about to write this entry – and I have to beg to differ from Tolstoy, the truth is not always beautiful. We have had four nice days, sunny, still, a saint's 'little summer', no doubt. This afternoon I decided not to wait for my telephone to ring, and went for a walk in the Forest of Ashes. I walked for about half an hour and was overcome with sleep, a result of my covering for Denis Woods who had taken Alyson and their children to the seaside for a holiday. I therefore branched off the ride and into the undergrowth, looking for a tree, an evergreen if possible, under which the earth would have been sheltered from rain. I found a hillock, a stony outcrop, part of which had once been quarried. The sun tempted me to climb to the top, and, although there was no shade and the ground was rock-hard, I lay down and shut my eyes. I slept for half an hour or so, and woke with a start – something had woken me, something that differed from the noises emitted by woodland birds and animals. It was laughter, male laughter, I thought; and it rose up from the ride below me. Two figures came into view, and one was Bruce Roecliffe. The other was a younger man or boy – I guessed at first that it was Tom: because a gun was hooked on Bruce's right forearm and a cartridge belt was round his waist, he must be going to teach Tom how to shoot. But then I saw that the second person was a man with a dark head of hair. One or both of them laughed again, and they turned into the undergrowth on that farther side of the ride. They were gone for six or seven minutes. When they reappeared, Bruce was tightening his cartridge belt and his companion held the gun. They walked on, Bruce again in possession of his gun, and passed out of sight. Later, as I gathered my wits about me and climbed down the hillock and headed for where I had left my car, I heard a gunshot.

No jumping to conclusions, I have told myself since then. The most acceptable explanation is that Bruce and his pal were out to shoot pigeons.

My notes will have to end here. It has passed the time for me to jot them down. The personal stuff I shall burn or shred at some stage. No word from Mary for nearly a month – I fear she is in trouble, also that I could make matters worse. Perhaps we have both needed time to ourselves. The future is dark.

No stopping after all – fate dictates and I do as I am told.
    Mary and I met by accident in Wates' pharmacy, and I brought her to The Poor Cottage. She looked pale and fragile. When I shut the door we faced each other, I held out my arms and she fell into them with her head on my shoulder. Our embrace was emotional rather than sexual, if love acknowledges such a division. She broke away and sat on the chair opposite mine by the stove.
    'I've tried so hard not to do this,' she said.
    'Thank heaven you haven't succeeded.'
    'My farewell hasn't lasted long.'
    'Long enough, too long.'
    'Maybe.'
    'Are you sorry to have failed?'
    She laughed.
    'Is someone not well?' I asked. 'You were in the chemist's.'
    'Yes ... I don't know. Are you well?'
    'Yes – I went to buy toothpaste. What does "don't know" mean?'
    'I was buying vitamins for Bruce.'
    'He hasn't seemed to me to need vitamins.'
    'He's ill.'
    'Really?'
    'Off and on, he's been getting ill for ages.'
    'What sort of ill?'
    'That's what we don't know – fatigue, exhaustion, the opposite of his normal constitution.'
    'Has he seen a doctor?'
    'Oh yes – in London – but they can't find anything wrong – he

says they can't. He's not a good patient, he doesn't like doctors, and he's quarrelsome when he's feeling bad.'

'Not good for you.'

'Would you see him?'

'Say that again?'

'Would you come to tea at Wisteria Lodge – today, a social visit – I could explain how we met – and you could give me your opinion – you wouldn't have to examine Bruce or do any doctoring?'

I put forward excuses. But she pleaded with me, she had no time to listen to my arguments, and I agreed to do as she wished.

We drove in the gloaming to Wisteria Lodge, she in her white Ford Fiesta, self in my Golf, and parked on the gravel sweep in front of the Gothic front door and windows. Melanie and Tom came out of the sitting-room to greet us in the hall. Mary asked Melanie to look after me, then went towards the back of the house. The sitting-room was brightly lit, and cheerful with the children's toys on the floor. Melanie wanted me to play cards with her, pontoon otherwise known as blackjack, and Tom showed me his model cars, a Bugatti with exhaust pipes extending from the bonnet and a gull-wing Mercedes. The children were more relaxed and chatty than ever before. After about ten minutes Mary returned and signalled to me from the doorway.

I told the children I was wanted elsewhere, and said quietly to Mary: 'If he doesn't want to see me I don't think I should barge in.'

'He's ready for you,' she replied, 'but he won't be cooperative.'

'Shall we call it off?'

'No – please,' she said, 'for me.'

I followed her along a passage and into an office.

She addressed her husband who sat in a big black leather reclining chair: 'Here's Dr Selaby, Bruce.'

The door closed behind me. Bruce offered me a chair on my side of the desk. The setting was dramatic: curtains drawn, illumination mostly by the winking screens of computers, one anglepoise standard lamp casting light on the black leather throne in or on which Bruce sat crumpled, wearing an open-necked shirt and red cardigan.

'This wasn't my idea,' he said with a wry and uncharacteristically feeble smile.

'Can I help you at all or would you like me to get out of your sight?'

'The latter, but not for a minute.'

I waited and he resumed: 'Okay – I'm sometimes grounded by a bloody bug – there was one doctor in London with a brain, he kept me on my feet without any fuss – I can't prescribe for myself – are you prepared to play ball?'

'What are your symptoms?'

'I'm not going into that.'

'Well, I'll leave you in peace.'

'Don't do that! I'm run-down and my stomach's not right in the present instance.'

'Have there been other instances?'

'Some.'

'Have you had tests?'

'I've had a few, and don't intend to have any more.'

'What did the brainy doctor do for you?'

'He cured me.'

'How?'

'With a hell of an antibiotic.'

'What was it called?'

'God knows.'

'Sorry – I'm not playing. Why not go back to the doctor who cured you?'

'He's turned up his toes, he was old and he's left me dangling.'

'You could try to find a doctor who's more amenable than I am.'

'I'm not in a fit state to find anybody or anything – can't you see?'

'My advice is to go for tests.'

'Clever you! You've made me feel a lot worse, Doctor.'

'Good night – good luck!'

I left the room, and met Mary in the passage.

'Did you hear any of our conversation?' I asked.

'I couldn't hear.'

'He should have tests.'

'Did you suggest them?'

'Yes.'

'What happened?'

'He more or less pointed to the door.'

'I'm sorry.'

'I did it for you. I'd do more than this for you.'

'Thank you. I must go into him – he won't like to think he's being discussed. Can I talk to you?'

'Any time.'

[427]

'About Bruce.'

'I understand – not *War and Peace.*'

'Good night.'

She kissed me again, fleetingly, gratefully, and turned away before I had a chance to make much contribution.

I headed for the sitting-room and said goodbye to the children. They wanted me to stay – they too wanted me to play – but I again refused, this time regretfully – and returned to The Poor Cottage, feeling upset for lots of reasons.

It must have been the day after when I spoke to Denis Woods. I pushed one of my upsetting reasons to a logical conclusion, and detained Denis in the rest-room after evening surgery.

'Can I ask you a hypothetical favour?' I began.

'You can, but I reserve the right not to give you the answer you're hoping for,' he replied.

Did he know the Roecliffes?

By name, he thought there was a pretty wife, and had an idea they lived near Taylton.

I said: 'Bruce Roecliffe's unwell, he may be ill, I've advised tests, and he may or may not agree to follow my advice. I'm not his doctor, I've treated one of his two children, a girl with asthma, and I'm friendly with his wife. If Bruce should wish to sign on with our Practice, would you accept him as a patient?'

'What's the catch?'

'I couldn't and wouldn't be Mary Roecliffe's doctor, owing to our friendship, and therefore couldn't be Bruce's. He's a bit of an awkward customer, a freelance financier, and he spreads it about.'

'Does "spreading it about" mean what I think it means?'

'Probably.'

'You're not asking Audrey to be his hypothetical doctor?'

'Certainly not.'

'How ill is he?'

'I can't say – my interview with him lasted four minutes in a half-dark room, and we didn't shake hands. He's not a nobody, he's an interesting man.'

'To wish an interesting patient on a doctor sounds like a Chinese curse.'

'Hypothetically, Denis, in the unlikely event of Bruce being sensible, will you do it?'

'I will,' he replied: 'and I haven't said "I will" since I married.'

As a result, I wrote with relief to Bruce – calling him by his first name as I used Mary's – to hope he was better, to clarify my professional position, and inform him that Dr Denis Woods, my experienced colleague, would be ready to offer assistance if need be.

Frank Cunningham, our senior partner, was not involved in these proceedings. I had been afraid that he would not allow Bruce to curse and swear at doctors in our Surgery.

Waiting for a bomb to fall in your vicinity is not the most pleasant of pastimes. I visited Ma again: it was late evening, when I was less expectant of a particular telephone call. Ma had had flu, a nasty strain of it, but was now convalescent. She thanked me for having been so attentive, and I thanked her for having been a good mother to me. I privately thank heaven for both my parents. I have personal experience of the opposite, not only in connection with Mary's children, but some of my patients with theirs. Everything costs something, what you do and fail to do will cost you, and the price of procreation should not be borne by innocent and uninvolved other people.

Mary was with me for nearly an hour: Melanie and Tom were at their classes. She asked me what was wrong with Bruce, and I had no answer – his only symptom I was told about could be caused by any number of diseases, some more serious than others. I asked if he was still suffering from digestive trouble and exhaustion, and then if he had had constructive second thoughts on tests: her answers were yes and no.

It was our most emotional meeting. I could not conceal my mingled joy and anxiety at seeing her again, and she made no secret of her sighs of relief to be in my arms. We had embraced as lovers do in the lull of a storm.

She said: 'I owe you explanations, I've broken my word twice now, by calling for your help and by coming here again. I didn't mean to. I couldn't help it. I need to explain my marriage so far as I can, and if possible spare you sorrow.'

I found it hard to listen to her, I was distracted by her voice, way of speaking, movements of her lips, expressions, gestures. She said she had been orphaned, her father perishing in the army in a war, her mother dying of TB when she was twelve. She lived then with an aunt and uncle in Shropshire. She went through college and she landed a job in a finance house. A man did her wrong and left her to cope with her pregnancy.

She said: 'I was ready to rear my child, my aunt understood my predicament and my uncle would have helped with money, but Bruce had a different idea. He was a friend of Melanie's father. He was a star turn at that time, launching his own business, handsome and surrounded by girls. He offered to marry me out of the blue. We were not lovers and scarcely friends. He said a good deed would be the making of him, he called himself rotten and a lost soul, and I imagined the task of remodelling him was worthwhile. We married in a Register Office, not church, and it was all on impulse and convenient for me, I admit. Problems took over at once. He was eccentric. He was forgivable, but his promises weren't kept. I conceived Tom, and things got worse. Bruce paid me less and less attention, he had other interests, and I made an unwelcome discovery Our marital life ended there. I would have left, but he persuaded me not to, and I stayed on partly for the sake of the children and partly to support him. He seemed to be cursed. He wasn't well, although his spells of ill health were short-lived. He was moody, yet had redeeming features, his dependence on me, his guilt and unhappiness. I couldn't leave him. I can't. I don't know if you would ever want me to leave. I don't presume, but my conscience has nagged for not telling you outright that all I have to offer is friendship. Bruce must be iller than he or anyone else knows, and I have loyalties that refuse to be divided.'

My paraphrase is the gist of her story. None of it cooled my ardour. I admired her honesty, and even her scruples. That she was cognisant of the range of Bruce's sexual antics, and I did not have to add to her burdens with my suspicion, was a weight off my mind. In my turn I made my confession, trying not to speak ill of Iris or too emotionally of Rose. I emphasised that my feelings for Iris were nothing like my feelings for herself, nothing whatsoever.

Before she left I asked her if Bruce had mentioned my letter about Denis Woods, and told her what was in it and why I had written.

She answered no, and said that Bruce was extremely secretive.

Schizophrenia beckons. Manic-depression is round the corner. I swing between optimism and pessimism, lightheartedness and gloom. Denis is another secretive man, he does not discuss his patients publicly, and I dare not dig for information about Bruce Roecliffe. At any rate the 'understanding' that Mary and I have arrived at is a lovely thing.

Is the news good? Is the news bad? It has reached me from an unexpected quarter. Ma tells me that she was told by Gabriella Shelby that Bruce Roecliffe has submitted to tests and been given a clear bill of health. I am sceptical – Ma said I was too much so. And I have to be glad for his sake, for Mary's, and contrarily for my own. I would not have liked to step into a dead man's shoes in a hurry. I am not altruistic or a saint: I foresaw pain for him and anguish for her, and possibly inextricable and insurmountable complications, which I no longer need to name or contemplate.

I wrote Mary a note to say how pleased I was to hear that Bruce had 'passed' his tests, and asking her to offer him my good wishes.

Months have passed. It is the next year. The short paragraph of a sentence above was to all intents and purposes my final note. But life has brought my story to a more recognisable end – coincidentally, my double notebook is running out of pages. What follows will be written not in the form of notes approximating to a journal, but like a narrative in a book.

I have to guess, since my notes were not dated, that it was a year ago when I congratulated Bruce Roecliffe and wished him well. My congratulations were premature. A few days after I heard that he had been given the all-clear, I received a call from Mary. She sounded agitated and was ringing me from London – I was at The Poor Cottage after evening surgery. She said Bruce was in a sort of hospital. He had suddenly developed a combination of symptoms almost simultaneously, in a matter of twenty-four hours, and had chosen to be treated by the successor of his old London doctor rather than by Dr Woods. He and she had been fetched by private ambulance, he was in the clinic where Dr Wolverton worked, and she was staying in their flat near Victoria Station. Bruce was awfully ill, she said, but well looked after, she believed, and she herself was okay – Melanie and Tom were with the abigail, Ursula, at Wisteria Lodge. Apart from letting me know what had happened and where she was, and wanting to hear my voice, she wondered if I would explain things with apologies to Denis Woods.

[431]

Two days later she rang me in tears: Bruce had AIDS.

I still know very little about the disease. In the case of Alec Whitehead, my treatment consisted of a single consultation and a prescription for painkillers. When I saw Bruce in the grip of fatigue it crossed my mind that he with his equivocal libido might have contracted HIV, the precursor of AIDS. But there were many possible causes of his thin neck and bony hands. I could not bear to think of the effects of AIDS on his wife, my Mary, her children and maybe many other people.

Mary's second call to me, the tearful one, confirmed my fears. She asked for information, she begged me to tell her the truth. I knew enough to be able to describe the stages of the development of AIDS, first HIV, which could become ARC, AIDS related complex, and finally the disease itself. Round about the transition from HIV to ARC there was a chance of the infection disappearing: Bruce's constitution might be able to seize such a chance.

'But...' she said, between a question and a statement.

One 'but', I replied, was that I had to ask her whether she had ever experienced an unusual symptom, and, if she would forgive me, selfishly for my peace of mind, and less selfishly for her own protection, when she had last had sexual relations with Bruce.

'Ages ago,' she sobbed.

'You understand my question?'

'Yes.'

'How long has it been?'

'Not since I was pregnant with Tom.'

'How old is Tom?'

'Nine and a half.'

'Ten years since you slept with Bruce?'

'This is painful, Joe.'

'For both of us.'

'He wanted me in other ways – I was essential – but always expected him to leave me – and I had the children – and wasn't happy. Sorry – I'll try again – yes, ten years.'

'And symptoms?'

'I've never been ill.'

'Thank God!'

'Why? How long is the incubation period?'

'I believe the average age is eight or nine years.'

'Tom...'

'Tom can't have AIDS if he hasn't been ill already – children develop it in months rather than years.'

'Are you sure, Joe?'

I took a risk and answered in the affirmative.

A little later I asked, 'How's Bruce?' and apologised for remembering the invalid belatedly.

'He's not surprised. He was HIV for a long time – he never told me – I was oblivious – and he's been afraid it had turned into AIDS. The disease accounts for a lot, but I can't say that knowing he was ill would have made our marriage easier. Now I'm sorry to see him so unlike himself. Thank you, Joe – please understand me. Now I must go back to the clinic, I promised I would.'

Soon after that conversation Mary returned to Wisteria Lodge – Bruce sent her back to be with the children. She travelled up to London and down again every few days for a month or two. We met, she came to The Poor Cottage, but we were discreet, we were equally keen not to be the subject of gossip while her husband was stricken. Moreover, we were careful not to discuss a hypothetical future: we stuck to practical subjects like the children's schooling and Bruce's pills.

Eventually, in confidence, I informed Denis Woods of his potential patient's condition, and conveyed the Roecliffes' apologies. He said he had wondered if AIDS might be the villain of the piece. What about the all-clear, I asked. He replied that mistakes are sometimes made when the disease is in its formative ARC phase.

Bruce improved slightly, and Mary was adjusting to the situation so far as was possible.

But subsidiary troubles befell the Roecliffes, and I was powerless to shelter the innocent one from their impact.

Ma was the first agent to bring a consequence of Bruce's sickness to my attention. I called on her at Silver Court one evening and guessed she had something on her mind.

She began by saying, 'Lisbet Tinnislea's not at all well.'

I mumbled a word of sympathy.

'She's supposed to have a ghastly disease.'

'Oh?'

'It's name is initials, HIV. That's serious, isn't it?'

'Yes.'

'Is it like AIDS?'

'It can become AIDS, but can also disappear.'

[433]

'Well, it isn't disappearing. Is it fatal, Joe?'

'HIV isn't, AIDS used to be and still is often; but they're working on a cure and they'll find one before too long.'

'Lisbet's seventy and sinking. A cure in the future probably won't help. She's such a nice dear person.'

'I'm sorry, Ma.'

'She's told us she knows how she caught it.'

'How is that?'

'From the husband of your friend, Joe.'

'I don't think that's possible.'

'Bruce Roecliffe visited her to talk about the money he was going to invest, and they had an affair. It happened at their only meeting. She hasn't known any other man since she lost her husband. Now she's heard that Bruce is dying of AIDS, and she believes she is, too.'

'When is the affair supposed to have occurred?'

'Nine years ago. She was always pretty, you see, and generous.'

'And truthful?'

'Oh yes, truthful and not fanciful. You needn't think that her age makes the story unlikely. Bruce Roecliffe came to see Gabriella Shelby about money and tried to have an affair with her – and Gabriella's much older now than Lisbet was then.'

Again I commiserated.

Ma said: 'Anyway, why I'm telling you is that Lisbet wrote to Bruce Roecliffe and his wife answered her letter. Mary Roecliffe wrote back so kindly, poor woman, and the message from Bruce she conveyed was a comfort to Lisbet.'

On another occasion another consequence was revealed to me and to Audrey Fletcher in the rest-room at the Surgery.

Frank Cunningham referred to Bruce's AIDS and told us that David Havior was HIV-positive and in hospital. David was the surviving son, and last presumptive heir to the ancient Havior barony: he must also have been the younger man I saw with Bruce in the Forest of Ashes. Apparently old Lady Havior, Helen, who lives in Maeswell, was always against David's friendship with Bruce, and had now written a furious letter to both Roecliffes, accusing them of ruining her family. Frank explained that if or when David died the Haviors would be done for emotionally, also financially, since there would be a second charge of death duty to pay, and because their name would be extinct. Frank then asked if Audrey and I would assure Mary Roecliffe, if we had a chance, that David might have picked up the infection elsewhere, and bring them round to believing as he did that she had nothing to blame herself for.

His revelations did not stop there. Shell Perry was HIV, he said, and the dermatologist blamed Bruce and was divorcing her.

'It's a bad business,' Frank wound up, 'but we doctors aren't judges.'

The third and last of the consequences I heard about was less bad than the others – at least Mary was not dragged into it. A Mrs Munsley with son aged two booked an appointment with me. A new receptionist had taken the booking and knew nothing except the name of the lady. Mrs Munsley wearing a hat, dark glasses and a scarf wheeled in a pushchair and disrobed to the extent of uncovering the Nicky Benning of yore. We embraced. She cried. What was wrong? She was scared. She was friends with a nurse who worked for Dr Wolverton in the clinic where Bruce Roecliffe was treated for AIDS. She had spent a weekend with Bruce, two nights in Brighton, long before she and I nearly got together, before she worked at St John's Surgery: how much at risk was she? She had a beautiful son, Timmy, and a great husband – they were all happy – she was a reformed character, she had married in church – was she, was her son, was her husband, in danger? She had AIDS hanging over her head and theirs. She had come to see me secretly, hoping no one would recognise her. Was there anything she could do? What should and could she do? How was she to recognise a symptom?

I answered her questions as best I could. She had youth and strength on her side, Timmy ditto, and her looks did not pity her. Should the necessity arise, there was an AIDS specialist not far from where she was living.

'Come and see me again in a few years,' I said, and she hugged me goodbye and went away bravely.

Meanwhile the planet continued to spin. Bruce was still in London, Mary visited him, and when she was absent I spent afternoons at Wisteria Lodge, playing games with Melanie and Tom. I played tennis with Melanie and cricket with Tom, and cards and Monopoly with both, and we ate teas produced by Ursula. Melanie benefited from Bruce's absence, the longer he was absent the more she relaxed and came out of her shell, and Tom too seemed increasingly carefree – the gun with which he had been going to shoot pigeons was not mentioned. I enjoyed their company, they reminded me of their mother, and they were less boring than the majority of children of their ages. We discussed their schools and schooling, their likes, dislikes and plans, and somehow skirted round the subject of Bruce.

One day at Wisteria Lodge, Mary arrived back from London just as I was leaving. We had a moment together in private, and she said that Bruce had expressed a wish to see me. I could not refuse.

He had been in and out of the clinic, and on the occasion of my visit was in his London flat and Mary was in the country. The flat was on the 'ground' floor – up steps but with other flats above it – of an Edwardian purpose-built block. A nurse was in attendance, she let me in and escorted me into the front room, which must have been the sitting-room. The time was between six and seven o'clock – I had skipped evening surgery. Curtains were drawn, the room was dark except for an extendable reading lamp on a table by the bed on which Bruce lay – furniture had been pushed aside and stacked to create space. He was propped up on pillows. The beam of the lamp was directed away from him – I could only see a half-lit profile of his face. He had a colourful scarf round his neck and wore dark blue pyjamas, and was smart even if his head was skeletal and he kept his arms and hands under the covers.

His voice was low and his breathing difficult. He greeted me by saying, 'My dear chap!' I spoke to him and waited.

'Find a chair,' he said, and after another pause, 'Sorry for the heat and gloom, eyes and circulation not what they used to be.'

I sat down where he might be able to see me.

We talked as I remember, he taking the lead.

'How are you, Doctor?'

'Well, I think.'

'That's the spirit, not to be too sure you're well. I'm the proof that pride comes before a fall. I thought it couldn't happen to me, and it wouldn't dare to turn nasty. Won't you have a drink? Ring that bell and my nurse will oblige – she might give you morphia if that's your fancy.'

I said I wanted nothing, and he was polite enough not to press me.

'Thank you for being kind to my children. I wasn't always kind to Melanie, and now she sends me cakes without poison in them, I'm told – I was never a cake-eater. She takes after her mother, she has a talent for tolerance, and she'll be another beauty one fine day. Give her my love. Give her confidence – I don't want her to think all men are as bad as I've been – but don't let her fall in love with you! Tom's a wax tablet – I haven't made too much impression on him, I hope, and Mary knows better than to bag all his affections. Let him be straight, for goodness sake! I wasn't cut out to be a father, more's the pity.'

'I've no children of my own, I'm not an expert in that line.'

'No, but ... I used to be rude about doctors, but I've revised my opinion, and I know for a fact that, in spite of all the pills you've prescribed, you haven't done a fraction of the damage that's down to yours truly. Are you aware of what I'm talking about?'

'Yes.'

'I'm haunted – I'm like Macbeth. You knew Nicky Benning, didn't you?'

'I've seen her recently.'

'Is she okay?'

'So far.'

'And other girls, other women, and not only women – too many, too many – have you seen them?'

'My mother's a friend of Lisbet Tinnislea.'

'She's ill, isn't she?'

'Yes.'

'Will you think of a suitable message from me to her?'

'Yes.'

'"Each man kills the thing he loves" – true words, aren't they?'

'Yes indeed.'

'I have, except for Mary – she escaped me, she resisted – the good in her was stronger than the bad in me. She believes I have a soul. It's my mind that's suspect. My disease affects the mind. But it's too late for excuses. Thank you for being Mary's friend.'

'I thank her for being mine.'

'You're right, you're lucky. I wasn't religious, I was a satyr; but, by God, if you catch AIDs you see the point of religion – you see it with a vengeance. No, that's a silly way of putting it – I mean, you appreciate the religion that's forgiving. I get tired quickly, which isn't a help to a host. Sorry...'

His voice trailed away and I thought he was asleep.

But he rallied, woke and said: 'I may go to America and get the medication that can cope. On the other hand, I may decide I don't deserve it. Who knows? I asked you here to give you my blessing – how ridiculous! – as if I had the right to bless you – but Mary values your friendship. Do you catch my meaning?'

'I think so.'

'Stand by her.'

'I will if she'll let me.'

'And if she won't?'

'I'll be there.'

'Thanks, Joe.'

There was a long pause. He was alive but no longer with me. I tiptoed out of the room.

There is room for one more note in notebook five.

I would never have chosen to be Bruce's friend, yet we are drawn ever closer – another unintended consequence. Not only do I love his wife, depend on him not to hurt or harm her, entertain his children, and obey the summons to visit him while he wrestles with death, but we are also linked by guilt. I killed Rose, he may have killed 'many'. We seek forgiveness. The advantages of the permissive society do not come cheap. The oaths Bruce and I swore, the laws of nature, the commandments of God, we got round them. We are chips off the block of the history of mankind. We did as we pleased and were licensed to do by science and fashion, atheism and amorality. We are the children of our forefathers who had inquiring minds and rebellious temperaments, Adam and Eve, for example.

Some days ago Ma asked me to visit her at Silver Court. She told me that Bruce had repaid the friend of the Cunninghams' whose money he had lost – the cheque was signed by Mary.

'Perhaps he had some good in him,' she remarked.

'He loved people in his fashion.'

'Is he dying?'

'I can't be sure, he seems to be.'

'If he died, how would it affect Mary?'

'Again I can't be sure.'

'And yourself, Joe?'

'I don't know.'

'How old is she?'

'Thirty-nine.'

'She could still have children.'

'Yes.'

'Will you wait for her for ever?'

'Please, Ma!'

'I'm sorry.'

'Don't be sorry for me.'

That day or the next I saw Mary, she came to The Poor Cottage. Her report was that Bruce had taken a positive turn, benefited from my visit, eaten food and talked of getting back to Wisteria Lodge as soon as his appearance would not alarm the children. I was congratulatory, notwithstanding the ultimate irony of my reviving my rival.

She said: 'I love you too much, Joe, to go on like this – I can't, I know I shouldn't – it's too awful.'

'It is awful.'

'What must your mother think of me!'

'Not relevant.'

'The disease can stretch out. There are new pills. Isn't that right?'

'Yes and no.'

'I can't say don't wait, I haven't the strength, but I think you should decide not to, I'm afraid you should. Honestly, Joe! Darling Joe, I'm being contrary, but you can read my mind. Tell me! Help me to read yours!'

'I won't tell you, but I will give you a present. Yes, a present, a small one. Ever since I arrived in this place, in The Poor Cottage, I've taken notes, not a diary, not *War and Peace*, just jottings. There are five notebooks now, and they tell the truth, our story, my side of our story, from when I got lost in your eyes in my consulting room. You remember, don't you? You've said something similar happened to you. Well, it's all here. You don't have to read my notebooks, but if you do you'll find my answer to the question of whether to wait or not to wait. They're my life in a manner of speaking, and they're for you.'